SHIPHANDLING FOR THE MARINER

SHIPHANDLING
FOR THE MARINER

THIRD EDITION

BY DANIEL H. MacELREVEY

ILLUSTRATIONS BY EARL R. McMILLIN

CORNELL MARITIME PRESS
Centreville, Maryland

Library of Congress Cataloging-in-Publication Data

MacElrevey, Daniel H.
    Shiphandling for the mariner / by Daniel H.
    MacElrevey. — 3rd ed.
      p.   cm.
    Includes bibliographical references and index.
    ISBN 0-87033-464-6 (hard cover)
    1. Ship handling.   I. Title.
VK543.M23   1994
623.88—dc20   95-5938

Manufactured in the United States of America
First edition, 1983. Third edition, 1995; second printing, 1998

For the shipmates and friends
who have shared their knowledge of the sea and ships
so unselfishly through the years

CONTENTS

PREFACE TO THE THIRD EDITION

Piloting and shiphandling skills have received much greater attention in the years since the publication of the second edition of *Shiphandling for the Mariner*. This is an exciting development for anyone interested in the art and science of moving ships and, by all indications, it is a long-term process that will benefit both mariners and the maritime industry in which they work.

This new interest in shiphandling skills has been prompted by several factors, including a greater awareness of the impact that marine collisions and groundings have on the environment, and new federal legislation and international conventions affecting ship operation, ship-owner's liability for marine casualties, vessel manning, and watch officer training requirements. The training is very much technology-driven, as sophisticated computer-driven simulators become more readily available at a lower cost. Before simulation, there was no practical way to teach shiphandling, except by handling an actual ship under tutelage of senior officers or pilots. Now, thanks to the ubiquitous microchip, it is possible to provide formal shiphandling, piloting, watch-keeping, and bridge resource management training ashore in a class-room environment.

Simulation has not yet reached a level where it replaces hands-on experience, but it can be used effectively for initial and specialized training to enhance shiphandling skills, and as a forum for experienced mariners to compare techniques with their peers and evaluate their own performances. Discussions of shiphandling have moved from coffee time to class time, and the professional is better off for the change.

This type of training has been needed for decades, particularly for ship's officers serving aboard larger, more deeply loaded ships on fast turnaround schedules, where it is increasingly difficult to accumulate traditional shipboard training, master to mate to cadet, aboard ship. Now, several excellent facilities at the Masters, Mates, and Pilots MITAGS facility; the Marine Engineers Beneficial Association STAR centers; the United States Merchant Marine Academy; the state maritime academies; the Seamen's Church Institute in New York; and the commercial simulator facilities operated by MarineSafety and others are using rapidly evolving simulator technology to provide the training. Similar facilities are also opening in almost every major maritime nation around the world.

This third edition of *Shiphandling for the Mariner* includes new material that reflects this development, particularly in discussions of training, voyage planning, and discussions of bridge team training and bridge resource management in chapters nine, ten, and twelve. Much of the new material is based on suggestions and papers prepared by Captain Charles Pillsbury of MITAGS, Captain Orlando Allard from the Panama Canal Training facility, Mr. Harry Crooks from the STAR center, Captain Richard Beadon from the Seamen's Church Institute school, Peter Barber of the Southampton Institute, and Captains Robert Meurn and George Sandburg of Kings Point's CAORF facility.

A greater understanding of the use of simulation in training, gathered in the course of visiting marine and aircraft simulator facilities, and from reading a two-foot high stack of material supplied to members of the Ship Bridge Simulation Committee by the National Research Council Marine Board, has also found its way into this new edition.

Other material has been added and changes made based on suggestions sent to the author by working mariners and instructors at the various maritime academies and schools. I hope that others will send material for future editions so that this text may remain as up-to-date and as useful as possible for seagoing professionals working to improve their shiphandling skills.

Practice maneuvers are again included in the text. The exercises can be used with this book as a self-taught shipboard shiphandling course or, better yet, they can be part of a formal maritime academy or simulator school program. In any case, training and books explain the science of shiphandling, but the art is learned by doing, and so it is hoped that these maneuvers and this expanded third edition of *Shiphandling for the Mariner* will help many mariners become skilled in moving ships.

ACKNOWLEDGMENTS

Those who make their life and living on or around the water are a special breed. They are always willing to help a shipmate and pass on the seaman's skills from one generation to the next. This is fortunate since no one person can write on a subject as diverse as shiphandling, and it has been the contributions of others that have made this book possible.

The marine industry has provided much of the background material and most of the photographs. I am indebted to, and greatly appreciate the assistance from, Texaco Incorporated; Exxon Corporation; Sperry Marine Systems; LOOP, Incorporated; MarineSafety International; American President Lines; Seaward International; Black Star Publishing Company; and the training facility of The International Organization of Masters, Mates & Pilots, the Maritime Institute of Technology & Graduate Studies (MITAGS).

Acknowledgment is gratefully made of the permissions granted by publishers to quote short passages from their books: Harper and Row and J.M. Dent for Joseph Conrad's *The Secret Sharer* and *The Mirror of the Sea*, respectively; Hamish Hamilton Ltd. for Jan de Hartog's *The Distant Shore*; Dodd, Mead & Company for Guy Gilpatric's *Mary, Queen of Scots*; and American Heritage Publishing Company for Captain Charles Porter Low's "Recollections," quoted by Alexander Laing in *Seafaring America*.

Mr. Earl McMillin read every page. His writing skills and professional expertise as both mariner and lawyer helped put the text into readable form while his cartoons make a potentially dry subject a bit more interesting.

Captain Brian Hope also read every page between trips on the Chesapeake Bay where he serves as a pilot, offered professional advice, and contributed photographs of some of his beautiful paintings of maritime scenes on "the Bay."

Many master mariners, including Captains Warren Leback, Carl Dingler, Marshall Irwin, William Deaton, George Quick, Dean Colver, Wilbur Vantine, Axel Munck, Douglas Hard, Curtis Fitzgerald, Philip Tomlet III, Gene Guest, Bill Lewis, Robert Boyd, Albert Wilder, Robin Erixon, George Smith, George Markham, and James F. McNulty, contributed both time and material—irreplaceable information based upon years of experience in some specialized area of our profession. Mr. Raymond Letulle, classmate and "Philadelphia lawyer," gave some order to the chapter on the master/pilot relationship. In reality, this text does not represent the thinking of any one person but instead brings together the expertise of many.

Lastly, a special thank you to Carolyn, my wife and shipmate in life, for her support, help, and patience. Only those who have been involved in a project such as this can understand why the author invariably expresses these sentiments.

SHIPHANDLING FOR THE MARINER

INTRODUCTION

The ability to handle a ship, especially in confined waters, is one of the most demanding and satisfying of the mariner's skills. It is a skill both as old as the first ship and as new as the latest vessel to be launched, yet little written material is available to the professional seafarer on shiphandling and much of what is available is either sparse or inaccurate. Hopefully, this volume will help to fill that void so the master, mate, naval officer, and Coast Guard officer will be able to gain some insight into the techniques used by the skilled shiphandler or pilot to move a vessel to her berth.

No master or mate of any type of vessel can be considered a fully qualified mariner unless he can handle that ship in a competent and seamanlike manner. This is especially true when considering the classic master/pilot relationship, a relationship which makes it essential for the master to be able to judge whether a pilot's actions are proper and whether the ship is being handled in a safe manner. While it certainly is not possible for the seaman to read this short book and then do the work of a pilot who has spent years refining shiphandling skills, the book will at least help mariners to better understand the handling of ships.

Until recently, little significant study was done on the behavior of large ships in shallow water. The science of hydrodynamics is now being applied to shiphandling and much is being learned that will allow the seaman to better predict a ship's behavior. Ships do respond in a predictable manner to the forces of wind, sea, and current, so these studies are important.

Years of experience are needed before the shiphandler can put this information into a "real world" perspective. So many variables and so many learned techniques are involved when actually handling ships that shiphandling remains more art than science—and this book's nonmathematical presentation, stressing application over theory, reflects that fact.

3

No single volume can possibly cover all the conditions that will be encountered by the mariner when handling a ship nor can any single technique be agreed upon by all professionals as the "best way" to do a job. Shiphandling is a learned art and it is only possible to give a background upon which to build the necessary skills.

A sincere effort has been made to separate fact from fiction and all that is contained herein is based upon actual experiences of practicing pilots and professional mariners. There are too many myths about shiphandling, especially in the use of anchors and the behavior of ships in narrow channels, and where this volume differs from commonly held opinion those differences are based upon the experiences of mariners who have performed such evolutions hundreds of times. It is time to replace the myths, born more of an overactive imagination than of experience, with facts that are applicable to today's ships and conditions. Further, this text is written for the practicing mariner who already possesses some degree of professional knowledge, experience, and training in navigation and seamanship.

Material that is not original has been credited to its source but the bulk of this information has been gleaned from the community of seamen and has been passed along from master to mate, pilot to apprentice. It is not possible to credit that information to any single source. The assistance of the many mariners and pilots who reviewed this material is appreciated and the unselfish manner in which they donated both their time and expertise is indicative of what makes the community of the sea different from that of other professions.

Just as a voyage is a natural progression of events from departure to final arrival at a port of destination, so too is this book organized to follow a vessel and her officers from the time she is preparing for arrival until she is again back at sea. This should put the information into a logical order. After following that hypothetical passage to its conclusion, special evolutions that are not often encountered by the mariner are described in the concluding chapters. Since it is inevitable that such a list of evolutions will be incomplete, it is hoped that others in the maritime profession will put aside their coffee cups and add to this collection; as professionals we would all appreciate the opportunity to learn from their experiences. It is time that more is written by active professionals, as at present we are over our marks with the inaccurate and unapplicable theorizing of the bureaucrat and the desk bound seaman.

Incidentally, for brevity, the pronoun *he* is used throughout the text to refer to an officer or a crew member serving in any capacity and obviously means a professional mariner of either gender. I trust the reader will accept this convention as readily as another—the use of *ship* and *vessel* to mean a vessel of any kind or size. A love of work on the water is not restricted to deep water, nor peculiar to men alone.

Okay, Mate . . . notify the engine room that there are two hours to arrival.

Departing the Pilot Boat *Maryland* on Christmas day. From an oil painting by Maryland Pilot Captain Brian Hope.

CHAPTER ONE

ARRIVAL

> . . . the place to enlarge upon the sensation of a man
> who feels, for the first time, a ship move under his
> feet, to his own independent word.
> —Joseph Conrad,
> *The Secret Sharer*

You are two hours from arrival at your first U.S. port, after a three-month trip that has been a good one for most of the crew aboard. The mate on watch called you from your warm bunk about half an hour earlier. After showering, and while savoring the morning's first cup of coffee that he had ready for you, you contemplate the day that lies ahead. The ship is starting to feel the shelving bottom as she comes on soundings, and shortly the pleasant routine of life aboard a ship at sea will be replaced with the activity, some might say the intrusion, normal to any port call.

The master has reviewed the appropriate sailing directions, light lists, local notices, and charts of the area, and has prepared a course card showing courses and the distances between the significant navigational aids in place along the channel to the dock. Soon the gear will be tested and required log entries made, and the chief mate will be called to stand by the anchors forward. The mariner's duties of open sea navigation and the myriad other tasks required of the deck officer at sea will be replaced by those of cargo handling, port administrative work, paying off, piloting, and shiphandling—the latter being perhaps the most interesting of all these duties.

MASTER'S TRIAL

In preparation for those tasks, the prudent master has familiarized himself with the handling characteristics of his ship. This is best done by putting the vessel through a series of maneuvers such as those proposed here to give the master or mate the information needed to predict confidently how the ship will behave in shallow water. Preferably these

7

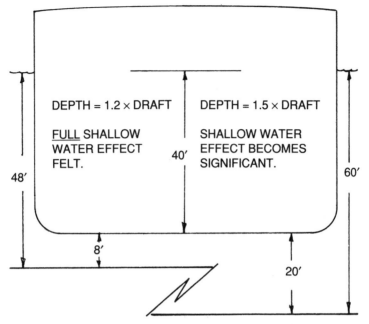

Fig. 1-1. Depth versus shallow water effect.

tests will be done in water of depth less than 1.5 times the vessel's draft (Fig. 1-1) so the marked changes in ship behavior that occur in shallow water will be apparent. The series of maneuvers should include:

1. Hard right turn at 6 knots.
2. Hard left turn at 6 knots.
3. Backing and filling maneuver starting from dead in the water.
4. Half astern to bring the vessel dead in the water from 6 knots, leaving the rudder amidships.
5. A series of backing maneuvers, until the vessel is dead in the water, using the rudder and engine as required to keep the ship's head within 10 degrees of her initial course.
6. Backing for ten minutes, starting with the vessel dead in the water, keeping the rudder amidships.
7. Turning with the bow thruster, if fitted, to the right and left across the wind. This should be done at 3 knots and at 1 knot.

All these maneuvers should be done with a sufficient number of mates on the bridge so the necessary data can be collected. These data will be analyzed later and compared with information collected aboard

WEATHER CONDITIONS

SS/MV_____ WIND_____

SHALLOW WATER DATA   CURRENT_____

AT_____

DATE_____

TIME (SECONDS)	HEADING (TRUE)	SPEED (KNOTS)	RPM	TELEGRAPH/ THROTTLE	TURN RATE (°/SEC)	RUDDER (DEGREES)	DEPTH OF WATER(FT.)

Fig. 1-2. Data sheet for trial maneuvers.

previous ships that a master or mate has served in. With a little planning, the time required to perform these maneuvers can be found without interfering with the ship's schedule. Since there is no other way to gain the "feel" for a ship necessary to handle her in a professional manner, it is important that these maneuvers be completed.

A sample data sheet to be used by the person making these tests is shown in Figure 1-2. Let's discuss these maneuvers in detail and give some thought to the things to look for when doing the tests.

HARD RIGHT TURN AT 6 KNOTS

This maneuver is made at 6 knots so a feel of the turning radius of the ship can be gotten at normal maneuvering speeds rather than in the full sea speed conditions with which the seagoing mariner is more familiar. During the turn do not change engine speed, and remember that the rate of turn will be affected by both current and wind. Record the data as shown on the sample data sheet. At the same time, observe the area required to make this turn and compare it with a known reference length, such as the distance from the bridge to the bow, for future use when judging whether a vessel has sufficient room to turn in an anchorage or harbor.

Keep in mind that the depth under the keel will cause the turning diameter to increase until, in shallow water, it may be as much as twice the diameter found for the same ship in deep water. Since for practical purposes the rate of turn is about the same whether maneuvering in

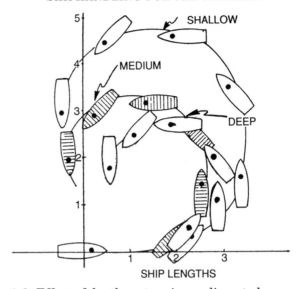

Fig. 1-3. Effect of depth on turning radius at slow speeds.

shallow or deep water, the larger area required to complete a turn is not immediately obvious to an observer. For these reasons it is stressed that the shiphandler should carefully observe the turn and *compare the turning diameter with a known reference* for use when planning maneuvers in the future. (Fig. 1-3)

HARD LEFT TURN AT 6 KNOTS

Make the same maneuver but this time turn to the left and again observe the turning diameter. When handling smaller ships, the smaller diameter and greater rate of a low speed turn to the left is apparent to the observer, as compared to the turn to the right. These differences become less significant, however, as ship size increases. Trial data for VLCCs and ULCCs indicate that the differences between the turns to the right and turns to the left for these largest of vessels are insignificant.

However, there are disadvantages to turning to the left when maneuvering in confined waters that far outweigh this one advantage of slightly reduced turning diameter. These other considerations, such as the ability to back and fill, are discussed in following sections.

BACKING AND FILLING

For the purpose of these trials, this common maneuver is started with the vessel dead in the water. The engine is brought to half ahead and the

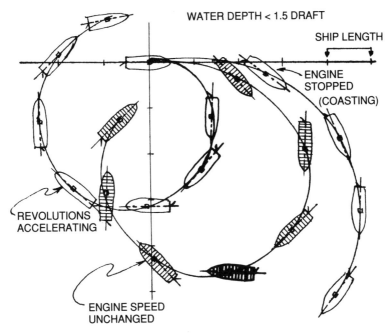

Fig. 1-4. Accelerating turn diameter.

rudder is put hard right. It will be immediately apparent as the ship moves ahead that the turning diameter for this accelerating turn is significantly less than for a turn using constant revolutions, and most ships will turn in about half the diameter required for the turn in maneuver 1, assuming both turns are made in the same depth of water. (Fig. 1-4)

When the vessel has picked up a good swing and some headway (the amount of swing depending on the sea room available for the turn), the engine is put half astern (or full astern for low-powered or deeply laden ships). The rudder becomes less effective as the ship loses headway, so it is first put amidships and then hard left as the ship begins to gain sternway. Again, the duration of backing and amount of sternway depend primarily on the space available for the turn, but the vessel can be turned in about one-and-a-half-times her own length if required, by reducing the amount of ahead and astern speed the vessel is allowed to develop. (Fig. 1-5)

Again observe the diameter required to make this turn, and get a feel for the maneuver and the time required to reduce headway. The effectiveness of the rudder while the ship is going astern can also be ascertained at this time.

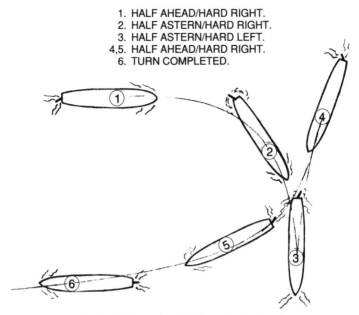

1. HALF AHEAD/HARD RIGHT.
2. HALF ASTERN/HARD RIGHT.
3. HALF ASTERN/HARD LEFT.
4,5. HALF AHEAD/HARD RIGHT.
6. TURN COMPLETED.

REPEAT 2, 3, 4, AND 5 AS REQUIRED.

Fig. 1-5. Backing and filling maneuver.

Do not be fooled by the fact that, during both this backing and filling maneuver and the steady state turns, the ship at first develops a good swing and then appears to be losing that swing as the rate of turn decreases. This effect is sometimes misunderstood and the shiphandler feels that the ship is going to stop swinging. The rate of turn will only decrease until the forces affecting the ship reach a state of equilibrium, after which a constant rate of turn is maintained. Be patient!

Do not attempt to back and fill to the left unless you have no other alternative, as a ship will normally lose her swing in that direction when the engine starts turning astern. An excessive number of engine maneuvers are required to back and fill to the left, and in many cases the ship simply will not make the maneuver. Some of the uses of the backing and filling maneuver are discussed in later sections.

There is not much point in collecting data during this maneuver. The rate of turn and the turning diameter required to reverse the vessel's heading are more a factor of the shiphandler's skill than the ship's characteristics, so comparisons are not particularly meaningful.

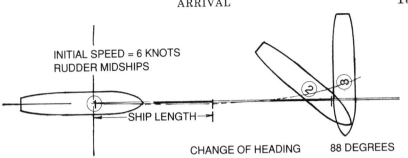

SHIP LENGTH

CHANGE OF HEADING   88 DEGREES

Fig. 1-6. Half astern to dead in the water.

HALF ASTERN TO DEAD IN THE WATER

The ship's behavior when backing can only be learned by observation. It is a characteristic of each individual ship that the master and mates aboard must have a feel for if they are to maneuver their ship properly.

While proceeding at 6 knots put the engine half astern and the rudder amidships. Do nothing further except collect required data as the ship comes to a stop. The data is most useful if the maneuver is performed when there is a minimum of outside influences and the wind is less than force three. Use visual and radar observations to fix in your mind the distance required to bring your ship to a stop using just the engine. (Fig. 1-6)

You will find that the ship changes heading significantly, in some cases as much as 80 to 90 degrees in shallow water and somewhat less in deeper water, although she doesn't travel a significant distance from her original track. Despite the differences in ship behavior in shallow water as compared to deeper water, there is not much difference in the stopping distance required. The data collected during this maneuver are useful both for routine and emergency maneuvers—you have a better feel for the ship and can better predict her behavior.

The ship's tendency to twist in this manner when backed directly affects her performance of certain routine maneuvers. The greater the magnitude of this twisting effect, the more effectively she can be backed and filled in an anchorage or other confined area, but the more difficult it is to stop in a narrow channel when it is necessary to keep the ship's heading within reasonable limits.

Depending on the ship's configuration, and especially the location of the house and any large objects such as containers on deck or an exceptionally high freeboard, the backing and filling maneuver can be significantly distorted by the wind. If you think ahead though, this wind effect can be used advantageously when maneuvering in tight quarters. Since the ship moving forward usually wants to head up into the wind once the rudder's effectiveness is lost, and to back into the wind once sternway develops, the twisting effect that occurs when backing the engine can be used to the shiphandler's advantage: plan to back when the wind will amplify or dampen this twisting effect to your advantage.

STOPPING WHILE MAINTAINING CONTROL OVER HEADING

Again the ship is proceeding at 6 knots on a selected base course. The rudder is put left and as the ship begins to swing to port, the engine is backed. The ship loses headway while the swing left decreases in rate and finally reverses. When the bow starts swinging right, come ahead again with left rudder to check and reverse the swing. Repeat these maneuvers as required until the ship is down to the desired speed.

It may be necessary to put the rudder amidships when the engine is going astern, so that the ship loses her swing to the left as desired. This can only be determined by trial so it is important to practice this maneuver at every opportunity. Don't wait until the ship is proceeding up a narrow river on a rainy, windy night to learn how the ship behaves when the engine is put astern.

This particular maneuver is obviously important since it is used to stop or reduce a ship's speed so a tug can be made up, to shape up for docking, or any number of other important maneuvers in confined waters. There is little need to collect data during this maneuver since this is primarily a shiphandling exercise that yields little quantitative data.

Keep in mind that bottom configuration and the proximity of a bank affect this maneuver. A ship may back "the wrong way," especially if the starboard quarter is close to the bank or a shoal area at the edge of the channel, so that the swing to the left is not checked. This effect is minimized if the ship is kept at or near midchannel when backed.

These possible variations in ship's behavior make shiphandling interesting and assure that the handling of ships will always be an art rather than a science.

HANDLING A SHIP WITH STERNWAY

When the ship is dead in the water put the engine half astern and back for a period of ten minutes so good sternway develops. Note all the previously discussed effects of backing and also note the degree to which the ship follows her rudder—the ability or lack of ability of a ship to steer while going astern is quite important when moving in confined waters.

Collect the usual data and note particularly the direction of the wind relative to the ship. Since the ship with sternway wants to back into the eye of the wind, it is especially important to be aware of the wind. Back first with the rudder amidships and then try to steer with the rudder after sufficient sternway develops.

BOW AND STERN THRUSTERS

Bow thrusters are becoming increasingly common aboard merchant ships and stern thrusters are also seen occasionally. The bow thruster has its advantages and disadvantages as does any other equipment.

ADVANTAGES	DISADVANTAGES
Located at the extreme end of the vessel for maximum effectiveness.	Becomes ineffective as speed increases.
Available at all times, unlike a tug.	Less powerful than a modern tug.
Gives good lateral control without affecting headway.	Cannot be used to slow a ship, or hold against a current from ahead or astern.
Saves some expenses by reducing the need for tugs.	Requires continuous maintenance to assure reliability.
	Unusable at very light drafts.

Thrusters are used much like a tug to move the bow and stern laterally, steer the vessel when going astern, hold the ship alongside a wharf or pier, and hold the ship into the wind at slow speeds and when anchoring. The thruster's uses are more obvious to the seaman than its shortcomings. The thruster is a useful tool to supplement the anchor and tug but certainly does not replace a tug in all cases.

Keep in mind that the thruster is most useful at speeds of 2 knots and less, and should not be relied upon at higher speeds. This is very important.

TURNING WITH A BOW THRUSTER

The bow thruster's effectiveness can only be determined by experimentation. The many diagrams that show this equipment being effective at speeds of 6 knots and more are a figment of some naval architect's imagination. More than one ship has a similar carefully drawn but incorrect graph posted in her wheelhouse. The person who developed this graph obviously never got beyond sailing model boats in a test basin and the graph only demonstrates the gap that remains between the theoretician and the real world.

Try your bow thruster first to the right and then to the left, making it a point to orient your ship so you bring her bow through the wind each time. This is an interesting maneuver for the mariner since the data collected makes it possible to predict with confidence the thruster's effectiveness when steaming through a crowded anchorage or holding the bow into the wind while the mate drops the anchor.

Perform this maneuver first at 1 knot and again at 3. To see how far the theoretical data is from reality try the thruster again at 6 knots. It won't have the effect shown on the previously mentioned posted card and it probably won't even be felt by the helmsman holding the ship steady on a course!

Collect the usual data for later study in the comfort of your fo'c's'le. Prepare a graph of speed versus bow thruster effectiveness (change of heading in degrees per minute as measured by observation or rate of turn indicator, if that equipment is available) for both your own infor-mation and for the use of pilots. There is no doubt that the graph prepared aboard ship will be more accurate and useful than the one supplied to the ship at delivery.

Remember that it is not so much the power of the thruster that is of interest in these tests but the ship's speed through the water at which the thruster is effective. A few years ago a tanker turning in the Dela-ware River collided with another tanker at her berth while trying to use the bow thruster at 6 knots to assist in making the turn. It is better to learn the capabilities of your equipment during this trial maneuver.

MOST EFFECTIVE MANEUVER

Professionalism in shiphandling entails looking for *the most effective maneuver*, not just a random series of maneuvers, that will put the ship in a desired position using a minimum number of bells and helm orders.

Having completed the trial maneuvers, the shiphandler has a feel for the ship and is better able to anticipate her behavior. It is therefore possible to choose the most effective action to take in a situation.

The most effective maneuver accomplishes several tasks simultane-ously so the ship is handled with the minimum of orders and is always under control.

For example, when it is necessary to alter a ship's heading to starboard and reduce her headway, the less experienced shiphandler might first make the starboard turn, then check the ship's swing and put the engine astern to reduce headway. The accomplished shiphandler puts the engine astern first and the resulting starboard swing caused by the ship's tendency to twist in that direction when backed takes the ship around the turn while headway is simultaneously being reduced.

APPROACHING SHALLOW WATER

You have familiarized yourself with the local conditions of the port at which you are about to arrive, planned your passage from sea to berth, and have become confident that you have a good feel for your ship and what she will do under various conditions. You now feel ready to bring your command into her first discharge port.

The vibration felt throughout the ship's hull tells you the depth of water under the keel is decreasing. Test gear, and then reduce speed to minimize this vibration. Other changes to expect include: (Fig. 1-7)

DEEP WATER (AT SEA)	SHALLOW WATER
DIRECTIONAL STABILITY A FUNCTION OF HULL FORM AND TRIM.	DIRECTIONAL STABILITY BECOMES MORE POSITIVE. (STEERING "IMPROVES.")
RATE OF TURN DEPENDENT ON HULL CHARACTERISTICS AND DIRECTIONAL STABILITY OF VESSEL.	RATE OF TURN ESSENTIALLY THE SAME AS FOR DEEP WATER.
DIAMETER OF TURNING CIRCLE APPROXIMATELY THREE TIMES SHIP'S LENGTH.	DIAMETER OF TURNING CIRCLE INCREASES TO AS MUCH AS TWICE THAT OF DEEP WATER TURN.
SPEED LOSS SIGNIFICANT WHEN MAKING LARGE COURSE CHANGES.	SPEED LOSSES OCCUR WITH LARGE CHANGES IN HEADING, BUT TO A LESSER EXTENT THAN IN DEEP WATER.
LOSS OF HEADWAY IN CALM WATER, WITH ENGINE STOPPED, A FACTOR OF DISPLACEMENT, TRIM, AND HULL FORM.	LOSS OF HEADWAY WITH ENGINE STOPPED, IN SHALLOW WATER, LESS THAN IN DEEP WATER. (SHIP CARRIES HER WAY LONGER IN SHALLOW WATER.)
VESSEL'S HEAD FALLS OFF TO STBD. WHEN ENGINE GOES ASTERN.	HEAD FALLS OFF IN THE SAME DIRECTION, BUT AT A GREATER RATE, AS DEPTH DECREASES.

Fig. 1-7. Shallow water effects on vessel maneuvering characteristics.

1. Improved steering characteristics as the underkeel clearance decreases until, in shallow water, a directionally unstable ship becomes easier to steer and less unstable. This is true only if the ship does not squat so much forward that she goes by the head, in which case the stabilizing effects of the shallower water are negated by the change in trim.
2. The ship's turning radius increases until, in shallow water (depths of 1.2 times the vessel's draft or less) the radius can be as much as double that experienced at sea.
3. The vessel twists more when backed.
4. The trim of the ship changes, the draft increasing more at the bow or stern depending primarily on the hull form.

These changes are significant and must be kept in mind as water depth decreases.

DIRECTIONAL STABILITY

Directional stability affects the ship's steering characteristics, the degree to which she can be checked when swinging, and the change in her rate of turn when the rudder is put amidships. A hydrodynamicist looks at directional stability in other ways, and tests for the degree of directional stability that a ship possesses by putting the ship through a series of "Z" maneuvers.

A vessel can have positive, negative, or neutral directional stability. A ship that tends to steady up when the rudder is put amidships has positive directional stability. If she swings at increasing rates of turn when the rudder is amidships she has negative stability. A vessel with neutral directional stability continues swinging at the present rate, or continues along on her current heading until external forces take charge. She has no tendency to either increase or decrease her rate of swing when the rudder is left amidships.

The ship's directional stability is especially important when proceeding up a channel or attempting to steer with a minimum of rudder at sea. *More rudder for a longer period of time is needed to check the swing of a directionally unstable ship than is required to start that swing.* It may not be possible to check the swing of a directionally unstable ship before she leaves the channel even though the rate of turn is quite normal for an average ship. Large rudder angles and constant attention are required to steer her, especially in confined waters and when making

Fig. 1-8. "A few feet of drag changes the entire personality of a ship, Cap'. . ."

course changes. As a greater number of full-bodied ships, and especially ships with open sterns and full sections forward, are launched, the condition of negative directional stability becomes more common.

Because this condition is to a large extent draft critical, it is affected by even small changes in trim. A few feet of drag will change the entire personality of an otherwise "cranky" ship and give her positive directional stability. An alteration in trim changes the underwater form of the hull, shifting the greatest submerged cross sectional areas of the hull. For this reason, any ship significantly trimmed by the head has negative directional stability and a seaman finds that the characteristics of a ship with inherent negative directional stability are the same as those always associated with a ship trimmed by the head. More time is required than usual to start such a ship swinging, and very large rudder angles for longer periods of time are needed to check that swing. If she gets away from the helmsman, watch out!

Directional stability is obviously a condition with which the mariner has long been familiar, although that term may not have been used to describe the condition. As more ships are constructed with hulls that are inherently directionally unstable it becomes increasingly important to be alert for this condition. You are better able to predict your ship's behavior both when handling the ship yourself and when turning her over to a pilot if steering behavior is considered to be a function of directional stability.

Because the changes in directional stability are significant as draft and trim are altered, and because large, full bodied ships with large block coefficients often squat by the head, it is especially important that these potential changes be given careful consideration when trimming such ships for arrival.

It is apparent then that directional stability:

1. Increases as the underkeel clearance decreases.
2. Becomes more positive as length increases.
3. Becomes more positive as drag increases.
4. Decreases as the block coefficient increases.
5. Decreases as the beam increases for a given length (length/beam ratio decreases).
6. Decreases as the area of the forward sections increases relative to the area of the after sections (as the pivot point shifts ahead).

EFFECTS OF BOTTOM CONTOUR ON HANDLING CHARACTERISTICS

Changes in ocean bottom contour do not affect the ship's behavior until shallow water conditions are encountered. Shallow water effects as shown in figure 1-7 vary in magnitude with changes in *average depth*. The additional effects of specific changes in bottom contour are superimposed on these shallow water effects and cause: (Fig. 1-9)

1. The ship's bow to move away from more shallow water. This well known "bank cushion" effect is caused by the pressure built up on the area of the bow, as seen in the raised water that forms between the ship's bow and the shoal or bank.
2. The ship to move bodily sideways toward a nearby shallow area, as her parallel midbody passes that area. This movement is caused by the increase in velocity of the water flowing through the restricted area between the ship and shoal, and the resultant reduction in pressure on that side of the ship.

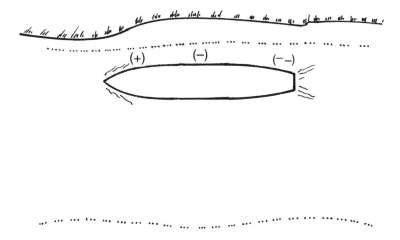

Fig. 1-9. Effects of changes in bottom contour or a near bank.

3. The stern of the ship to move toward shallower areas or banks due to the reduced flow of water to the area behind the ship, and to the ship's propeller on the side closer to that shallow area.

Bank cushion is unfortunately often exaggerated in marine texts which describe hypothetical ships "smelling" shallow water and heading away from it, saving themselves from grounding. These tales are untrue and dangerously misleading and should be filed along with those about sea monsters and falling off the edge of the world. It is more correct to say that "a ship tends to head away" from shoal water—the effect is not as strong as often indicated in classic books on seamanship.

Bank suction is more strongly felt than bank cushion and causes a ship to sheer away from a shoal or bank. This is a significant effect that can make steering difficult as the bottom contour changes in shallow water.

All these effects are felt to some degree during the arrival phase of a voyage as water depth decreases. The effects are more pronounced as the ship proceeds up a channel and are discussed more fully in applicable chapters.

HANDLING OF LARGER SHIPS IN SHALLOW WATER

A study was conducted by a group of shipping companies and organizations in July 1977, using *Esso Osaka* to determine the handling charac-

Fig. 1-10. The VLCC *Esso Osaka*. Courtesy Exxon Corporation.

teristics of VLCCs in shallow water.* This study has been widely circulated and used to refine previous theories. The data were also used to improve computer programs for the various shiphandling simulators used to train deck officers.

While most of the information contained in the tests is discussed in this text, it should be stressed that the tests proved that, contrary to oft-stated opinions, VLCCs remain highly maneuverable in shallow water and steer quite well both with the engine turning ahead and stopped. This now well-documented fact, based on both the *Esso Osaka* study and on the experiences of masters and pilots who have handled these larger ships in shallow water, should be comforting to the master bringing a VLCC into shallow water for the first time. In fact, large ships usually steer better in shallow water with the engine stopped than they do in deep water. There is no need for a ship to move at excessive speed to maintain steerageway.

It is encouraging to see greater attention being given to real ship/real time data on shiphandling and maneuvering characteristics. The data collected during the *Esso Osaka* trials, and several other shallow water

*W.O. Gray, *Esso Osaka* Maneuvering Trials.

trials, such as those done by El Paso Marine Company with liquefied natural gas carriers, can only result in safer handling of present vessels and the design of better-handling ships in the future.

APPROACHING THE PILOT STATION

It should be standard practice to station an engineer in the steering gear flat when arriving and maneuvering in restricted waters. It's too late to send someone to shift to the trick wheel after steering is lost. The engineer assigned to stand by must be trained in shifting over to the emergency system and then steering by both compass courses and conning orders.

This operation must be practiced at sea before an emergency arises. It is difficult enough for an experienced helmsman to steer in a confined area with no visible horizon, let alone an untrained person under emergency conditions with the noise of the steering gear machinery making it difficult to hear helm orders. The half hour a month required for practice is time well spent.

There must be a tested and reliable means of communicating between the steering gear flat and the bridge. A good headset with a long cord that leaves the wearer free to move about and use both hands is recommended. The headset cuts down on background noise so instructions can be heard.

Prepare the anchors for letting go with the claws and pawls off (or clear whatever gear you might have aboard your particular ship for securing the anchors at sea). Break the anchors out of the hawsepipe to assure that if needed they will run free, unless the ship is rolling too heavily to allow this. The anchor may need to be lowered to the water's edge if a large bulbous bow prevents dropping it from the hawsepipe. (See Chapter 8 for a discussion of the uses of the anchor.)

STOPPING OR REDUCING HEADWAY

You now want to reduce ship's speed so the pilot can be safely embarked and the ship maneuvered among other traffic and anchored vessels. The most common methods to reduce a ship's headway include:

1. Using the ship's engine astern. (See Fig. 1-6)
2. Slewing a vessel about a base course.
3. Large changes in heading, including a complete round turn. (Fig. 1-11)

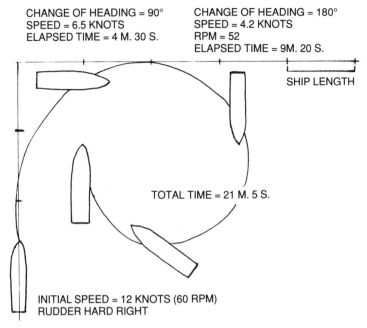

CHANGE OF HEADING = 90°
SPEED = 6.5 KNOTS
ELAPSED TIME = 4 M. 30 S.

CHANGE OF HEADING = 180°
SPEED = 4.2 KNOTS
RPM = 52
ELAPSED TIME = 9M. 20 S.

SHIP LENGTH

TOTAL TIME = 21 M. 5 S.

INITIAL SPEED = 12 KNOTS (60 RPM)
RUDDER HARD RIGHT

Fig. 1-11. Loss of speed during round turn.

The use of the engine astern to reduce a ship's headway is the easiest and most common method for slowing or stopping any ship. It is also often the least effective. A propeller is less efficient astern than ahead, a large turbine plant may have as little as 25 percent of the power astern that it has ahead, and a ship becomes difficult to handle when the engine is put astern at higher revolutions. Time and searoom are required to back a ship to a stop—so with a large ship it is often impractical to use this maneuver alone. This maneuver becomes more useful as headway is reduced to lower speeds, and is generally carried out as described in the previous section of this chapter, so that the ship remains reasonably close to the desired heading.

A preferred method for reducing headway, and with VLCCs often the most practical method, is a series of course changes to starboard and port of the base course. Using this slewing maneuver the ship loses a significant amount of headway each time she swings, yet makes good her desired track towards the pilot station or anchorage.

Keep in mind when other vessels are about that this slewing maneuver may be confusing to them. They don't know if your change in heading is an actual course change that will affect a meeting situation between your two ships, or only a temporary heading change as you slew ship to reduce headway. This is especially true at night when the watch aboard the other ship sees your large tanker or containership showing first a green and then a red sidelight, and then sees both sidelights as you head directly for them. Good seamanship dictates that you contact by VHF any ship that might be concerned and let her know your intentions when slewing ship to reduce headway.

The round turn maneuver, or even a large change in heading, quickly takes the headway off any ship, with the reduction being greater for larger ships. This maneuver disputes the claim that VLCCs can't be handled safely in crowded waters "because it requires miles to stop those big babies." A rule of thumb is that a VLCC loses 25-30 percent of her headway for every 90 degree change in heading.* If the ship is proceeding at 12 knots, her headway is reduced to 2 to 3 knots at the completion of a round turn even though the engine continues to turn ahead for steerageway. The ship completes this turn in about three times her length in deep water, or a bit less than six times her length in shallow water. (See Fig. 1-3) That is much less than the oft-claimed "several miles" stopping distance supposedly required for these ships.

This round turn maneuver is useful:

1. When in a crossing situation at sea it is necessary to maneuver to avoid collision.
2. To slow a ship before arrival at a pilot station.
3. To make a lee for a pilot.
4. To stop a ship after losing the engine.

The round turn maneuver used in a crossing situation at sea accomplishes several tasks simultaneously. Your ship is turned away from the other vessel and makes a 360-degree course change while reducing headway. At the completion of the turn she is back on her original heading at a minimum speed and you probably find that the other ship has crossed your course line and is safely on her way.

If a round turn is used to make a lee for a pilot, the ship both sweeps a calm area for boarding and loses headway.

The round turn can be used to stop your ship after losing her engine, since she will usually respond to her rudder if given a chance. The ship remains in the limited area needed to make the turn while losing

*Ship Performance Data for VLCCs.

headway until stopped or nearly so. While she might carry her way for an extended period if moving straight ahead, she stops in a surprisingly short time when put into a hard-over turn. It is stressed that the ship does respond to her rudder without the propeller turning ahead at even very low speeds.

A master or deck officer, accustomed to the ship's immediate response to rudder movements at sea, might feel that she does not steer effectively when the engine is stopped. Often a master advises the pilot that the ship does not steer without the engine, or will not steer at less than some excessive speed, such as 6 knots. In waterways such as the Panama Canal, or in a port area where speed is naturally restricted, this lack of steering capability would create an interesting situation if it really existed. The Panama Canal locks certainly could not be entered at such a speed and yet the ship must be steered all the way into the jaws of the lock. Ships do, in fact, respond to rudders at very low speeds if given a chance.

This is a comforting fact as the world's merchant fleet becomes almost exclusively powered by diesel engines. The odds increase to some extent that the engine will not go astern if a ship is diesel propelled since it is stopped and restarted astern in most cases—but you can still get the ship safely stopped using a round turn. The round turn is useful in these and other situations and every master or watchstander must keep the maneuver in mind to reduce headway and avoid casualties both in the open sea and when maneuvering.

PICKING UP THE PILOT/MAKING A LEE

As you approach the pilot station after several days steaming at sea speed, a conscious effort is required on the part of conning officers to reorient themselves to the lower speeds necessary for maneuvering. When making a lee for the pilot be sure speed is reduced to 3 to 4 knots. There are ports with high powered boats and special boarding facilities where it is preferred that the ship proceed at higher speeds. You are usually aware of this requirement or the pilot will inform you of it via VHF when you call the station two hours before arrival. Unless informed otherwise, the 3-to-4-knot speed is comfortable and yet not so slow that the boat has difficulty staying alongside while transferring the pilot to the ladder.

Make your approach so as to give the pilot a good lee and remember that it is possible to knock down a short chop by putting a swing on your

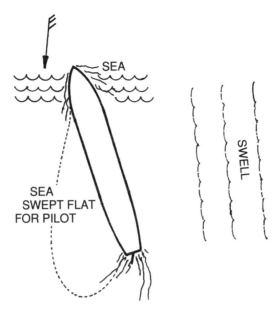

Fig. 1-12. Ship in hard over turn "sweeps a lee" for the pilot.

ship just before the pilot boards so *the quarter is swinging away* from the pilot boat. "Sweeping a lee" in this manner is especially helpful when there is a cross sea and swell since you can block the swell with the ship's hull and then knock down the contrary sea as the pilot boards. (Fig. 1-12)

Making a lee often requires some careful planning, especially when a shoal area or traffic restricts maneuvering. Here again, a complete round turn may be the best way to make a good lee, even if it appears at first to be very time consuming. Since the turn takes off a great deal of the ship's headway, you can make up for some of the time required to make this round turn by being able to approach the station at a greater speed than would have been possible had you proceeded directly and then slowed with the engine alone. More important, while it may not look rough from the bridge, it is rough down there in that small launch, and the transfer will often be hazardous. Professionalism demands that you make the situation as safe as possible for the pilot, regardless of how late you are arriving at the terminal, or how many gangs might be waiting at the dock.

To further assist in sweeping a lee without gaining excessive headway, you can use the previously described backing and filling maneuver. Come ahead to start the ship swinging to the right and then put the

Fig. 1-13. "It's a long way up." Courtesy Lee Klimo.

engine astern. The vessel turns about her pivot point while headway is simultaneously reduced so the maneuver does not require any great amount of searoom. Remember, though, that all the way must not be taken off the ship as this makes it difficult for the pilot boat to stay alongside. It is also important not to back so long that the wash reaches the pilot ladder and sweeps the pilot launch away from the ship's side.

ESTIMATING SPEED THOUGH THE WATER BY SHIP'S PROPELLER WASH

How, on a dark night without a Doppler log, do you tell what speed you are making? By watching the wash from the propeller. When the engine is going astern, the ship's speed is down to about 2 knots when the wash from the propeller begins to move up the starboard side of the ship. So long as that wash is being left behind the ship, you are making something in excess of 2 knots. Of course, as every seaman knows, once the wash reaches halfway up the ship's hull, the ship is dead in the water. (See figure 4-2.)

Would you want a good, sound ladder to scale a two-to-four-story swaying building? The pilot wants at least as much when boarding your rolling ship in a seaway.

Be sure a clean pilot ladder meeting current IMO and USCG standards is properly rigged under the supervision of a licensed deck officer. This officer must visually and physically inspect the ladder as it is rigged and be in attendance while the pilot embarks or disembarks. Two seamen must also be on hand at these times. Use only a proper ladder, reserved for use as a pilot ladder, that is made up so that:

1. The rungs are of one piece hardwood. (That often-used chain affair should be thrown over the side.)
2. The bottom four rungs are of reinforced hard rubber.
3. The rungs have a nonskid surface.
4. Rungs are at least 19 inches long, 4 inches deep, and 1 inch thick.
5. The ladder is hung by single lengths of manila or prestretched (low stretch) Dacron.
6. There is a clear space 16 to 19 inches between the lines across each rung.
7. There are 12 to 15 inches between the rungs.*

Have a heaving line available to handle the pilot's bag (it may contain your mail, so handle the bag with care!) and a life ring with waterlight. Maintain communications by walkie-talkie between the pilot ladder and the bridge when the pilot is boarding or leaving. Keep the ladder and the deck area at the head of the ladder well lighted. Place a light aft but near the ladder so it illuminates the ladder without blinding the pilot boat operator.

Coming aboard on a winter night is dangerous enough without having to use an iced-up ladder. Keep the ladder on deck in icy weather and put it over the side only when the pilot boat is alongside.

Spreaders are required if there are more than nine rungs in the ladder, to keep the ladder from twisting. These spreaders must be at least 70 inches long, placed at intervals not exceeding nine rungs apart, and be secured behind and in line with rungs.†

The maximum distance that a pilot should have to climb is 9 meters (30 feet), and an accommodation ladder must be used in conjunction with

*Malcolm C. Armstrong, *Pilot Ladder Safety*, 8-12.
†Ibid., 15.

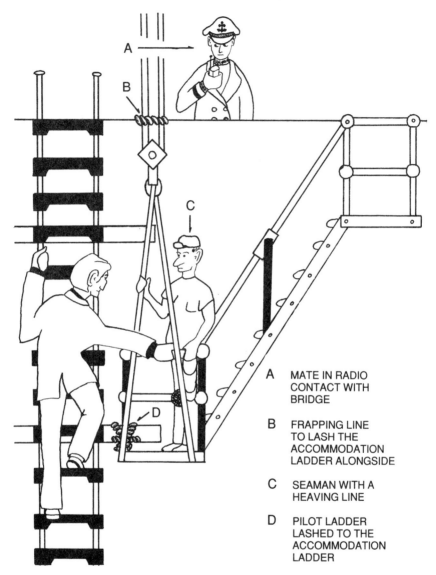

A   MATE IN RADIO
     CONTACT WITH
     BRIDGE

B   FRAPPING LINE
     TO LASH THE
     ACCOMMODATION
     LADDER ALONGSIDE

C   SEAMAN WITH A
     HEAVING LINE

D   PILOT LADDER
     LASHED TO THE
     ACCOMMODATION
     LADDER

Fig. 1-14. Use of combination of pilot and accommodation ladders.

the ladder as shown in Figure 1-14 when the distance from the water to
the deck exceeds that amount.

Be sure to lash the accommodation ladder tight alongside the ship
with the frapping line "B" (fig. 1-14). This important line is often

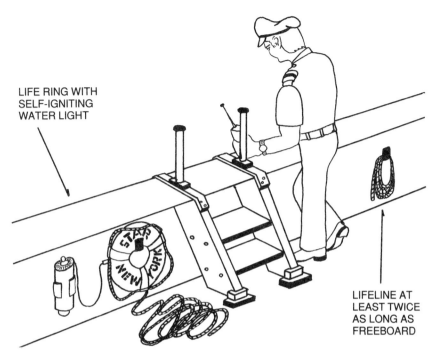

LIFE RING WITH
SELF-IGNITING
WATER LIGHT

LIFELINE AT
LEAST TWICE
AS LONG AS
FREEBOARD

Fig. 1-15. Typical bulwark steps and boarding area safety aids.

forgotten, leaving the accommodation ladder free to swing away from the hull as the ship rolls in a swell at the pilot station. The frapping line also holds the accommodation ladder alongside when the ship has a small list and, since the pilot ladder is lashed to the accommodation ladder at point D, this in turn minimizes the amount the long pilot ladder is free to swing.

The access to the deck must be either through an opening in the bulwark or over the rail using stanchions at least 40 inches high secured into the bulwark together with a sturdy set of steps down to the deck. Too many pilots have been needlessly hurt trying to climb over the rail or gunwale. (Fig. 1-15)

Rig manropes alongside the ladder. Not all pilots use the manropes, but they should be available to assist a pilot in transferring safely from ship to launch. Have the manropes and ladder rigged well above the water so they clear the deck of the launch lying alongside. A ladder lying on the launch's deck may trap and injure the pilot, while a ladder lying between the launch and the ship's hull may be pulled down from the ship by the pitching launch.

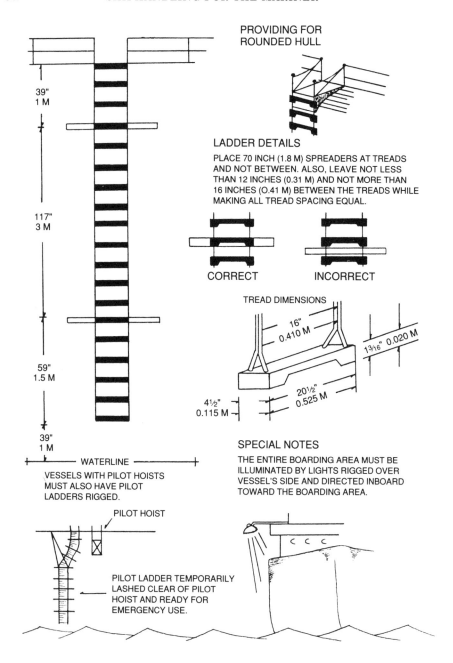

PROVIDING FOR
ROUNDED HULL

LADDER DETAILS

PLACE 70 INCH (1.8 M) SPREADERS AT TREADS
AND NOT BETWEEN. ALSO, LEAVE NOT LESS
THAN 12 INCHES (0.31 M) AND NOT MORE THAN
16 INCHES (O.41 M) BETWEEN THE TREADS WHILE
MAKING ALL TREAD SPACING EQUAL.

CORRECT   INCORRECT

TREAD DIMENSIONS

16" 0.410 M

1³/₁₆" 0.020 M

20½" 0.525 M

4½" 0.115 M

39"
1 M

117"
3 M

59"
1.5 M

39"
1 M

WATERLINE

VESSELS WITH PILOT HOISTS
MUST ALSO HAVE PILOT
LADDERS RIGGED.

PILOT HOIST

PILOT LADDER TEMPORARILY
LASHED CLEAR OF PILOT
HOIST AND READY FOR
EMERGENCY USE.

SPECIAL NOTES

THE ENTIRE BOARDING AREA MUST BE
ILLUMINATED BY LIGHTS RIGGED OVER
VESSEL'S SIDE AND DIRECTED INBOARD
TOWARD THE BOARDING AREA.

Fig. 1-16. Pilot ladder pointers.

If a pilot hoist is used be sure a conventional ladder is also rigged alongside and available. Many pilots have had enough bad experiences with these hoists that they refuse to use them, and even if the hoist is used, the ladder must be available in case a problem develops.

Rigs for proper boarding facilities with various combinations of freeboard and hull type are shown in Figure 1-16. Titles of some useful books and pamphlets about pilot boarding techniques and facilities are included in the Bibliography.

WIND EFFECTS ON STEERING

As the ship slows, she begins to feel the wind and become more difficult to steer if the weather is not the best. The freeboard or "sail area" that the ship presents will be the principal factor determining how much effect the wind will have on steering, although the ratio of the ship's draft to freeboard will also be important. Needless to say, even if the amount of sail area is not great, if you are only drawing 10 feet forward, you will find the wind a problem as you begin to reduce speed.

How much will your vessel feel the wind? As a rule of thumb, based on tests with various types of ships, at very low maneuvering speeds a high-sided ship such as a passenger ship or a containership will feel the wind significantly at a wind speed of three times the ship's speed, while a loaded tanker will require a wind speed of at least five times the ship's speed before being affected to the same degree. Other types of cargo ships will fall between these two factors, depending on their house configuration, deck load, and freeboard.* (Fig. 1-17) Keep in mind that a loaded containership, passenger ship, auto carrier, or high-sided liquified gas carrier with 75 feet of freeboard presents 50,000 to 60,000 square feet of side to the wind. *A full rigged sailing ship carried about 45,000 square feet of canvas.* Obviously, the wind direction and force is at least as important to a pilot or master handling modern motor ships as it was to ship's masters maneuvering ships in the days of sail. Ships may grow larger and look different but the wind and sea haven't changed and the basic principles of shiphandling remain very much the same, no matter how many flashing lights and alarms we put on the bridge.

Conversely, the ship's speed can be reduced to a point determined by that same ratio of wind force to ship's speed before you would begin to

*Brian Hope, *El Paso Consolidated Maneuvering Trials.*

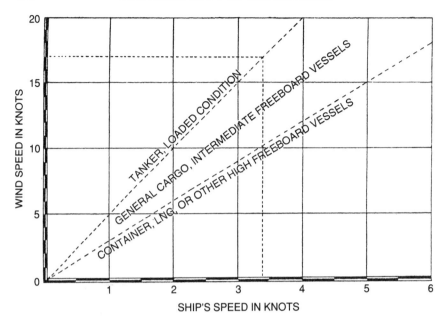

Fig. 1-17. Speed of vessel at which wind takes charge.

have problems steering. This is not to say that you cannot steer at that point, but rather that you will then need to use the engine to steer, giving a kick ahead as the ship starts to come up into the wind. When you are trying to stop the ship, this can obviously become a problem. By punching the engine ahead, that is, significantly increasing the revolutions for just long enough to start the ship swinging back to the desired heading, you will be able to control the ship without significantly increasing her headway. You should keep in mind that the wind will become an important factor in handling the ship as you reduce speed when making arrival or slowing to pick up the pilot, and consider this factor when planning your arrival.

How will the ship react as you reduce speed? Ships of most configurations will normally head up into the wind at increasingly larger angles as the ship loses headway. When finally dead in the water, the ship will usually want to lie beam to the wind. With sternway, the ship will want to back into the wind. Be aware, though, that every ship will behave a little differently, depending on the silhouette that she presents to the wind, i.e., the location of the house, deck cargoes, amount of freeboard, and trim. Only you will know exactly how your ship will behave in a strong wind, and then only after extensive experimentation with her.

Again, it is stressed that you should get as much experience as possible handling your vessel under varying conditions. Don't let your natural reluctance caused by lack of experience deter you from creating opportunities to handle your ship and develop a feel for her at slow speeds. Any damn fool can handle his ship at sea speed!

Here again, a potential problem such as a strong wind can be made an aid once the shiphandler begins to appreciate his ship's behavior and plans his maneuvers with that behavior in mind. An example would be a ship that must turn around and head to an anchorage, or perhaps to sea. If she is loaded with containers, it might not be possible to turn in a direction that requires the bow to come through the wind—she might be held on her heading by the wind much like a sailing ship in irons, and her speed would increase without any significant change in her heading. If the ship is instead turned away from the wind (or back and filled around if the amount of searoom available will not allow a normal turn), and her stern is brought across the wind during the maneuver, the wind will assist the ship in turning. As sternway develops the ship will turn easily as she backs into the wind, so that when she comes ahead again the wind, now on the quarter, will assist her in turning. This is true even if due to the configuration of the channel or anchorage the ship must back and fill in what ordinarily would be the "wrong way," to the left— since the normal tendency of the stern to go to port when the engine goes astern would be overcome by the wind as the ship gains sternway.

This demonstrates once again the value of appreciating the forces of wind and current, and the need to add sail training to the curriculum of our maritime schools. Apart from the important but more esoteric benefits of sail training such as self-discipline, attention to tasks at hand, and appreciation of the demands of the ocean environment, there are important direct benefits. The skills required to navigate and handle a ship being affected by wind and current are as important today as they were in the years of the Down Easters, and these seafaring skills can best be learned by working a ship under sail. Sail training should supplement the seagoing experience already given potential deck and engineering officers.

COMMUNICATIONS WITH OTHER VESSELS

With the advent of good radio voice communications, and especially the universal use of VHF radio, it is possible to avoid many dangerous situations as well as arrange passing and meeting situations so that those aboard can enjoy a degree of peace of mind not possible when conning a ship only a few years ago. Further, the third mate no longer has to stand out on the bridge wing manning the signal light on a cold, rainy winter night arriving at Ambrose. Unfortunately, this also means that this same mate probably can't read a message sent by flashing light when needed, nor will he or she enjoy the satisfaction of mastering that skill so as to be able to talk to a passing ship by flashing light on the long night watch at sea. Today, we instead suffer through long discussions on the VHF with every passing ship such as, "How was the weather behind you?" and other nonessential communication that interferes with important transmissions. Better we had stayed with the "What ship? Where bound?" of the Aldis light days.

Be that as it may, the VHF can be a great aid to ship's officer if it is used properly. While there are good references available on proper radio procedure, to assure that the VHF is used to its best advantage, there are also practices that may not have been discussed sufficiently.

1. Don't transmit overly long messages, with tiresome and *unnecessary repetition of your ship's call letters after each transmission.* It is necessary to give your call letters to another ship only when making an initial transmission, and after the last transmission of your discussion. Between the first and last transmissions you need only give your call sign *at ten-minute intervals*, although you will hopefully keep radio communications shorter than that.

2. Do call the pilot station, discuss the placement of the pilot ladder, update your ETA, and ask if there are any special requirements for boarding facilities.

3. Utilize the VHF to contact the pilot services before arrival at the station to discuss the traffic and weather that you might encounter as you approach the station. This is often better information than you can obtain from a traffic control system, which we'll cover in a later chapter when we will discuss traffic movements and control in general. Suffice it to say that the pilot is able to give you this information and make your arrival safer and easier.

4. When talking to other ships, remember that while U.S.-flag ships are accustomed to discussing meeting situations according to their intentions for meeting and passing, ships of most nationalities discuss how they will change course to pass. Therefore it is prudent

for the mariner to state any meeting arrangements in two ways, to be sure that the other ship understands those arrangements. For example: *"Golden Gopher, this is the tanker Prudence.* I will alter my course to starboard, to meet you port to port."

This will avoid any misunderstandings, even if there is little English spoken on the other ship. If you are in U.S. inland waters, add "for one whistle meeting." This phrasing of communications on the radio is commonly taught to apprentice pilots and should be adopted by ship's officers as well.

Use the ship's whistle to supplement radio communications and further clarify the planned meeting, whether or not this is required by the Rules of the Road. There is an unfortunate reluctance of deck officers to use the ship's whistle today.

There was a collision several years ago between a U.S. Navy *mariner*-class support ship and a Liberian-flag, Chinese-manned, bulk carrier at the entrance to the Chesapeake Bay. It could have been avoided if these recommended procedures had been followed. The non-English-speaking crew of the bulk carrier thought the naval ship was going to alter course to starboard, when in fact the naval ship had requested on the VHF radio a starboard to starboard meeting. The only word clearly understood by the Chinese master was "starboard" and, since the rules that most of the world operates under outside U.S. waters discuss course changes, not meeting situations, his mistake was natural and quite common. The seagoing community is international, speaks many tongues, and care is needed when speaking via VHF to arrange meetings and passings.

Lastly, do not call another ship by saying, "Ship on my starboard bow." A call on VHF can be heard at sea even under the worst conditions over an area of *at least 1400 square miles*, so it is obvious that you are certainly not defining the ship that you want to speak with. There are many other means of identifying that ship, such as adding an approximate course that she is steering, or a geographic location, the type of ship, or the hull color.

It is hoped that a practical method of identifying a calling ship will soon be developed, such as a distinctive mark on the other ship's radar presentation, that will finally make the VHF the useful aid that it is capable of being. With the plethora of existing sophisticated electronic aids, surely an electronics firm can develop a means of identifying a ship

---

transmitting on the VHF. This would be one of the greatest collision avoidance aids since the development of running lights. However, until such a system exists, you will have to use your imagination to make your communications more positive.

PILOT ABOARD

After the ship's officer brings the pilot to the bridge, there are several items that should be covered before the ship's conn is turned over for the passage up the channel. The first should not be to have the pilot write his name; there are more important things, such as shaping up for the channel and meeting other traffic, to be taken care of!

Several pilots were gathered around the table at the pilot station, waiting for the arrival of their ships so that they could begin their night's work. Coffee was passed.

"Got myself a Japanese containership tonight, which should make for a pleasant night's work. They will be as efficient as hell, make their ETA, and have a hot cup of coffee waiting for me when I get up to the bridge."

"Yeah, and can't think of anything I'd like more after boarding on a cold night like this."

The junior member of the group was to go aboard a German refrigerated ship. He joked that the first thing the captain would say was, "Where have you been pilot? We have been waiting for ten minutes, and we do not like being delayed like this."

This observation has been made by a thousand pilots, on a thousand nights such as this, and always raised a laugh.

"I have an American ship, light draft, and a long way to the bridge. After going up 30 feet of icy ladder, and climbing six decks, I'll be panting like a race horse."

"Yeah, and the first thing you'll be handed won't be coffee!"

"That's for sure. They'll stick the damn bell book in my hand and want me to write my name!"

This brought a bigger laugh from all in the room.

This is a scene common to pilots from all over the world. Before a pilot can get a U.S.-flag ship headed fair, or even catch his breath, he is asked for his name. No coffee, no sandwich, no "May I take your coat, pilot?" Professionalism calls for something better than this. Keep it in mind the next time you welcome a pilot aboard your vessel—let the man catch his breath, get the ship steadied up on course, hand him a cup of coffee, and then ask for his name.

Fig. 1-18. "Welcome aboard, Mr. Pilot. She's on full ahead, steady on 275, and all yours."

The pilot will need information from the master. While IMO regulations now require a card to be posted in the wheelhouse showing some of the ship's particulars and maneuvering characteristics, this card is not much good on a dark night on a ship that is underway. The same information will be much more useful if it is also contained on a small pocket-size card that the pilot can look at with a flashlight while starting up the channel. Further, there is other information of more use than that found on the maneuvering card which should be supplied by the master. Is the engine in proper operating condition? Does it respond quickly? Does the ship have any steering peculiarities? Can she maneuver on heavy oil, or must you change to diesel prior to reducing to maneuvering speeds? Will there be any problem letting go the anchor if it is required, or in making up a tug, due to deck cargo or the ship's construction? This and many other items must be exchanged as it is obviously to the master's advantage that there be no surprises for the pilot at a later time in the passage. The additional information required will vary from ship to ship, and voyage to voyage. It is here that the professional knowledge of the master alone can serve, and he must give some thought before arrival at the pilot station to making up his own list of pertinent information, to supplement the posted information required by regulation.

POSTING OF MANEUVERING CHARACTERISTICS

The applicable sections of the Code of Federal Regulations are excerpted to show the information required on the posted card, and the minimum information that should be presented to the pilot on the recommended wallet-size card. Several other items should also be included, such as the ship's length, beam, displacement, horsepower, and the distance from the bridge to the bow and stern, distance from the bridge at which visibility is restricted, the present draft, and a check-off list showing the operating condition of the engine, radar, and other navigational equipment, the bow thruster, and any other items pertinent to your particular vessel.

The information required by law is general in nature and is for deeper water than the pilot would ordinarily be interested in. Since the data is for specific conditions, and is too often based on analytical calculations or model tests, it is of limited use at best. Here again, it is obvious that the master should collect his own data based on actual trials that he will have conducted at the earliest available opportunity after taking command of a new vessel. Since there have been so few actual trials under shallow water conditions, any data derived by calculation, or from simulations based on such calculations, should only be considered as being a good approximation of a vessel's performance. As more tests are conducted, such as the aforementioned El Paso Marine Company and *Esso Osaka* tests, there will be more valid data available. Hopefully more complete shallow water tests will be conducted in the near future for other classes of ships, as well.

As stated in the Code of Federal Regulations:

Aboard each ". . . ocean and coastwise tankship of 1600 gross tons or over, the following maneuvering information must be prominently displayed," etc. in the pilothouse on a fact sheet.

(1) For full and half speed, a turning circle diagram to port and starboard that shows the time and the distance of advance and transfer required to alter the course 90 degrees with maximum rudder angle and constant power settings.

(2) The time and distance to stop the vessel from full and half speed while maintaining approximately the initial heading with minimum application of rudder.

(3) For each vessel with a fixed propeller, a table of shaft revolutions per minute for a representative range of speeds.

(4) For each vessel with a controllable pitch propeller, a table of control settings for a representative range of speeds.

(5) For each vessel that is fitted with an auxiliary device to assist in maneuvering, such as a bow thruster, a table of vessel speeds at which the auxiliary device is effective in maneuvering the vessel.

(6) The maneuvering information must be provided for the normal load and normal ballast condition for:
  (i) Calm weather—wind 10 knots or less, calm sea;
  (ii) No current;
  (iii) Deep water conditions—water depth twice the vessel's draft or greater; and
  (iv) Clean hull.

(7) At the bottom of the fact sheet, the following statement must appear:
                            WARNING

The response of the (name of vessel) may be different from those listed above if any of the following conditions, upon which the maneuvering information is based, are varied:

(1) Calm weather—wind 10 knots or less, calm sea;

(2) No current;

(3) Water depth twice the vessel's draft or greater;

(4) Clean hull; and

(5) Intermediate drafts or unusual trim.

* * *

(8) The information on the fact sheet must be:
  (i) Verified six months after the vessel is placed in service; or
  (ii) Modified six months after the vessel is placed into service and verified within three months thereafter.

(9) The information that appears on the fact sheet may be obtained from:
  (i) Trial trip observations;
  (ii) Model tests;
  (iii) Analytical calculations;
  (iv) Simulations;
  (v) Information established from another vessel of similar hull form, power, rudder and propeller, or
  (vi) Any combination of the above.
  The accuracy of the information in the fact sheet required is that attainable by ordinary shipboard navigation equipment.

(10) The requirements for information for fact sheets for specialized craft such as semi-submersibles, hydrofoils, hovercraft, and other vessels of unusual design will be specified on a case by case basis.

When you are sure that the pilot is fully briefed, and only then, can the conn be turned over to him. For some reason, it is the custom aboard too many ships to have the ship on full ahead and on the general heading for the channel when the pilot gets to the bridge. The turnover of the conn then consists of, "She is on full and heading 330, pilot." Too many masters think that the faster the changeover takes place, the more professionally it has been done. Ridiculous! And that is just how the pilot involved in such a turnover feels about it. Give the pilot sufficient time to get his eyes adjusted to the night, gather all the needed information, and then turn the conn over to him. A professional is never in a hurry to do anything aboard ship, yet more often than not aboard the merchant ships of most nationalities this hurried evolution takes place. It has taken you two weeks to get to this port. What is five more minutes?

CHAPTER TWO

SHIPHANDLING IN A CHANNEL

Seamen, with their inherent sense of order, service,
and discipline, should really be running the world.
—Anonymous

*The squall passed as suddenly as it had arrived and all that remained
was the mist rising off the hot, wet deck. Only a few minutes ago we had
been feeling our way up the winding river channel as the driving rain
blinded those on the bridge. The pilot had navigated primarily by radar,
alternating between that equipment and the forward wheelhouse windows where he peered through the heavy rain to verify what he was seeing
on the scope. Never was a voice raised, as courses and engine speeds were
given to keep the ship in the channel, and this display of skill and
confidence was appreciated by all on the bridge.*

*The aura of professionalism that surrounded this pilot's actions is as
much a product of experience and attitude as it is the result of technical
training and skill. It is essential that all seagoing professionals develop
this aspect of their work along with their technical skills. Professionalism
is a learned trait, qualitative in nature and difficult to define. We have
all observed the shipmaster or pilot who is obviously in command of a
situation, a person who is a professional, and the manner in which they
performed their work was, of itself, a definition of professionalism.*

*Because of the uniqueness of the seagoing environment and of the
seaman's work, the "showboating" often resorted to in other professions
to impress one's peers and superiors is out of place aboard ship. Decision
making committees and the substitution of rhetoric for content are mech-
anisms that can be used to hide inability in some fields. Not so aboard
ship. Here you must be competent and confident about your work, and
any lack of skill will become evident in a short time. Further, you must
also appear competent to those you work with so they too have confidence
in your skills and respond without the delay or questioning that leads to
confusion.*

Since professionalism cannot be learned from a book, those who teach at the various maritime academies and schools, and more importantly, the senior officers aboard ship, have a responsibility to nurture its development among younger officers just starting out in their careers. This offers a significant challenge in an era when it is fashionable to denigrate traditional skills and quiet competence. Demand professionalism from all aboard. Ships cannot function properly without a singular high standard of performance and sense of responsibility.

BANK EFFECTS

In the portion of a river where the channel narrows, the ship begins feeling the steep bank close on the starboard hand. She wants to sheer to port as the combination of suction on the starboard quarter and, to a lesser degree, the cushion of water built up between the ship's starboard bow and the bank become more strongly felt. The problem is compounded when it is necessary to slow the ship; the rudder loses some effectiveness as the flow of water is reduced, while the suction at the stern, which is primarily a factor of the ship's speed through the water, remains strong. The ship must be moved further from the bank and the rudder angle increased.

But what if the ship gets so close to the bank that she starts to sheer across the channel? *Don't reduce engine speed*, as at this point the rudder needs to be as effective as possible and any reduction in the ship's speed that might result from a change in engine revolutions will be negligible in such a short period of time. Rather, let the head fall a few degrees off course across the channel while maintaining some rudder angle toward the near bank, and *increase engine speed* so the flow of water past the rudder increases significantly. When the heading has changed a few degrees toward the center of the channel, increase the rudder angle toward the near bank to first check the swing, and then to bring the ship back on course as she reaches the center of the channel, or at least reaches a distance from the closer bank that will allow her to be steered safely. Only after getting away from the bank should the engine speed be reduced so the ship loses some headway and the tendency to take a sheer is reduced. It is obvious that a ship should not proceed in a narrow channel at full maneuvering speed, since she would not have any revolutions in reserve should they be required.

Fig. 2-1. "The quiet manner in which the pilot went about his work . . . "

Remember too that a ship wants to move closer to a bank, due to the increased flow of water and the resultant reduced pressure along her side closest to the bank. For reasons explained by Signore Bernoulli, a ship wants to move laterally toward a closer bank even though her heading is parallel to it. Either keep the ship headed at some small angle away from the bank or hold her in the center of the channel when not meeting another vessel.

As is pointed out again and again in this text, the forces acting on a ship can often be put to your advantage, making an aid of what seems to the nonmariner to be a hazard. When making a turn, a bank can be put close enough to the quarter to cause the ship to sheer in the direction of the turn and thus make a turn that she otherwise could not navigate, or at least could not navigate at the speed that is possible utilizing these forces. As an example, there are turns in the Gaillard Cut in the Panama Canal that theoretically cannot be negotiated by many ships without tug assistance and yet ships have been making these turns easily throughout the life of the Canal with the aid of bank suction. If your ship should transit the Panama Canal or another narrow waterway, watch the rudder angle indicator and the position of the ship and you will find the

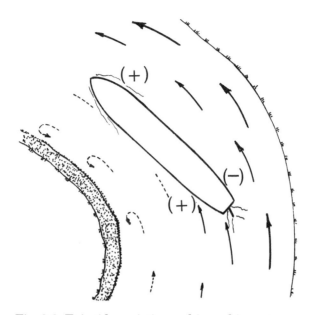

Fig. 2-2. Fair tide assisting a ship making a turn.

ship going around many turns with the rudder amidships. A seaman routinely uses learned skills to turn potential hazards into aids, both in close water and offshore.

This same bank suction can also assist a ship to pass another vessel in a narrow channel, to locate the center of a channel in times of limited visibility, or to make routine maneuvers, as long as it is planned and allowed for. Keep in mind, though, that speed must be restricted so the ship can come ahead if the sheer should become greater than desired.

PLANNING AHEAD

Once again we see the importance of planning ahead to use natural forces to advantage. Thinking ahead and planning maneuvers based on an understanding of the forces acting on the ship, much like a chess master who wins by planning several moves at one time so they follow in a logical order, is essential if a ship is to be moved efficiently and safely. The process of thinking several steps ahead underlies every maneuver discussed in this text. Its importance in your development as an excellent shiphandler, rather than just as an acceptable shiphandler, cannot be exaggerated.

Understand ship behavior, properly reduce ship's speed, use existing conditions and forces to advantage to assist the ship's rudder and engine in maneuvering and, most important, *think ahead of the ship* so that she is reacting to your orders rather than your orders being given in reaction to the ship's behavior—these are the basics of excellent ship-handling. Think ahead of your ship at all times.

TIDE AND CURRENT

Many rivers cannot be negotiated by larger ships without a fair tide since a head current hinders them in making turns. As shown in Figure 2-2, a fair current helps the stern around a bend when it strikes the quarter, so the stern comes around at a greater rate. At the same time the bow is assisted by the eddy currents reflected out of the bend and the lack of current on the bow on the point side of the bend. In contrast, for a given speed over the bottom, a ship stemming a tide has a greater flow of water passing between her and the bank, retarding the stern's motion around a turn and forcing the bow and ship bodily towards the bank. (Fig. 2-2)

Since a ship that is closer to the bottom is more difficult to control, high water makes the pilot's job easier—aside from just putting enough water under a deep loaded ship to assure that she is in the desirable state of being always afloat! By moving with a rising tide to ensure a fair current and deeper water, a ship is using both tide and current to her best advantage.

The current changes at each area of a channel at a different time, and is affected by several factors such as freshets resulting from heavy rains upriver, and strong off- or onshore winds, so tides may occur at significantly different times than predicted. Keep a seaman's eye on the current. Develop the habit of looking at pilings, buoys, and other fixed objects to check the actual current against that which has been predicted until the practice becomes as natural as breathing. It's the difference between the neophyte and the professional.

TYPES OF RUDDERS AND PROPULSION SYSTEMS

While the mariner has an academic interest in the characteristics of all the various types of rudder and propulsion systems used on ships today, the shiphandler must first be concerned with how the ship responds to the system with which she is fitted. He can't change that rudder or engine, whether or not the ship handles poorly, but must live with the ship as she is. A practiced shiphandler will know in a very short time how effective the rudder is and how the ship will respond to varying amounts of rudder angle. Unfortunately, the tendency towards smaller rudders on larger ships has made the shiphandler's task more difficult.

Again, plan ahead so the rudder and propulsion system can be used as effectively as possible. Proceed at a moderate speed so greater engine revolutions can be used as needed to increase the flow of water past the rudder and thus increase the rudder's effectiveness without creating other problems. By using the engine in this manner, for only as long as needed to obtain the desired results, the shiphandler can usually overcome any inherent deficiencies in the ship's design. This tactic is particularly effective with a diesel ship since immediate, large changes in revolutions can be obtained; a steam turbine ship increases revolutions more slowly and more care is necessary to keep the ship's speed down while still controlling steering. Obviously then, speed is important when steering a ship—sufficient headway is needed to make steering possible, yet speed must be kept down to minimize unwanted hydrodynamic effects and to have sufficient engine speed in reserve to increase rudder effectiveness when required.

Ships fitted with balanced spade rudders often will not steer when large rudder angles are used. A turbulent flow develops over the rudder's surface so its lifting effect is lost and it stalls. Occasionally a ship is still designed with such a rudder and all those involved in her design and construction seem surprised when she goes aground early in her life while trying to negotiate a normal turn. A few years ago, a class of large German containerships was fitted with such a rudder and suffered several groundings within a few months. Tug assistance was required so those ships could make turns that other ships of similar size navigated routinely. If a ship's profile drawings show a spade rudder, beware of turns requiring the use of more than 5 to 10 degrees of rudder angle. The rudder may stall, and the loss of effectiveness means that the ship will just continue along her course as if she had no rudder until she fetches up at some point where you never intended to be.

Propeller design has a significant effect on the handling characteristics of a ship. The direction of rotation affects the ship's behavior, the direction in which the vessel tends to twist when the engine is put astern, and the diameter of the turning circle for right and left turns, as discussed in Chapter 1. The size of the propeller affects the stopping and steering ability of the ship since higher revolutions are required to get a good flow over the rudder at reduced speeds when the ship is fitted with a smaller diameter propeller.

The handling characteristics of a ship fitted with a variable pitch propeller are significantly different from those of a ship with a fixed blade propeller. Variable pitch propulsion systems have advantages since a diesel engine so fitted does not have to be stopped and restarted to go astern, and an almost infinite choice of speeds is available. Further, you can go astern indefinitely, which isn't possible with a turbine-driven ship, and, unlike a conventional motor ship, you can change the direction of propulsion repeatedly without being concerned about exhausting the supply of starting air. These advantages have at times been used as a basis for recommending that VLCCs be fitted with this type of propulsion. The drawbacks should also be considered, however, before deciding whether variable pitch propulsion is as desirable as claimed:

1. When reducing the speed of a ship fitted with a variable pitch propeller, the flow of water past the rudder is significantly disrupted unless the pitch is reduced very gradually. The adverse effect on steering is significant. The propeller cannot safely be put at zero pitch to reduce the ship's headway since this completely disrupts the needed flow of water to the rudder.
2. A variable pitch propeller going astern is less effective than a conventional propeller. This compounds the aforementioned steering problems since, because it is more difficult to drift the way off a ship fitted with a variable pitch propeller, it is often necessary to use the engine astern for longer periods of time to stop her.

When approaching a berth, lock, or pilot station it is therefore necessary to start slowing a ship equipped with this type of propeller sooner than would be required with a conventional propeller, and to then use minimum pitch to steer at slow speed once headway is sufficiently reduced.

Since a variable pitch propeller is normally turning at high RPM, even when in position and stopped at the berth at zero pitch, be sure to keep stern lines clear of the water when docking. Inform linehandlers on the dock that this is necessary, as a line can become fouled in this rapidly turning propeller in an amazingly short period of time. A tug working at the stern must also be cautioned.

EFFECT OF TRIM ON HANDLING CHARACTERISTICS

As a ship's trim by the stern increases, she becomes more directionally stable and her tactical diameter increases. The latter change is minor and of no practical significance to the shiphandler so long as the drag remains within practical limits. There is, however, a marked increase in the diameter of the ship's turning circle as the bow comes out of the water.

From the shiphandler's point of view, assuming there isn't an excessively strong wind on the higher bow, a ship usually steers better as drag increases.

The steering characteristics of a ship on an even keel vary depending on the ship's hull form. A ship with a large block coefficient steers poorly, tending to be directionally unstable. This condition is amplified if the ship trims by the head as she enters shallow water. A ship with finer lines may be directionally stable, or have neutral stability when on an even keel. The behavior of a ship with moderate block coefficient can only be determined by trials since there is insufficient data available at present to allow an accurate prediction of her steering characteristics.

A ship trimmed by the head is directionally unstable for almost all hull forms. When in this condition the ship requires large amounts of rudder for excessive periods of time to check her swing. The vessel becomes cranky and difficult to handle. If she trims by the head in shallow water the problem is compounded.

Why does a ship behave in this manner when the difference between the forward and after drafts decreases? One must look at the immersed sections of the ship to better understand this phenomenon, and especially at the location of the sections having the maximum submerged area.

The ship is turning as a result of couples formed at the rudder and through the center of gravity. One of the forces forming the latter couple is the imbalance of pressures about the submerged portions of the hull. (Fig. 2-3) As the ship begins turning, there is a new increase in pressure below the waterline on the bow away from the center of gravity, i.e., the outward bow. This resultant imbalance of forces in that location, *forward* and outside of the center of gravity, causes the ship to be directionally unstable.

All ships experience the same imbalance in the initial stages of a turn. If a ship is trimmed by the stern though, the pressures shift further aft along the side of the hull as the ship stabilizes in the turn, while

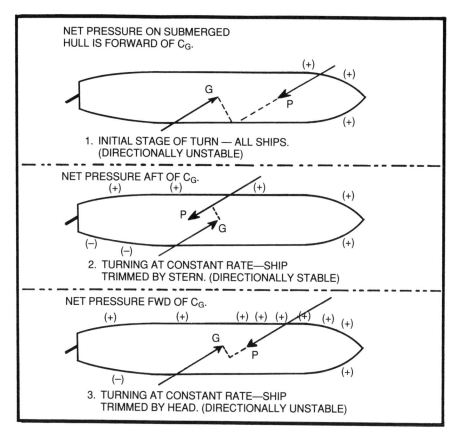

Fig. 2-3. Effect of trim on steering.

the corresponding pressure drop on the quarter on the inboard side of the turn continues to increase. The resultant couple has then shifted aft of the center of gravity so the ship becomes directionally stable.

Ships trimmed by the head experience a larger initial positive pressure at the bow due to the increase in submerged area forward, while the negative pressure is reduced at the quarter due to the reduction in submerged area. The couple therefore remains ahead of the center of gravity throughout the turn and the ship continues to be directionally unstable.* This condition is indicated to the shiphandler by the shift forward of the apparent pivot point of the ship, so the ship seems to pivot about a point nearer the bow than normally expected,

*John H. La Dage, *Modern Ships*, 203-4.

and by the ship wanting to continue to swing after the rudder is placed amidships.

A large VLCC with full sections forward will experience the same distribution of pressures in a turn when on an even keel as a finer ship does when trimmed by the head. Obviously then, if a VLCC is trimmed by the head she will be even more unstable since the resultant couple is magnified accordingly.

The effect of trim by the head on a vessel's steering can be anticipated by referring to the curve of areas of the immersed sections. This curve is developed by the naval architect by measuring on the ship's lines drawings with a planimeter that portion of the cross sectional area at each station that will be submerged at a particular draft and trim. These areas are then put into the form of a curve by measuring outward from a baseline a linear distance equal in units to each station's submerged area. After plotting the corresponding point at each station, a curve is faired through the points. The curve will reach a maximum at that station having the greatest submerged area—the location of a vessel's center of buoyancy—and as the vessel is trimmed by the head the apex of that curve will shift progressively forward. More use should be made of this curve since it is one indication of the changes that can be expected in directional stability of a particular hull as trim changes. Sample curves should be included with the ship's stability and trim booklet for use by the ship's officers.

The value of this curve is unfortunately limited at present since, like all relative indicators, some norms must be established against which the mariner can compare the curves for his own ship. Hopefully, these norms will be developed as part of future model, simulator, and trial testing. Larger ships are being built, with higher block coefficients and a greater percentage of their total submerged area in their forward sections, so this curve and the steering characteristics that it indicates are becoming increasingly important.

With this in mind, what steps must a mariner take to safely handle a potentially directionally unstable ship? First, she must not be trimmed by the head. Keep sufficient drag to assure that the ship maintains positive directional stability, allowable draft permitting. Second, on a ship with marginal directional stability the rudder will have to be used for a longer period of time to start the vessel swinging, after which large amounts of rudder are needed for longer periods of time than normally expected to check a swing. The rudder is put back amidships as soon as the swing begins since the rate of turn will increase even when the rudder is amidships. If the rudder is kept on too long the ship will get away and it might not be possible to check her swing in time to avoid leaving the channel.

Don't overlook the importance of having a trained helmsman who is experienced in steering your particular ship. A directionally unstable ship requires special treatment and the helmsman's experience can be invaluable.

Even this potentially unsatisfactory condition can be put to advantage if the shiphandler watches the steering closely, since a directionally unstable ship can turn in a very small area. It is not suggested that the ship be purposely loaded to obtain this condition, but often the mariner must live with a ship "as she is" and in such a case he or she can at least take advantage of the situation.

MAKING A TURN IN A CHANNEL

There are two basic considerations when making a bend or turn in a channel—where to begin the turn and how much rudder to use.

It is impossible to make a turn properly if the turn is started at the wrong place in the channel. Obviously, if the turn is started too late excessive amounts of rudder and engine revolutions are necessary to complete the turn while remaining in the channel or in the desired location in an anchorage. A more common error, though, is to start the turn too soon, since it is human nature both to be conservative and to become impatient when waiting to reach a desired point. This results in having to check the ship's swing and then start the turn again at a later time. Starting a turn too early may not always cause a problem and is certainly preferable to starting a turn too late, but if you have to check the ship's swing in a channel where suction can be experienced it may be difficult to start the ship turning again once that swing is lost.

Begin the turn when the ship's *pivot point* is nearly at the turning point at the end of the reach or range, not the ship's bow or bridge. (Fig. 2-4) Remember that ships turn circles, not corners. Since you have fixed the diameter and advance of the turning circle in your mind during the previously described trial maneuvers, you should be able to judge when to start a turn. (Fig. 2-5)

While it is possible to determine this point by constructing diagrams based on channel widths and the theoretical turning radius of the ship,

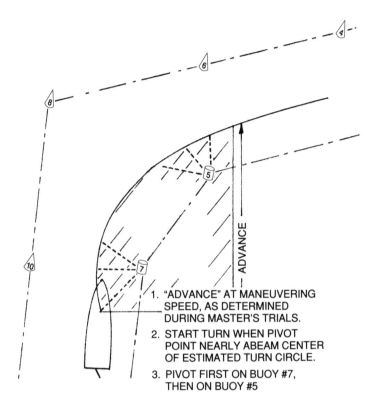

1. "ADVANCE" AT MANEUVERING
   SPEED, AS DETERMINED
   DURING MASTER'S TRIALS.
2. START TURN WHEN PIVOT
   POINT NEARLY ABEAM CENTER
   OF ESTIMATED TURN CIRCLE.
3. PIVOT FIRST ON BUOY #7,
   THEN ON BUOY #5

Fig. 2-4. Use the pivot point to position a ship in a turn.

such an approach to a routine maneuver is not practical and encourages
the mariner to get involved with unworkable methods. It is better to
learn to handle the ship by instinct and feel developed from experience
and trial maneuvers.

If in doubt about the amount of rudder required, use a larger amount
than you feel necessary. Reduce the rudder angle as needed to place the
ship at the desired point in the reach using the reference point method
discussed in the next section. Practice making exact turns at every
opportunity, even if a ship is in an open anchorage and there is no need
to put the ship in an exact location at that particular time. A professional
makes turns neatly and with a minimum of helm orders and it is only
through practice that the feel for making precise turns can be developed.
Turns can also be practiced with great benefit on a simulator since you

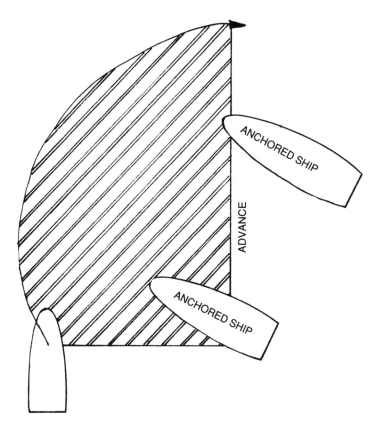

Fig. 2-5. Allow for ship's turning characteristics when starting turns
and maneuvering.

can get a very realistic feel for both rate of turn and relative movement
when working at such an installation. These are skills that, like riding
a bicycle, are never lost once learned.

USING AIDS TO NAVIGATION WHEN TURNING

As the ship proceeds up the channel, numerous aids to navigation are
available to the pilot and master. While the primary purpose of these
aids is to determine the ship's position relative to the axis of the channel,
there are other ways in which these aids can be utilized.

A buoy at a turn can be used as a rate of turn indicator by aligning
the buoy with a fixed point on the ship such as a stay, stanchion, or
window frame. (Fig. 2-6)

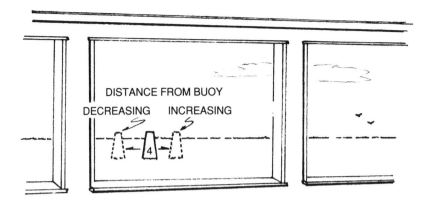

Fig. 2-6. Pivoting on a reference point when turning.

1. If the *relative bearing changes* toward the bow, so the buoy is
   moving forward relative to the reference point, the ship is turning
   at a rate that will bring her closer to that buoy. She will be closer
   to the buoy at the completion of the turn than she is at present.
   If the *rate* at which the buoy is moving ahead of the reference
   point is increasing, then obviously the rate at which the ship is
   turning is increasing.
2. If the buoy is *remaining steady* relative to the reference point
   the ship is turning at a fixed rate. She will maintain her present
   distance from the buoy as she makes the turn. In practice, the
   ship will actually be a little farther from the buoy when the turn
   is completed, since she is sliding sideways during the turn at a
   rate relative to the speed at which she is moving. For practical
   purposes though, the ship can be considered to be maintaining
   a constant distance from the buoy during the turn.
3. If the *bearing is opening* away from the bow so the buoy is moving
   aft relative to the reference point, then the ship's distance from
   the buoy is increasing. If the *rate* at which the buoy is opening
   is increasing then the rate of turn is decreasing.

Using a buoy in this manner is especially effective when turning in
a strong current since it is the vessel's movement relative to the buoy
and channel (the net movement resulting from the combination of vessel
momentum, swing, and current effects) that is of interest to the shiphandler. This resultant motion is immediately apparent when the ship is
turned using a fixed reference. By adjusting the rudder to alter the

buoy's relative movement a shiphandler can position the ship in a turn with great accuracy.

The angle between the lines of buoys marking the port and starboard sides of a channel can be used with great accuracy both to predict the ship's future position in a reach into which she is turning, and to know the vessel's position relative to the centerline after she has steadied up in that reach. Further, the rate at which a vessel is sliding laterally can be quickly determined by watching the change in angle of those buoys during a turn.

A range can obviously be used to determine the ship's position relative to the channel, but do not overlook the fact that the rate at which a range is opening or closing is of equal importance. This information is used in the same manner as the change in angle of a line of buoys to position the ship in a reach or channel.

MEETING ANOTHER VESSEL OR TOW

If a channel is of sufficient width, meeting another vessel is simply a matter of staying on your own side. The problem then is one of determining what "sufficient width" is, this being primarily a question of ship size and especially of draft and beam.

Ships routinely meet in the 500-foot-wide reaches of the Panama Canal with no problems, when their combined beams total up to 170 feet. (The only exceptions are the *Panamax* class vessels which do not meet any ship in those 500-foot-wide reaches due to their own inherent handling limitations.) This limit was established based upon the operating experience of the pilots in that waterway and confirmed by simulator tests, and can serve as a guideline although ships do meet in channels of less width than 500 feet under the proper conditions.

As ships approach the 170-foot-combined beam limit it becomes necessary to meet in the manner shown in Figure 2-7. In such cases the ships:

1. Meet nearly head-on and, when approximately one-and-a-half ship lengths apart, put their rudders to starboard to move to their own side and pass safely.
2. When one ship's bow is abeam the bow of the other, her helm is shifted to move her stern to starboard until she is parallel to the bank.
3. The rudder is again put to the right to check the swing. Caution is required at this point, so watch the ship's head closely. Your

vessel wants to continue swinging due to a combination of the bank suction on the starboard quarter and the effects of the other ship as her quarter comes abeam your bow, i.e., your ship wants to turn to port as her bow passes the other ship's stern. Use sufficient rudder to check this swing and maintain control despite the effects of suction at the bow and stern.

4. Do not increase the right rudder at this stage, but instead allow your ship to sag slowly to port so she is heading away from the bank once again. It is now unlikely that you could hit that ship if you tried since she has passed your bow and is moving away. So long as you don't come together laterally, which is unlikely unless you are close enough to shake hands with the mate on the bridge of the other ship, you will pass safely.

5. Finally, as the stern of the other ship passes your stern there is a mutual suction effect which moves your stern away from the near bank as the two ships pass clear and proceed on their way.

Again, the ship's speed is a key. The ship must be moving at less than full maneuvering speed so suction is minimized and sufficient engine speed remains to come ahead and increase the effectiveness of the rudder as needed. This passing maneuver is not as difficult as it might sound, and is probably best demonstrated in the Houston Ship Channel where the pilots have perfected what for them is a routine meeting maneuver.

A great deal of study is being done using both simulators and actual ship trials to determine the limits for safe navigation and meeting in various types of channels. The results of this research can be used to safely handle vessels in narrow channels as ship size continues to increase without a commensurate increase in channel width and depth. Hopefully, the practice of using the services of experienced shiphandlers to perform these tests will continue. A great gap still exists between theoretical hydrodynamics and the real world, which limits the value of any tests not performed by competent shiphandlers.

OVERTAKING ANOTHER VESSEL OR TOW

The mechanics of handling a ship while overtaking another vessel are routine and safe so long as the shiphandler realizes that it is the speed at which the maneuver is performed that is most important. If the overtaking ship is abeam of the other vessel or tow for any length of time

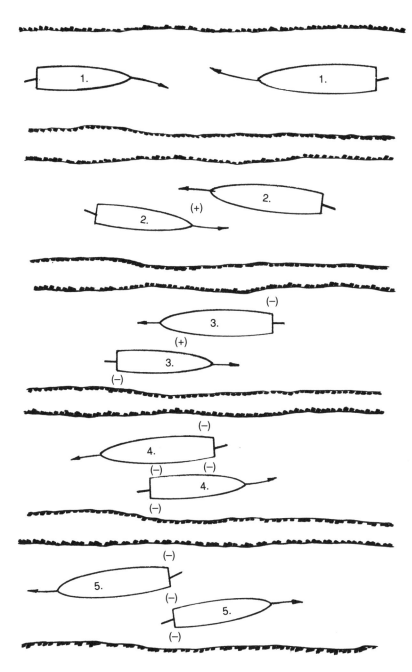

Fig. 2-7. Meeting in a narrow channel.

she increases the chances that the overtaken vessel will become unmanageable, particularly when her stern is abeam the bow of the vessel being overtaken. Give the overtaken ship as much room as possible and maintain a moderate speed to minimize the period of time that the two ships are abeam.

The overtaken vessel reduces her speed as much as possible before the maneuver begins while still maintaining steerageway, to further reduce the time required to complete the overtaking maneuver. While being passed, the slower vessel increases revolutions as needed to increase the flow past her rudder and maintain steerage.

The Rules of the Road give the ship or tow being passed the responsibility for agreeing to any passing situation. It is obvious why this is so. It is the overtaken vessel that is most likely to have a problem, and which will be the most likely to go aground should any problem arise. No prudent mariner agrees to be passed until the maneuver can be performed under conditions that he or she feels comfortable with.

UTILIZING SHIPHANDLING INSTRUMENTATION

While the seaman's eye remains the best aid to shiphandling and maneuvering in channels and restricted waters, other aids are available to supplement experienced judgment. Radar and other electronic aids are useful for navigation in restricted visibility, but the gyro and fathometer remain the shiphandler's primary tools.

The gyro is used, of course, to maintain direction, supplying the point of reference for almost all maneuvers. The gyrocompass also serves as an accurate audible rate of turn indicator as it clicks off the fractions of each degree during a turn. It is surprising how accurately an experienced seaman can judge the rate of turn and, of equal importance, whether a desired or undesired swing has begun, without having to continuously watch the gyrocompass. Hopefully, the solid state era will not bring with it an "improved" silent gyrocompass.

The fathometer provides the soundings that the mariner needs to predict when a ship might become difficult to handle due to shoaling, and to know the clearance beneath the keel. Squat can then be anticipated as well as the need to reduce speed as bottom clearances change. The fathometer must be routinely watched; the development of the digital fathometer mounted on the forward bulkhead of the wheelhouse to supplement the recording fathometer in the chartroom has done much to increase shiphandling safety. The fathometer seems to often be forgotten once the pilot is aboard—this is unfortunate since the depth of water is a basic shiphandling parameter.

Due to the mass of today's larger ships and the greater height from the water at which the pilot is now working, it has become more difficult to detect an error in judgment and to recover from that error. It is important to have an accurate means of determining the ship's movement—both ahead and astern over the bottom, and her lateral motion at the bow and stern. The ship can then be accurately positioned at a pier or at the single-point moorings commonly used by VLCCs, and also steered at the low speeds involved when the bow and stern are moving at a fraction of a knot. While a single-point Doppler log is useful at sea, the complete Doppler presentation showing ahead and athwartship movement is needed to supply the information required in maneuvering situations with large ships. (Fig. 2-8)

On larger ships and ships with restricted visibility from the bridge, such as containerships, it is important to have a rate-of-turn indicator to enable the mariner to detect and control the ship's rate of swing in a turn. A rate-of-turn indicator usually supplies turn information in tenths of a degree per second, although degrees per minute are used occasionally, showing a rate to the right or left which corresponds to the direction of the movement of the ship's bow. This information in itself is not of great value. It is the relative indication that is important—that is whether the rate is increasing or decreasing, and by what amount. It is both interesting and instructive to watch a helmsman do his first trick aboard a ship fitted with a rate-of-turn indicator. After a short time, he begins to steer by using the indicator, as well as watching the jackstaff move across a point of reference as helmsmen have done for centuries. While holding the ship steady on a compass heading the rudder is used to keep a zero rate of swing. As soon as swing is indicated the helmsman uses sufficient rudder to check that swing, often applying the rudder before any movement of the bow to the right or left can be detected by eye. (Fig. 2-9)

When a ship is directionally unstable due to her hull form or trim, the rate-of-turn indicator becomes essential, making it possible to navigate restricted channels safely. By accurately knowing the rate of turn the shiphandler can limit that rate to a known safe maximum and always keep the ship under control. As an example, a current class of liquefied natural gas carriers, which have to be trimmed to an even keel to meet the draft requirements of their terminal port, are safely handled in spite of being directionally unstable at that trim. By limiting their

Fig. 2-8. Three-point Doppler speed log. Courtesy Sperry Marine
Systems.

rate of swing to less than of 3/10 of a degree per second it is always
possible to easily check their swing. While the readout is basically a
relative indication, this rate of turn of 3/10 of a degree per second is
comfortable under most conditions. A rate of turn of 6/10 of a degree per

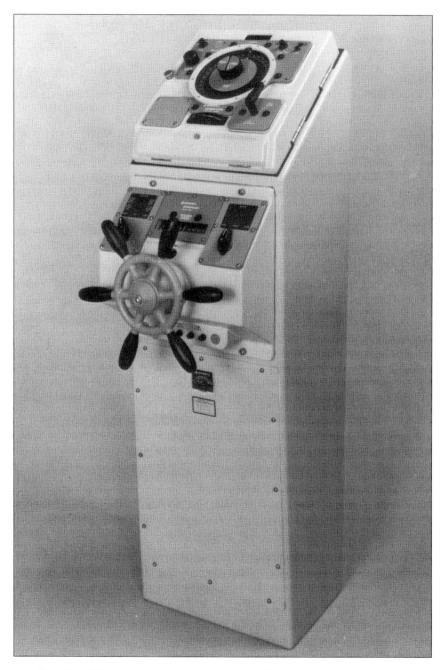

Fig. 2-9. This modern helm station is fitted with a rate-of-turn
indicator. Courtesy Sperry Marine Systems.

second is a safe maximum for an ordinary turn, i.e., a 36-degree change in heading in one minute.

SQUAT

As a ship begins to make way through the water she undergoes a change in mean draft known as sinkage. This change may occur equally forward and aft or may be greater at the bow or the stern, the resulting change in trim being called "squat."

When passing through the water the ship displaces an amount of water equal to her own weight. This water must move outward from and around the hull in all directions. The water so displaced moves primarily along and under the hull and returns astern of the ship to "fill" the space left by the ship as she moves on. Naturally, the faster the ship is moving the greater the velocity of this flow under and along her hull, and the greater the corresponding pressure drop as a result of that increased velocity. Depending upon where the greatest drop in pressure occurs along the length of the hull, this reduced pressure will result in greater sinkage (increase in draft) at the bow or stern, although the draft increases to some degree all along the length of the ship.

As the ship enters shallow water the flow of water becomes increasingly restricted due to the reduced clearance both under and on one or both sides of the hull. The effect of this restriction or "blockage factor" is dependent upon several variables:

1. The speed of the ship through the water.
2. Ratio of the ship's draft to the depth of water.
3. Ratio of the ship's cross sectional area to the cross sectional area of the channel. (Fig. 2-10)
4. The ship's block coefficient. (The previously explained effects on draft and handling characteristics of a high block coefficient are amplified in shallow water.)
5. The ship's displacement, which determines the amount of water that must pass around and under the ship's hull at a given speed.

Consider first the effect of ship's speed since this is the factor over which the mariner has the greatest control. It has been found, based upon observations of both actual ships and models, that squat varies in proportion to the square of the speed. If ship's speed is doubled, squat increases by a factor of four. With today's large ships and minimal

$$\text{BLOCKAGE FACTOR } f_B = \frac{b \times T}{B \times H}$$

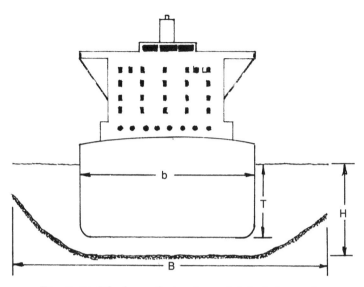

Fig. 2-10. Blockage factor in restricted channels.

underkeel clearances it becomes immediately obvious why speed and resulting squat must be very much on the shiphandler's mind.

The maximum cross sectional area of the submerged portion of the ship's hull, seen by looking at the midships section in the ship's file of drawings, is significant when compared to the cross sectional area of a narrow channel. The ratio of these two areas determines the clearance through which the displaced water must flow. Obviously, the less area available the greater the velocity at which the water must flow for a given ship's speed—and the greater the resultant pressure drop around and under the hull.

The other variables listed also affected the flow in a similar manner and their importance will be obvious to the mariner.

The total sinkage in *open water* can be calculated with sufficient accuracy *for a VLCC* using the formula:

$$S \text{ (meters)} = C_b \times \frac{V^2}{100} \quad \text{or}$$

$$S \text{ (feet)} = C_b \times \frac{V^2}{30}$$

Where S = sinkage

C_b = vessel's block coefficient

V = vessel's speed in knots

Sinkage *in shallow, confined waters* is computed by doubling the quantity S found by the above formula, i.e., in *shallow, confined waters* the sinkage equals 2 × S.*

When aboard a ship with a block coefficient of 0.8 proceeding in *shallow water* at 10 knots, she will sink approximately 1.6 meters (5.25 feet). If the speed is reduced by half, to 5 knots, the same vessel sinks only 0.4 meters (1.3 feet) or one quarter the squat experienced at the higher speed.

It would be appropriate at this point to also discuss the effect that these same factors of blockage and speed have on handling characteristics of a ship. Since a ship in confined waters can be compared to a piston in a cylinder, it is obviously more difficult to drive the ship ahead as the blockage factor increases. There is therefore a practical limit to the speed at which a ship can proceed up a channel: the ship which makes 16 knots at eighty revolutions in open water might make only 9 or 10 knots with the same number of revolutions in shallow water. This limit is reached when the water is flowing at relatively high velocities, the ship becomes difficult to steer, experiences heavy vibrations throughout her hull, and generates a much greater wave pattern astern. The wake becomes short and steep, breaking along its length and moving outward at a greater angle from the ship as the point of maximum flow around the hull is reached. The ship is now said to be "pulling a lot of water."

Will the squat occur by the head or by the stern? This can only be determined with accuracy by observation, but a commonly accepted rule of thumb is that a ship with a large C_b (greater than .75), which includes most very large oceangoing vessels, will tend to squat by the head. Vessels having such block coefficients are generally large tankers and bulk carriers which are very full in their forward sections. The previously discussed curve of submerged cross sectional areas is therefore also helpful in predicting squat by the head or stern. If the curve reaches its maximum point at a more forward station, the ship can be expected to trim by the head. Hulls having forward sections of varying fullness should be tested so some criteria can be developed and published to

* C. B. Barrass, "Ship Squat and Its Calculation," 11.

Fig. 2-11. All the effects expected in a confined channel can be seen in the Gaillard Cut.

determine how far forward this peak in the curve can be located before a ship will trim by the bow.

As ships get larger and load to deeper drafts, squat becomes increasingly important. It is imperative that the mariner allow for squat when loading and reduce the speed at which the deeply loaded ship navigates in a shallow channel. This requires a conscious effort on the part of many mariners since the operation of ships of this size is a relatively new phenomenon and most ship's officers have served in the past in ships where squat is not a significant consideration. Ships exist to carry cargo and by limiting speed to minimize squat, a ship can lift the maximum possible deadweight.

STOPPING AND MANEUVERING IN A CHANNEL

The berth is now in sight but the tugs aren't yet available, so it is necessary to stop your ship during her passage up the channel and hold her in that location until tugs arrive. It would of course have been better to have had the tugs made fast before needing to stop, but it is certainly not a problem to stop without them. The maneuver for stopping your ship while maintaining her heading is discussed in the section on master's trials in Chapter 1, and since you have kept the ship's speed moderate at all times, you are in control of the situation with or without tugs.

The experience gained during the master's trials helps you judge whether the ship can be stopped in the distance available using only routine maneuvers. Remember that it is often possible to perform two or more maneuvers simultaneously, such as using the tendency for the bow to swing to starboard when the engine is put astern to both make a turn to the right and reduce headway.

CHAPTER THREE

USE OF TUGS

We maneuvered in the outer harbor until it was dark. When we put in the Chief came to the bridge, wiping his hands with a wad of cotton waste and his forehead with his sleeve. "Blimey, Skipper," he said, "you certainly kept us busy." I had . . . I found out that she was indeed a lovely ship; you couldn't expect her to do more and still be called a tugboat.

—Jan de Hartog
The Distant Shore

The heavily bearded docking master burst through the wheelhouse door, grabbed the Old Man's hand, and welcomed him to the port in a voice two tones deeper than our whistle. Taking the radio in hand, he instructed the two tugs that would be assisting us to the dock to come alongside and make up.

"How do you like your coffee, Cap'?"

"Black please. Just black and hot will be fine," the docking master replied to the captain.

"Call the standby and have him bring up a pot of coffee, Cadet."

"I'll get it, sir. It will only take me a second to go downstairs for it," replied the cadet.

The docking master glowered at the cadet, but said nothing until he had left the wheelhouse. Obviously, he didn't like the young man's reply.

"Downstairs! Downstairs! Where the hell does that kid think he is," bellowed the heretofore jovial docking pilot.

"They don't go down below anymore, they go downstairs. Decks are floors, lines are ropes, and the other day one of these kids called a mooring wire a cable." He paused long enough to catch his breath but it was obvious that he had hardly begun his dissertation on the preservation of the seafaring language and the use of proper shipboard terminology. In fact, we were lectured on that subject for the rest of the docking.

Unfortunately, it is true that the vocabulary of the mariner is often ignored and those who have been working around ships for any length

69

Fig. 3-1. Tugs alongside, arriving Baltimore Harbor. From an oil
painting by Captain Brian Hope.

*of time are not happy about it. Perhaps this is because so many landsmen
rush to the water on weekends to play, and most of what is written and
filmed in the United States about living and working on the water is
directed toward, and produced by, these neophyte admirals who do not
understand that the language of the sea is steeped in tradition. Nautical
vocabulary allows those aboard ship to communicate orders and ideas
clearly and concisely in a manner that is not open to misinterpretation.
For this reason it is important that the shiphandler use proper and accepted shipboard terminology when giving orders.*

*While practitioners in the medical, legal, engineering, and scientific
fields have and use a specialized vocabulary peculiar to their profession,
the language of the sea is now being misused with regularity. This is sad
since seafaring is not just a job, it is a way of life, and the seaman's
vocabulary captures the very essence and spirit of life on the water.*

*The argument has been made by some that the seafarer should
"modernize" nautical language so it could be immediately understood
by all, even though this would actually mean that it would be clearly
understood by no one. Without a unique nautical vocabulary it would
be impossible to accurately express ideas or describe conditions in the
marine environment. A whole series of long and ambiguous sentences
would be needed to express the same thoughts that the seaman can now
convey with but a few words. Consider the paragraph of instructions
that would have to be given to a seaman tending the spring line to get
the same reaction that the mariner gets from the three words: "Check
the spring."*

Just as doctors or lawyers would not bastardize the language of their professions, nor tolerate others in their field who do not master that language, neither should the mariner accept the misuse of the language of the sea. It is another aspect of professionalism.

After being properly chastised the cadet went forward to assist in the docking, having assured the docking master that his point had been made.

The work of the tugmaster is a subject unto itself, and it is beyond the scope of this text to discuss that work. Only the use of tugs to assist in the movement and berthing of ships will be covered here.

There are several types of tugs, each of which has its limitations and advantages. The single-screw harbor tug is still predominant in many ports and will serve as the basis for this chapter. It's essential that the shiphandler understand the tug's work, and her limitations and capabilities, so that he can do the best possible job without endangering the assisting boats.

MAKING UP A TUG

Having proceeded to within sight of the berth and taken the docking master aboard, the crew makes the tugs fast and gets ready to go alongside. The tugs can be made fast in several ways depending on where they are to be placed and the work that they are going to do.

If the tug is to assist in a routine docking or undocking and is to be made fast on the bow or quarter, she generally puts up two lines. The first line sent aboard, to be led forward and put on a bitt on the ship's deck, is the *backing line*. This line is made fast to a bitt on the tug's foredeck. Since this line will take a heavy strain as the tug backs against it to pull the bow or stern, it *must* be put on a bitt aboard the ship. Too often, the mate on the bow or stern puts the backing line on a small cleat on the bulwark, or on some other unsuitable fitting that is out of the tug master's line of sight. When the tug later backs on that line for the first time, the cleat pulls off the bulwark with the very real danger of injuring or killing someone aboard either vessel. The second line sent aboard from the tug is led from the tug's foredeck to her bow, and then up to the ship. This *come ahead line* is led aft on the ship's deck and used by the tug to work against and get into position to push. (Fig. 3-2)

If the ship will be backing into or from a slip, a *stern line* may also be rigged so the tug does not fall around as the ship gathers sternway.

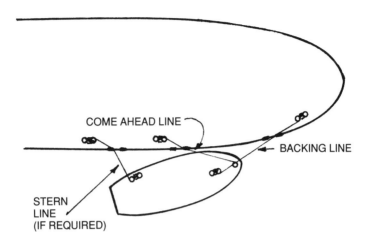

Fig. 3-2. Making fast a single-screw tug.

The ship's speed must then be kept to a minimum since the tug is at nearly right angles to the ship while backing, with the full length acting as a drag and putting a heavy strain on that line that increases geometrically as ship's speed increases. Two of the ship's crew must stand by to let the line go promptly on signal from the tug and slack it *with a messenger* to the tug. If the line is not let go promptly the tug is either unable to get in position to work or the line is parted by the strain as the tug and ship maneuver. There is a very real risk of getting the stern line in the tug's propeller if the messenger is not used and properly tended when slacking the stern line down to the boat.

Twin-screw tugs, due to their ability to maneuver, will often give the ship only a backing line since they can use their two engines to get at right angles to the ship to push without a come ahead line.

Tugs having one of the various patented drives that allow maneuvering in all directions will need only to send a hawser to the ship, which allows the tug to work with greater freedom and to be more useful to the shiphandler. Patented drive tugs such as the Voith-Schneider can do everything that twin-screw tugs can do with the added advantage of being able to work (to direct their thrust) at right angles to the ship when the ship has headway. Obviously, the closer the tug is to being at right angles to the ship, the more of her power is being used to move the ship in the desired direction. These patented drive tugs can also work closer to the stem or stern of the ship because of their ability to maneuver around the flare of the bow or curvature of the ship's run aft. The closer to the ends of the ship that the tug is able to work, the more effective it can be in moving the ship.

The patented drive tugs usually keep their working line on a winch with sufficient power to shorten or lengthen the line while working against it. The tug is thus able to change position without losing effectiveness and to work at more than one location around the bow or stern without having to shift lines.

COMMUNICATING WITH A TUG

While various tug signals have been developed that are peculiar to a port or even to a particular berth, certain basic signals and maneuvers are common to almost all ports at which you will call in the United States. Signals to be given with a hand whistle or the ship's whistle include:

One blast	If pushing or backing, stop. If stopped, come ahead with normal power.
Two blasts	Back with normal power.
One long blast	Come ahead dead slow.
Series of short, rapid blasts	Increase to full power, ahead or astern, depending on the direction in which the tug is presently working.
One long and two short blasts	Tug is dismissed. Let go the tug's lines.

Now that the radio is supplementing the whistle, the shiphandler can verbally instruct the tug to perform these same maneuvers. The use of the radio has resulted in safer and more professional work since it is possible to specify a tug by name, and to give more precise instructions to the tug. When using a radio to work more than one tug, good practice dictates that the name of the tug be repeated twice so that there is no misunderstanding about which tug should follow a particular order: "(name of tug) Come ahead full (name of tug)."

USING A TUG

Rule one—don't use the tug.

Make the needed tugs fast but plan the job so as to deliberately minimize their use. Let's look at the reasons for this. The tug is simply another tool available to the shiphandler to accomplish the task at hand, supplementing the engine, rudder, bow thruster, anchors, and mooring lines. Use the tug only when these other tools will not by themselves accomplish the task. There are several reasons for this.

1. The only way to develop a skill in and a feel for handling ships is to do the work. If a ship is pushed and pulled into position primarily using the tug, you aren't developing any skill in shiphandling, you are only learning to push and pull with tugs.
2. If a job is planned to minimize the need for the tug, then those tugs are available as additional tools if required—an ace up the shiphandler's sleeve. If the job is done in a manner that makes the use of tugs essential, this backup capability is lost. By making the tugs fast, and then working as if they weren't available, the tugs can be used to correct any problem that might arise.

There unfortunately seems to be an inverse relationship between shiphandling ability and the availability of powerful tugs. No great skill is required to berth a ship under normal conditions with a little common sense and a few powerful tugs to push and pull the ship into position. It is a pleasure, though, to watch a skilled pilot or master move a ship using only her engine and rudder, making her perform without fuss or confusion. The only way to develop that degree of skill is by handling a ship with minimum assistance.

The tug's power when working alongside is used primarily to move the ship laterally. It can also be used to reduce a ship's headway by backing the tug so the force of the tug is opposing the ship's movement ahead. The properly made up tug can also be used to move a ship ahead or hold her in position. It is this flexibility that makes a tug preferable for many maneuvers even though a ship is fitted with a bow thruster.

A bow thruster can only be used to move a ship laterally. The tug can have two or more simultaneous effects. This is one of the reasons a pilot will sometimes use a tug on a ship even though she is equipped with a bow thruster.

Keep in mind, when using a tug to maneuver, that ship's speed has a crucial impact on the tug's and bow thruster's effectiveness. The tug has only a limited amount of power available and, as the speed of the ship increases, more of that power is needed just to "keep up" with the ship and therefore less power is available to assist the ship's maneuvers. Keep the ship's speed to a minimum for maximum tug effects when maneuvering.

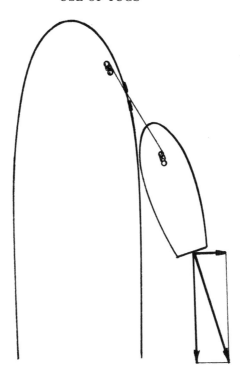

Fig. 3-3. A tug's force affects both the ship's lateral motion and her headway.

As stated, backing a tug also slows the forward speed of the ship, and simply dragging the tug along with its deep hull at some angle to the ship's centerline will have some slowing effect. Keep in mind that the opposite effect occurs when the tug comes ahead. The tug's force increases the speed of the ship since some of her power is pushing the ship ahead. It is possible to compute by vector diagram the percentage of the total force being generated by a tug that is acting in the desired direction under a given situation, but in the real world it is sufficient to know that the tug is in fact having more than one effect and to use these effects to your best advantage. (Fig. 3-3)

Other than the pushing and pulling effects on the ship's bow, the bow tug can also be used to follow a ship which is going astern, working stem to stem to steer the ship by pushing on either bow as required. The tug trails the stem and comes ahead against the port bow to move the stem to starboard and thus turn the ship to port. Pushing on the starboard bow has the opposite effect.

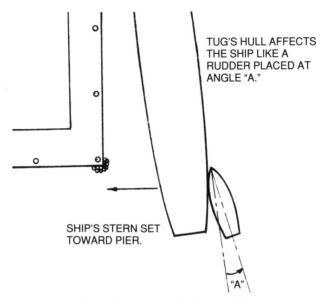

Fig. 3-4. Effect of a tug made fast on the quarter.

The bow tug is used to hold the ship alongside in position after arriving at the berth until mooring lines are out and tight. By keeping the tug at some angle to the ship, that ship can be held against a flooding or ebbing current as well as alongside her berth until she is secure. Other uses of the bow tug are covered in sections on approaching the berth in Chapter 4, and going alongside in Chapter 5.

The after tug or stern tug, if placed on the quarter, is made fast in the same manner as a tug on the bow, i.e., with a backing line and a come ahead line. The tug backs and pushes against the hull in the same manner and with the same effects as the bow tug, with two important differences:

1. The after tug acts as a drag, reducing the effectiveness of the rudder, especially at slow speeds when the shiphandler is trying to move the stern laterally without any significant increase in speed.
2. The stern tug tends to set the stern away from the side on which she is made fast, toward the pier or wharf in a docking situation, which creates an additional problem for the shiphandler. This effect increases as the angle at which the tug lies to the ship increases, since the tug is acting as a rudder of the dimensions of the tug's underwater profile. (Fig. 3-4)

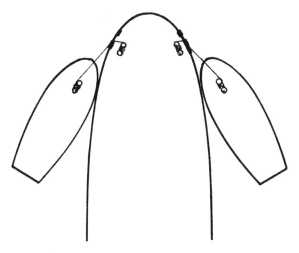

Fig. 3-5. Using a tug on each bow.

For these reasons it is best to have the stern tug stand off until actually needed to assist the ship, and to be let go after undocking at the earliest practical time.

Occasionally a tug will be secured *on each bow* when the ship is approaching a berth or lock, or holding a position in a channel. (Fig. 3-5) Either tug can then back or come ahead, alone or together, to move the ship's bow as required. More importantly, when both tugs are backed simultaneously the ship's heading is maintained while reducing the ship's speed, as the tugs back against the ship's headway. The ship's engine can also be used as required, so that she is both steered and stopped with maximum control.

A tug can be placed astern of the ship and made fast with one or two lines. (Fig. 3-6) In this position the tug backs to slow the ship or comes ahead to either the right or left to move the stern, acting much like an active rudder to supplement the ship's own rudder. The tug can also be used to steer without the ship's engine, controlling the ship without developing excessive headway. It is claimed in some shiphandling texts, and occasionally by pilots in ports that do not normally use tugs in this manner, that there is some hazard to a tug made fast on the stern. This is simply untrue. For example, tugs have been used astern to assist literally thousands of ships through the Gaillard Cut in the Panama Canal at speeds of 6 to 8 knots without any problems. Often texts recommend using a tug on a hawser ahead of the ship to assist the ship

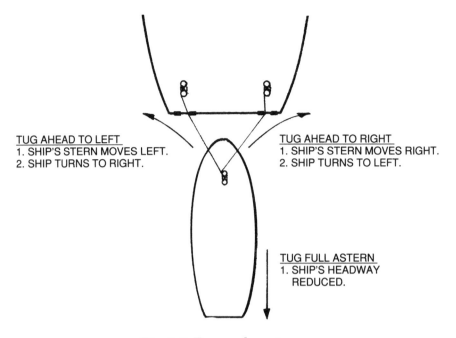

TUG AHEAD TO LEFT
1. SHIP'S STERN MOVES LEFT.
2. SHIP TURNS TO RIGHT.

TUG AHEAD TO RIGHT
1. SHIP'S STERN MOVES RIGHT.
2. SHIP TURNS TO LEFT.

TUG FULL ASTERN
1. SHIP'S HEADWAY
   REDUCED.

Fig. 3-6. Tug used on stern.

to steer. This arrangement is both less effective and potentially more hazardous. A conventional U.S. harbor tug working ahead of a ship with any significant headway is always in danger of being tripped or rolled over.

The ship should always keep an officer and two crew members standing by the tug lines, especially when they are led through the ship's quarter chocks, in case the tug should have to let go on short notice. Too often, ship's crews make a tug fast and then walk off, giving the tug on the stern no alternative but to let go the lines from her end should it be necessary to break away. This leaves the lines in the water near the ship's propeller—not a desirable situation!

TUG ON A HAWSER

Although it is not as common to see a tug work on a hawser in the United States as it is in other parts of the world that use what might be called the "European style" of shiphandling, the use of a hawser should be considered. There is no point in discussing the relative merits of the European and U.S. systems, since the design of the tug used, the

Fig. 3-7. "The pilot wants a tight lashup, Harry, so . . ."

experience and habits of the shiphandler, and the physical layout of the
port all determine the style of working.

As Shottel and Voith-Schneider tugs become more widely used in the
United States, there will be a corresponding increase in the amount of
hawser work seen by the mariner. These tugs are designed to be used
on a hawser, having winches that are properly located relative to the
tug's pivot point so they can work safely in this manner. This is not
generally true of conventional U.S. harbor tugs.

There are occasions when a conventional harbor tug can be put on a
hawser, most commonly when handling a dead ship or a ship with such
a light draft that it is not possible to make up alongside. In this case,
keep the ship's speed and the use of the ship's engines to a minimum to
avoid getting the harbor tug in irons, abeam the hawser, and rolling her
over.

When working a tug in this manner, it is common to use radio
communication to give the tug a speed and direction to pull, and otherwise to use that tug in much the same way as has been previously

described for a tug alongside. Tugs on a hawser can also be used in opposition to one another to increase or reduce the way on a ship, or to hold a ship in a particular position in a stream or at berth. In Chapter 4, other uses of tugs on hawsers when approaching a berth are discussed.

LASHING UP A TUG

When a ship is moved in a confined area or as a dead ship it is often effective to lash a tug up at her bow or stern. The tug lies alongside and puts up a head line, stern line, and an aft leading spring line to the ship. The head and stern lines are kept as short as possible, leading as much like breast lines as the situation permits, and heaved up very tight. It is important that these lines be tight so the ship and tug work as a unit, or the lash-up will be more of a hindrance than a help. Do not allow the ship to be moved if it is not possible to get a tight lash-up due to the ship's draft, hull configuration, or the location of her chocks and bitts.

The tug or tugs may be lashed up on the stern and used in place of the ship's engine and/or rudder. If a tug is lashed on each quarter, the ship is handled much like a twin-screw vessel. In sheltered waters a large ship can be moved significant distances quickly and safely in this manner. When using tugs in this manner helm and engine orders similar to those used aboard a twin-screw ship are appropriate.

When only one tug is lashed up, the off center location of the tug is felt until the ship has some headway, so the ship initially tends to move laterally away from the tug. It is more effective to back the tug to turn the ship to the side on which the tug is lashed up, i.e., back a tug lashed to the port quarter to turn the ship to the left (stern to right, bow and ship to the left). Once it has headway a small ship can be moved efficiently with only one tug lashed up.

The other common type of lash-up places the tug on the ship's bow heading aft. This might be done when only one tug is used to back a ship from a berth around another ship docked astern or to back a dead ship from a berth. After being lashed up (Fig. 3-8), the tug is backed to move the ship's stern off the dock to get clear of the berth and around any ship astern. When the ship has sufficient angle to the berth, the tug comes ahead as needed to steer the ship from the berth. Helm orders are used that are similar to those used to move the ship from a berth under her own power.

When leaving the berth stern first, left rudder is used by the tug to move the ship's bow to port and thus her stern to starboard. This can be

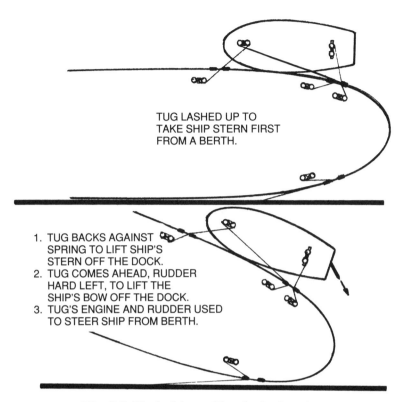

TUG LASHED UP TO
TAKE SHIP STERN FIRST
FROM A BERTH.

1. TUG BACKS AGAINST
   SPRING TO LIFT SHIP'S
   STERN OFF THE DOCK.
2. TUG COMES AHEAD, RUDDER
   HARD LEFT, TO LIFT THE
   SHIP'S BOW OFF THE DOCK.
3. TUG'S ENGINE AND RUDDER USED
   TO STEER SHIP FROM BERTH.

Fig. 3-8. Undocking with a lashed-up tug.

confusing, so face aft in the direction in which the ship is moving, and give helm orders to the tug. The maneuver is immediately simplified and the helm orders needed are obvious. Once clear of the berth, with sternway on the ship, the tug is given a course or steadied on a heading and the tug master steers the vessel much as a helmsman would.

A ship with a tug lashed up can be stopped by backing the tug. If the tug is lashed up on the starboard quarter when moving ahead, or lashed up on the port bow when moving stern first, the ship will twist and can be handled like a single-screw ship with a right-handed propeller.

A lashed-up tug can often do the work of two tugs when used together with the ship's engine moving a ship laterally without developing headway. Use of a tug in this manner requires close cooperation between the shiphandler and tug master, as well as a good tight lash-up. The tug lashes up at the bow heading aft. She comes ahead with her rudder hard over in the direction of the pier while the ship uses her engine ahead

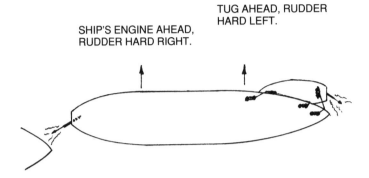

Fig. 3-9. Working tug and ship in opposition to move ship laterally.

and rudder hard over, also in the direction of the berth. The ship's bow and stern then move together away from the berth, the ship's engine working in opposition to the tug so the ship gains no way ahead or astern. (Fig. 3-9)

CHAPTER FOUR

APPROACHING THE BERTH

There are many old pilots, and many fast pilots, but
there are few old, fast pilots.

—Traditional

*The docking master hadn't left the center window of the wheelhouse since
beginning the approach to the pier. He continued to give helm orders
slowly and quietly, signaling with his hands to the right or left as he gave
the rudder commands to the helmsman. With a strong northwesterly
breeze setting us toward the dock it certainly was not going to be a routine
docking and yet he showed no signs of tension or concern. If the docking
master's demeanor was any indication, the docking apparently was not
going to be as difficult as those of us on the bridge had expected.*

*As the ship came up to the pier the docking master walked out on the
bridge wing where he stayed until we were in position alongside the berth.
Even when the bow fell off the wind toward the berth the orders came
slowly and deliberately, and if the docking master had any apprehension
about the evolution it never showed. Docking on this blustery afternoon
was uneventful—about as exciting as watching grass grow—just the way
it was supposed to be.*

GOOD BRIDGE PRACTICES

Several important aspects of the shiphandler's work have been touched
upon here, all of which are as important as the technical skills involved
in docking a ship.

1. The docking master did not move about the bridge while working.
2. Hand signals were given to clarify all helm orders.
3. The pilot remained calm and unexcited throughout the docking.

Select one location to work from when handling a ship and don't move
from the position until nearly alongside. Too often the shiphandler will
move from wing to wing and back again to the wheelhouse at a frantic
pace that increases as the ship gets closer to the dock. Ostensibly, this

Fig. 4-1. "He's planning the docking . . . says shiphandling is an art."

is done so it is possible to get an unobstructed view of the approach but, in fact, it only makes it very difficult to appreciate distance, speed, and motion. The ship's heading is immediately obvious from any vantage point, but less obvious is her motion both ahead and athwartships. It is important that the shiphandler pick one location, generally amidships, and stay there until close to the dock. When nearly alongside, when cargo and superstructure block the shiphandler's view, a move can be made to the bridge wing where the shiphandler should remain until the docking is completed.

Helm orders must be supplemented by hand signals to right and left to avoid any misunderstanding due to language differences or inattention. It is quite common, especially during a long passage, for a helmsman to repeat an order correctly and then put the wheel in the opposite direction. If the shiphandler points in the desired direction when the order is given, this mistake is rarely made by the helmsman.

The pilot's manner of working assures that a calm and orderly atmosphere prevails throughout the docking. Often, if a mistake in judgement or action occurs, it is because people become excited—and excitement is contagious. Even when a problem develops, if the shiphandler, be he pilot, master, or deck officer, controls emotions so his concerns are not obvious to others, there will be none of the shouting and running about that only complicates a bad situation. The shiphandler controls the mood of the bridge as well as the movement of the ship.

DISCUSSING DOCKING PLANS

Discuss the approach and docking plans well before reaching the berth. The docking master appreciates the opportunity to brief you and to be assured that the ship and crew are ready to respond as required. Don't expect him to predict each bell and helm order in detail but do get an understanding of:

1. The approach, including any special maneuvers or engine requirements.
2. The placement of tugs.
3. The configuration of the berth, including any special problems such as poorly located dolphins, ships to be maneuvered around or between, and any unusual space restrictions. This is the time to learn of potential problems, and to cancel the docking if you don't feel it can be done safely. Don't wait until the ship is halfway up the slip and being set down on the vessel in the berth astern.
4. Any special requirements such as a need for the anchor or for any unusual leads for the mooring lines.
5. The current and wind to be expected at the berth. This is often different from that indicated in the current tables and can best be ascertained from the docking master who has the local knowledge required to make accurate predictions.

In turn be sure to give all the same information to the docking pilot that is described in Chapter 1 for the channel pilot. Too often the docking master is not properly briefed since the "passage is almost over." It's at least as important that the docking master be as fully informed as the channel pilots.

Don't hand the docking master a two-page preprinted form asking for a detailed description of the "docking plan," including the engine bells that will be required and the heading of the approach. The docking master cannot do this, nor would you want to restrict him to any such predicted set of maneuvers. Such forms and procedures only reflect the lack of professional background of the originating party, and create an embarrassing situation for both the master and the pilot who must deal with such absurdities. An intelligent discussion between two professionals to ascertain the general plan for the docking will suffice.

If you don't agree with the proposed plan, let the docking master know about it. Don't wait until the middle of the evolution.

TIMING ARRIVAL—HOLDING IN A CHANNEL

For a number of reasons it may be necessary to plan a vessel's passage to arrive at a berth, turning basin, or lock at a specified time. The master or pilot may wish to dock at slack water, or the tugs or berth may not be available until a particular time. This is a routine navigational problem.

When timing arrivals, the mariner often attempts to arrive exactly as scheduled and allows no time for unforeseen delays. Any reluctance to arrive early and have to maneuver the ship to hold her in position in a channel for some period of time is natural but unnecessary. The ship can easily take an hour to go the last mile to a desired point so there is no reason not to allow some extra time when planning a passage.

The master or pilot can:

1. Anchor to a short scope of chain with a head tide.
2. Steam on an anchor at slow engine speeds and hold a position and heading in the channel even if there is a moderate wind from abeam.
3. Hold with a tug on each bow, using the engine as needed while the tugs minimize headway.
4. Back and fill as necessary with surprisingly little advance up a channel.

Further, by arriving early the master has an opportunity to practice any or all of these maneuvers to sharpen shiphandling skills and develop confidence. Arriving early presents no problems but arriving late causes the mariner to use excessive speed—the shiphandler's worst enemy.

SPEED OF APPROACH

The major difference between the neophyte and the experienced shiphandler is the speed at which they work. *The less experienced shiphandler generally works too fast.* Don't equate increased speed with increased ability.

When beginning an approach to a berth, speed should be reduced to bare steerageway. This is much slower than most mariners realize and it is a rare ship that, under calm conditions, will not steer at speeds of less than 2 knots if given a chance to respond to her rudder. Further, by using the engine in short bursts or kicks with hard over rudder, even the worst handling ships will respond. If additional response is needed, use the tug or work against an anchor rather than increasing headway. If unsure of speed take all headway off the ship—you are now certain of her speed through the water—and then come ahead as required to steer and make minimum headway to the berth.

There are several methods available by which the mariner can judge speed:

1. Doppler log giving direct readout.
2. Fixes by radar or visual bearings.
3. Position of the ship's quickwater.
4. Observation of passing objects and comparisons with known distances.

The Doppler log gives direct readout of speed over the bottom (or speed through the water when the ship is offshore and the log is indicating speed referenced to water mass). Both single-point and three-point Doppler logs have proven to be extremely valuable shiphandling tools, especially when moving larger ships where speed is critical and tolerance for error small.

Fixes by radar or visual bearings are neither convenient nor sufficiently accurate for determining speed in a docking situation.

The position of the ship's *quickwater*, that is, the wash from her propeller as the engine goes astern, is extremely useful to the shiphandler at low speeds. If that quickwater falls behind the ship when the engine is put astern, the vessel's speed is 3 knots or more. When the quickwater begins to move with the ship, the speed is about 2 knots. When the wash reaches the midsection the ship is dead in the water. Since 2 knots is a comfortable approach speed for an average size ship, it's convenient to be able to put a light on the water at night and then go astern until you see by the position of the ship's quickwater that the speed has been reduced to the desired 2-knot speed. (Fig. 4-2)

Some experience is needed before the relative motion of passing objects can be used to estimate ship's speed, although it is possible for an experienced seaman to judge speed visually with surprising accuracy. How does an experienced seaman become experienced? By practice! Estimate your ship's speed of approach at every opportunity and

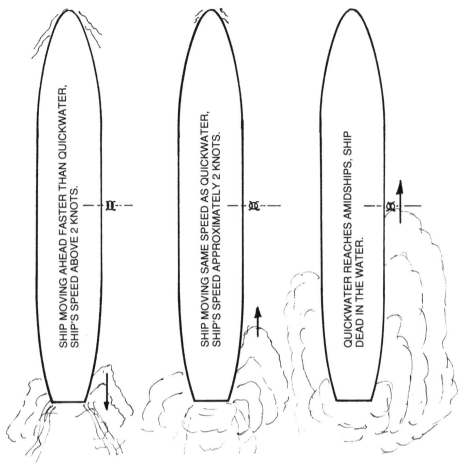

Fig. 4-2. Estimating headway when backing.

compare it with the speed shown on a Doppler log, or the speed indicated by the time required to advance along a pier of known length, or by comparing your estimate with that of a more experienced shiphandler such as the docking master. Apprehension is usually the result of uncertainty, and the ability to judge your ship's speed with reasonable accuracy will do much to make you a confident and capable shiphandler.

When estimating ship's speed look at objects abeam or a little abaft the beam since an optical illusion occurs when looking ahead. Objects forward of the beam do not seem to be moving and if you use them as a reference you'll find your ship is going too fast when she reaches the berth. Try an experiment to satisfy yourself that this is so. Stand in the wheelhouse at night when the ship's speed is most difficult to judge and, while watching an object ashore located forward of the beam, slow your ship to a minimal speed. Now look abaft the beam and see how fast you are actually moving.

Judging absolute speed visually can be difficult, but it is possible to develop some rules of thumb to improve your accuracy. For example, at the Panama Canal the pilots use the long fluorescent lights that illuminate the banks at night to judge a ship's speed. By aligning the after edge of the light with some point on the ship, such as the wheelhouse window, and counting the number of seconds required for the entire light to pass that point of reference, a surprisingly accurate estimate of speed can be made: the light passes in 2 seconds at 2 knots. It is because of aids and skills such as this that the pilots in the canal, where scheduling and timing are so important, are able to move ships as efficiently as they do.

The shiphandler must differentiate between speed over the ground and speed through the water. Obviously the speed over the ground determines the speed at which the ship arrives at the pier, while speed through the water affects the ship's response to her rudder. Docking while stemming the current is an advantage since the shiphandler can steer even when moving at minimal speeds relative to the berth; docking with the current from astern creates the opposite situation and requires a greater degree of skill.

All of the aforementioned means of judging speed give ship's speed over the bottom except the use of her quickwater.

REDUCING SPEED EARLY

Speed is especially important during the approach since a ship is less controllable when her engine is used astern to reduce headway. If speed is kept to a minimum it is possible to use the engine as needed without arriving at the berth with excessive headway. If speed is not reduced early in the approach, the shiphandler finds himself with a tiger by the tail—needing to reduce speed and yet having to use the ship's engines ahead to control the vessel when shaping up for docking.

Many shiphandlers make it a practice to stop a ship completely about one ship length from the berth, especially at night when it is more difficult to estimate a vessel's speed. They are then certain of the speed —it is zero—and can use the engine as required without concern about arriving at the berth at an excessive speed.

THE APPROACH

A good docking actually begins long before the ship comes alongside the pier. The approach is at least one third of the docking. If the speed is reduced, the ship properly lined up with the pier or wharf, and then steadied up so that all lateral motion is eliminated, she practically docks herself.

When berthing *starboard side to* the pier, assuming that the ship has a right hand turning propeller, the ship approaches at only a small angle to the dock. When the engine is put astern to take the last headway off the ship the stern moves to port, so if the ship is already at a significant angle to the berth it will be that much more difficult to get the ship flat alongside. It is natural for a ship to behave in this manner at any time when backed, and this behavior is amplified by the quickwater trapped between the hull and berth moving up the ship's side. For this reason a deeply loaded ship will normally require a tug aft to hold the stern up to the pier when docking starboard side to.

The same ship approaching to dock *port side to* must maintain a greater angle to the berth, approximately 10 to 15 degrees to the dock in most cases, with the bow heading for the area of the pier that will be amidships when the ship is finally in position alongside. (See Fig. 4-3.) After the engine is put astern to stop the ship, the stern will move to port and reduce the angle of approach so that the ship comes flat alongside. By using left rudder and a kick ahead with the engine to check that swing to port as the ship comes alongside, the ship can be stopped in position without needing a tug aft.

There will be some modifications to the basic angle of approach for a starboard or port side to docking, depending on:

1. Wind strength and relative direction.
2. Set and drift of the current.
3. Ship's draft and freeboard.
4. Ship's power and steering characteristics.
5. Whether the pier has an open or solid face.
6. Physical configuration of the berth.
7. Availability of adequate tug assistance.
8. Presence of other vessels in the berth or slip.

These factors all affect the docking of ship. Modifications will be discussed briefly in subsequent sections, but keep in mind that it is impractical to attempt to cover each step of a particular docking in a

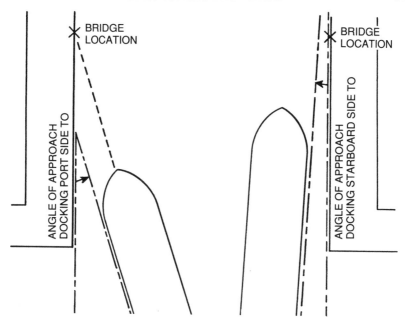

Fig. 4-3. Bow-in approach to pier.

cookbook-like fashion. By understanding the basics of shiphandling and approaching the pier in a proper manner, the mariner can use good seamanship to adjust to a given situation.

Ships generally approach either a pier constructed at an angle to the channel or a wharf that parallels the channel. The ship may dock either bow or stern in at the pier or heading upstream or downstream at the wharf.

BOW-IN APPROACH TO A PIER

A ship docking bow in should turn and line up at the greatest possible distance from the pier. This simplifies the docking and minimizes any lateral motion as the ship approaches the berth. The angle of approach described for starboard or port side dockings is increased or decreased to allow for set and leeway toward or away from the pier due to current and wind. If these forces are too strong to permit a safe docking, the ship can land on a camel or a cluster of pilings at the outboard corner of the pier and then either come ahead on a bight led as a spring line or have a tug push on the bow to bring the ship into the slip. As ships become larger it's increasingly impractical to come ahead against a spring in the classic manner to warp a ship into a slip or berth. Tugs are generally required in these cases. (Fig. 4-4)

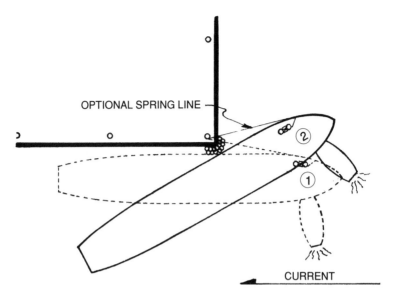

OPTIONAL SPRING LINE

CURRENT

Fig. 4-4. Docking in a slip with a strong crosscurrent.

STERN-IN APPROACH TO A PIER

When docking stern in, use the location of the ship's pivot point as a reference when estimating both the distance that you should pass off the end of the pier, and the point at which you should turn away from the pier and begin backing. (Fig. 4-5) The angle of approach is less important when backing into a slip since the tugs are used to steer. Because the stern tends to walk to port when the engine is backed it is desirable to have a small angle toward the berth when docking starboard side to. If the tugs have a problem holding the ship at the desired angle, the engine and rudder can be used to assist, coming ahead for sufficient time to move the stern in the desired direction but not so long that the ship gains headway. While Figure 4-5 shows the tugs made up on the bow and quarter, the after tug can also be used at the stern on a hawser when berthing the ship stern in. This has many advantages. The ship's engine can be used with ahead revolutions together with the rudder to steer the ship, while the tug continues to keep her moving astern by pulling in opposition to the ship's engine. Consider using a tug on a hawser in this situation.

Always avoid pushing with the tugs so long that excessive lateral motion is developed towards the berth, causing the ship to land heavily against the stringpiece. It is the lateral motion that the less experienced

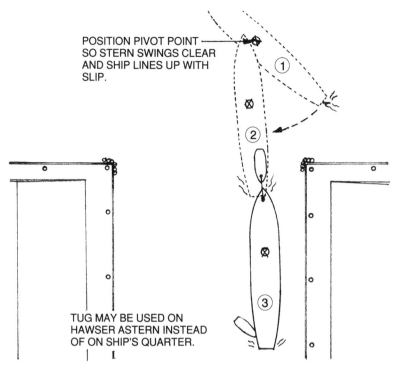

POSITION PIVOT POINT
SO STERN SWINGS CLEAR
AND SHIP LINES UP WITH
SLIP.

TUG MAY BE USED ON
HAWSER ASTERN INSTEAD
OF ON SHIP'S QUARTER.

Fig. 4-5. Docking stern in at a slip.

shiphandler has the most difficulty detecting and controlling, and a mariner will never become a shiphandler without being able to appreciate sideward motion.

The importance of having the stern tug stand off until actually needed was discussed in the previous chapter. This is especially important when planning a stern in docking. The stern tug must not make fast until the ship has turned to bring her stern toward the slip and is dead in the water. Until then, the tug aft is of little help and may fall around under the counter and have an effect opposite to that desired. Preferably, the aft tug does not come alongside until the ship is entering the slip, since once fast, the after tug—by her weight and underwater profile alone—sets the stern toward the pier as the ship comes astern. This effect is amplified when docking port side to since the stern tends to move to port anyway when the engine is going astern.

The bow tug is best made up with only a backing line so she simply follows the ship into the slip, trailing on the line in a position bow to bow with the ship. She comes ahead on either bow to steer the ship into the slip as required, without having the effect of setting the ship towards the berth that would result from being made up on one bow.

STEMMING THE CURRENT AT A WHARF

Berthing starboard or port side to a wharf while stemming the current is a straightforward job which should be approached as described earlier, with some adjustment for the prevailing wind and current. There is usually some set off the wharf as the ship comes alongside, in a direction contrary to the current in the stream which is running nearly parallel to the ship's heading. This set off the pier is caused by a combination of the eddy current that forms along the shore or shoal area, which exists in almost all cases under the wharf, and the hydraulic cushion that is created between the hull and the shallow area under the wharf. This cushion is quite significant when the face of the wharf is solid, or nearly so, as is often the case when a wharf is constructed using a bulkhead to contain the bank behind the stringpiece. This set off the wharf should be planned for so the ship can be brought alongside and held there until made fast. Tools available to the shiphandler to accomplish this include tugs, steaming against an anchor, or good breast lines. Do not expect to simply bring the ship alongside and have her lie there without some assistance until the lines are run ashore.

APPROACHING A WHARF—CURRENT ASTERN

Docking at a wharf with the current running from astern requires greater planning and skill. The ship comes up to the berth with the intent of backing into position since she will be making sternway through the water when stopped in position relative to the wharf. If the shiphandler thinks of the job in this way, that *the ship is coming stern first into the current to the berth*, the maneuver becomes much more straightforward.

Come abeam of the assigned berth with two tugs made fast and take all headway off the ship. Continue backing the engine while keeping the stern angled slightly toward the wharf and, as the ship gains sternway *through the water* (while stopped or nearly *stopped relative to the bottom*), the current on the ship's offshore side moves her laterally toward the wharf. (Fig. 4-6) Use only enough speed to hold the ship in position and use the tugs as required to control the ship as she is set alongside *by the current*.

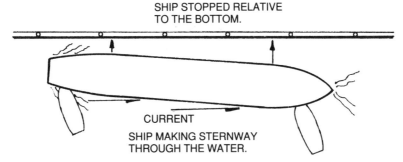

Fig. 4-6. Approaching wharf, current from astern.

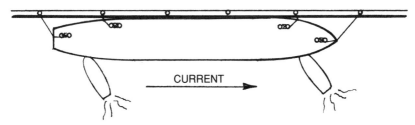

Fig. 4-7. Tugs work at an angle to hold ship alongside and into current.

Once alongside, the tugs hold the ship against the eddy current that exists at the wharf. The mate on the stern must keep the propeller clear while running stern lines since the engine is used continuously to hold the ship in position against the current. The tugs can also help to hold the ship in position by keeping an angle into the current rather than being at right angles to the ship's hull. Their thrust holds the ship alongside *and* up to the current. (Fig. 4-7)

Berthing with the current from astern is not a problem so long as it is kept in mind that the ship is effectively *backing stern first* into position. By adjusting the angle that the ship makes to the current—stern toward the dock to move in that direction, stern parallel to the dock to check the lateral motion toward the pier or move away from it—the ship can be efficiently and safely berthed. Any problems that arise when docking with the current from astern usually result from trying to push the ship alongside with the tugs, rather than letting the current set the ship onto the berth. The vessel gets away from the shiphandler because the current takes charge. Use the tugs only to assist to keep the needed angle as the ship is set alongside.

CHAPTER FIVE

DOCKING

Captain Ball, on the bridge, heaved a sigh. "Ring off
the engines," he directed; and somewhere down below,
the telegraph jingled. Suddenly, disturbingly, the
decks ceased to throb and the stanchions to tremble.
After eighteen pulsing days the ship seemed no longer
to be alive. Silence, torrents of silence poured in from
all sides.

"Hell's bells!" remarked Captain Ball, unbuttoning
his overcoat and taking a cigar from his nightshirt
pocket, "What a trip that was!"

—Guy Gilpatric
Mary, Queen of Scots

*"It's been a pleasure to watch your crew work, Cap', a real pleasure. They
know what is needed and go to it without a lot of talk on the damn radio."*

*The expression on the old man's face made it obvious that he agreed
with the docking master's observations and was proud of his ship and
crew.*

*"It's true, Pilot. They do work well—probably because most of them
are permanent aboard and know what is expected of them," replied the
captain.*

*"They rotate as a team—mates and engineers, and most of the unli-
censed crew—so they know the ship and each other. Makes for a safer
and more efficient operation, that's for sure."*

"How come more ships aren't manned this way, Cap'?"

*It is a subject the captain felt strongly about and he went into a lengthy
explanation, interrupted only by an occasional engine or rudder order as
the deep laden bulk carrier slowly approached the berth.*

*"Too few owners appreciate the importance of a trained and organized
crew, and of keeping a crew aboard ship as a unit. The same shoreside
manager who cries like hell if he has three personnel changes in his office
in one year thinks that the staff aboard ship can be shuffled from vessel
to vessel at random and still be well-trained, know their ship, and work
efficiently."*

"Well, it's obvious from the way that everyone aboard your ship works like a team that it makes a difference," replied the docking master. "We're getting close—better move out on the wing."

They moved to the port wing and continued the discussion.

"Another benefit of having everyone in the crew stay together is that they take a lot more pride in their work and the operation of their ship. Guess that's the key—since they keep coming back to a permanently assigned ship, they feel an interest in her and it shows in their work."

"I see a lot of this on the better run ships such as yours, Captain. They have bridge teams that are trained together, and permanent unit crews, shipboard management schemes, and a lot of other good ideas."

The subject was dropped as the first heaving line snaked ashore; the docking operation now required their full attention. After the engine was rung off the captain invited the pilot to his cabin for a heave ahead before going to his next job.

"Yep, this unit crew business should be started on more ships, Cap'. I sure see a difference when I move ships set up that way. Things go much smoother, and it makes shiphandling and docking a lot easier and safer."

"Hopefully, more companies will begin to appreciate that it's the key to efficient and safe operation of ships, Pilot. This crew even trained as a unit in navigation, bridge procedures, and shiphandling, and there would be no point in all that training if they were split up after their first vacation."

As they parted with a handshake, the captain added, "I've been going to sea for over twenty years and I know that having permanent, well-trained crews makes a difference in the standard of ship operation."

USING WIND AND CURRENT TO ADVANTAGE

Too often the seaman brings a shoreside mentality aboard ship and thus looks upon wind and current as hindrances to be overcome, rather than as aids to be used with the rudder, engine, tugs, and anchor to put the ship alongside a berth in a safe and seamanlike manner. A powerful tug can combat a moderate wind and current, although at best the docking will be sloppy, but even the finest tugs do not make it possible to fight a strong wind or current. Nor is it necessary for them to be asked to.

Before starting the docking get out on the bridge wing and feel the wind and weather on your face. Look up at the stack and down at the water. Look out to the horizon and check what the future weather conditions might be. Constant awareness of wind, weather, and current is essential to effective shiphandling.

How do the effects of wind and current compare? Air is about nine hundred times less dense than water, so *for a given velocity* wind has much less effect on the ship than current. An increase in the velocity of either the wind or current will increase its effect on the ship, both varying as the square of the velocity. The relationship of density and velocity to pressure is expressed:

$$P = \frac{pV^2}{2g}$$

P = resultant pressure
p = density of the fluid (air or water)
V = velocity of the fluid
g = acceleration due to gravity (32.2 ft./sec^2)*

A 30-knot wind exerts the same force on an equal area as a 1-knot current. This ratio is altered by variables such as the surface area of the superstructure, the ratio of the ship's draft to her freeboard, and the vessel's trim. While the shiphandler should not apply this formula to every docking situation, the ratio 30:1 can be used as a base to help understand the relative effect of wind and current.

As a ship's speed is reduced, the momentum of the ship and the effectiveness of her rudder and engine decrease while the wind and current remain the same. When the ship is dead in the water, only the wind and current act upon her, although at some prior point these outside forces have become dominant. If the docking has been properly planned, the ship is so positioned that *as the wind and current "take charge" they assist the shiphandler in docking the vessel.* Until that time, the ship's angle of approach and speed are adjusted to compensate for wind and current, and anchors and tugs are used as necessary.

Let's look at some of the ways in which the wind and current may assist the ship:

1. A wind blowing off the berth can be used to overcome a ship's lateral motion toward that berth, instead of using the tugs and engine.
2. A wind blowing on the berth can ease a ship alongside if the shiphandler stops her a few feet off the berth.

*R.S. Crenshaw, Jr., *Naval Shiphandling*, 15.

3. A current that runs across the end of the berth acting on the ship's quarter can assist the ship in turning into a slip. She is landed and pivoted on a cluster of pilings or a camel rather than being steamed into the slip while fighting the current. (See fig. 4-4.)

Don't fight a wind blowing off the berth. Position your ship at a greater angle to the berth and deliberately give the ship more lateral motion as she comes alongside. The engine is kicked ahead with the rudder hard over to move the stern towards the berth and the ship is then held alongside by tugs. The larger angle of approach compensates for the wind's effects while the ship has headway. As she slows, the lateral motion overcomes the wind. (Fig. 5-1) In stronger winds put an anchor down as described in Chapter 8 to check up the bow and amplify the lateral motion as the ship comes alongside into the wind.

The tugs and rudder move the ship toward the berth, the anchor holds her up to the wind, and the wind checks the lateral motion that develops.

A *strong* wind on the berth causes the ship to land with too much lateral motion, so it may be necessary in such a situation to back the

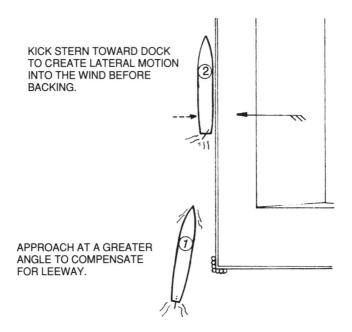

KICK STERN TOWARD DOCK
TO CREATE LATERAL MOTION
INTO THE WIND BEFORE
BACKING.

APPROACH AT A GREATER
ANGLE TO COMPENSATE
FOR LEEWAY.

Fig. 5-1. Don't fight external forces—work with them.

tugs or ease alongside with an anchor as described in Chapter 8. Plan so tugs are in position to perform this work, or have the anchor on the bottom and ready to use.

When the wind is quite strong onto the berth, put the ship alongside earlier in docking. Don't fight a strong wind: let the ship go alongside and slide up the stringpiece into position. The ship can't be blown heavily against the dock after stopping in position if she is already alongside. These are but a few examples of ways in which mariners use wind and current as tools rather than allowing them to become problems.

MEASURING SLOW RATES OF SPEED

The minimal speeds used while docking can be accurately measured without instrumentation or complication using this rule of thumb:

"A ship moves 100 feet per minute at 1 knot."

If in doubt of a ship's speed, note the time on your watch and the ship's position relative to a bollard on the pier. After any convenient interval of time (say thirty seconds), again note the relative positions and you will immediately know the ship's speed.

You don't know the distance between bollards or other convenient reference points? It can be estimated with sufficient accuracy by comparing the distance between points with the ship's beam.

Having moved in one minute between two bollards placed 150 feet apart you know the ship is making 1½ knots.

When determining ship's speed, don't ignore the obvious. Engine revolutions equate to speed through the water. This is so obvious that it is often forgotten during the approach to a pier or when proceeding in pilot waters, yet engine revolutions are nearly as good an indication of speed when maneuvering at low RPM as when at sea.

Learn your ship's RPM / speed ratio. If 10 revolutions equals 2 knots, then 60 revolutions equals 12 knots—it isn't necessary to continuously consult a detailed table to determine ship's speed through the water.

DETECTING LATERAL MOTION

It quickly becomes second nature for an experienced mariner, who lives and works more closely with the elements than perhaps any other professional, to make allowances for wind and current. It is equally important that the shiphandler also develop an appreciation for the less obvious lateral motion that results from:

1. Turning as the ship is approaching the berth.
2. Extended use of tugs.
3. Checking or holding the lines before the ship is alongside.

These actions cause sideward motion independent of any motion caused by the wind and current, even when the ship is making no headway. If not checked, the ship moves laterally toward or away from the berth or comes alongside with excessive force. Lateral motion may be desirable at times and is not so much an effect to be avoided as a factor to be watched for and used to advantage.

Lateral motion is easier to detect when working from the centerline of the ship because you have a better view of the vessel and her heading. Watch objects ashore located ahead or astern. Use their change in alignment as a range to detect lateral motion, and note when the distance from the pier increases or decreases independent of heading, wind, and current.

The ability to detect this sideward slide through the water and make use of it is a mark of an accomplished shiphandler because it is one of the effects that is least appreciated by an inexperienced pilot or master.

SETTING UP TO BACK

Prior to going astern, especially when docking without a tug aft, a single-screw ship should be set up so her inherent twisting effects are an aid rather than a hindrance. Since the approach is planned to allow for this effect, only one additional maneuver is required.

When going starboard side to the berth, put the rudder to port and kick the engine ahead until the stern develops a slight swing to starboard. Note that it is necessary to consider the rudder's effect on each end of the ship rather than simply on the ship as a whole. Near the berth the rudder is often used to move the stern rather than to change the ship's heading. After this slight swing of the *stern to starboard* has begun, go astern to slow or stop the ship. While backing, the stern checks up and probably moves to port as the propeller and quickwater take over, but any movement of the stern to port is minimized since you shaped up to back prior to putting the engine astern. The maneuver is repeated as required so the ship is stopped in position and parallel to the pier or wharf. (Fig. 5-2)

When berthing port side to, the ship is set up to allow for the same swing of the stern to port. Since the ship's angle of approach decreases

1. "KICK" THE ENGINE AHEAD, RUDDER HARD LEFT,
   SWINGING THE STERN TOWARD THE DOCK &
   COUNTERING THE TWISTING EFFECT AS

2. THE ENGINE IS PUT ASTERN. THE SWING IS
   CHECKED BY THE PROPELLER'S TORQUE AND
   THE QUICKWATER SO THE SHIP STOPS
   PARALLEL TO THE DOCK.

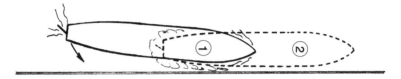

Fig. 5-2. Docking starboard side to—setting up to back.

each time the engine goes astern, the initial angle of approach is greater
for a port side to docking. The rudder and engine are used to check the
motion to port as necessary so the ship does not come parallel to the
berth until she is in position. The quickwater partially checks the swing
so the ship lands easily.

Knowing that the ship swings in this manner, it is logical to use
astern bells to change her heading to starboard rather than only the
rudder. This provides an opportunity to simultaneously slow the ship
and change her heading. (Fig. 5-3)

Don't overuse the rudder when docking. The rudder can often remain
hard left during the final stages of a docking maneuver whether docking
port or starboard side to, since it has so little effect at these slow speeds.
The hard over rudder is in the position in which it will most likely be
needed, and having it in this position saves time required for the
steering engine to move the rudder should it be needed to check the
ship's swing. Do the same when backing the engine in an anchorage or
during other maneuvers when the ship has little or no headway—the
rudder need not be shifted when backing the engine unless the ship
develops significant sternway.

QUICKWATER

Quickwater develops when the flow from the engine going astern starts
moving up the ship's side. This occurs first on the starboard side at about
2 knots and by the time the ship has little headway there will be considerable flow up both sides of the ship. The quickwater strikes first on

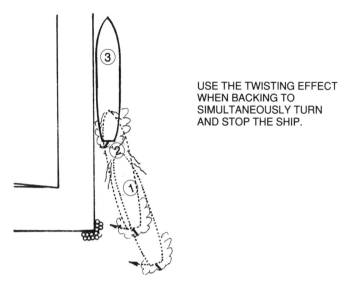

USE THE TWISTING EFFECT
WHEN BACKING TO
SIMULTANEOUSLY TURN
AND STOP THE SHIP.

Fig. 5-3. Coming alongside—port side to the dock.

the quarter so the stern moves away and the bow heads toward the berth, and its effect is more pronounced when docking starboard side to. The quickwater eventually moves up the full length of the ship so she is affected equally fore and aft, the cushion being used by the shiphandler to reduce the ship's lateral motion or move the ship away from the dock.

Like other forces which affect a ship, quickwater is planned for and used as an aid by the competent shiphandler. Quickwater affects a docking or undocking ship but is strongest when there is shoaling or a bulkhead under the berth. This contains the flow and increases the pressure acting upon the hull. If the ship approaches with excessive speed it is necessary to back more strongly than desired for a greater length of time, and resulting excessive flow of quickwater becomes a problem in spite of the best planning. This is one more reason for approaching at the minimum possible speed.

BRIDGE MARKERS

Common sense dictates that a marker or light be placed on the string-piece to show the location of the bridge when the ship is in position. Unfortunately, this is rarely done. Too often the ship is alongside with the first lines run before someone on the dock decides that she should shift 50 feet ahead or 30 feet astern. Aside from being both annoying and unprofessional, this practice costs both the ship and the terminal a great deal of time and money. The stevedore or terminal operator knows where the working hatch or manifold should be spotted, and every shipmaster knows the distance from the bridge to the bow or manifold, so the bridge location can easily be marked on the dock prior to bringing the ship alongside.

Shipmasters and pilots must work to make the use of bridge markers and lights more common.

USE FINESSE, NOT FORCE

Keep in mind when going alongside that you are bringing a moving object of considerable mass alongside an unforgiving and immovable pier or wharf, an evolution that requires some degree of finesse. Beware the shipmaster or pilot who tells in most graphic terms how the ship was "forced" into a berth against wind and current, having been "belted" full ahead and full astern until she was "driven" alongside the berth within feet of certain calamity. This is no professional speaking!

Shiphandling, like lovemaking, is a subtle art: the ship is not driven by the shiphandler, she is caressed, and this must be foremost in your

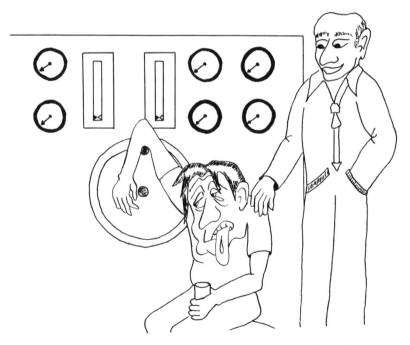

Fig. 5-4. "... and just think, First, that pilot docked with 'finesse'."

mind as you give those last commands to ease the ship alongside. (Fig. 5-4)

GOING ALONGSIDE

It is extremely important that the ship is flat to the stringpiece as she comes alongside. This is true for several reasons:

1. The frames through the entire midbody of the ship can absorb the impact of landing, rather than having the impact concentrated within a small area of the hull.
2. A parallel landing traps the maximum quantity of water between the hull and the pier or wharf, and thus develops the maximum cushioning effect.
3. The eddy current acts equally along the entire length of the ship, slowing her lateral motion and easing the landing.
4. If the ship is docking with any current, having the ship's upstream end hard alongside keeps the current from getting inside the ship and forcing her back off the berth.
5. The maximum cushioning effect is gained from the ship's quickwater when the ship is parallel to the berth.

When the impact of landing is spread over the entire length of the flat parallel midbody, and several hundred feet of nearly incompressible water cushions that landing, the ship can go alongside with surprising force without damage. The reverse is true when the ship lands at any angle to the berth. It is common to see water trapped between the hull and a solid-faced pier or wharf go several feet into the air as the ship comes alongside, indicative of the energy that this hydraulic cushion is absorbing. If the hull has any angle, the water rushes toward the end that is farthest off the pier and the cushion is lost.

ALL SECURE

The ship is alongside and the lines are being run ashore one after the other to make her fast. The number and placement of these lines varies with the location and construction of the pier, the type and size of the ship, and the weather and current conditions that are expected.

Ships usually run sufficient head, spring, and stern lines which keep the ship from moving forward and aft. Unfortunately, these lines are often a hindrance rather than an aid in keeping the ship alongside in a strong current—especially after the ship has been allowed to get off the pier at one end. The tidal current gets on the inshore side of the hull at the bow or quarter, an eddy current develops to further increase the strain on the lines, and the ship moves ahead or astern *into the current.* The ship rides outward and ahead on the lines, pivoting on them much like a waterskier at the end of a towline, while the lines at the opposite end of the ship pull her in so she begins surging up and down the pier. This surging occurs because there is a greater strain on the upstream lines than on those leading downstream, and causes *shock loading* that parts lines.

Breast lines, the lines that are most effective in keeping the ship alongside, are too often overlooked although they should be doubled up like any others. If there are sufficient breast lines to keep the ship alongside, the strain on the lines leading forward and aft remains equal and the ship does not begin surging.

The surging is aggravated by passing ships whose hydrodynamic forces move the berthed vessel first away from and then toward the moving vessel, while also pulling the docked ship off the wharf. A pressure wave moves ahead of the approaching ship, and there is a decrease in pressure between the two ships due to the flow of water as they pass. It is especially important that the ship be kept hard alongside, with sufficient breast lines run and all lines up tight, at berths exposed to passing ship traffic.

Remember too, Mate, to call the ship that is approaching at excessive speed on the VHF radio and tell her to slow down. No longer is it necessary to stand by and watch a catastrophe develop because you cannot communicate. Look over the side and make sure the ship is alongside, then go to the VHF radio and tell the passing ship to pass at minimum speed with the engine stopped to assure that your vessel is not pulled off the pier.

CHAPTER SIX

UNDOCKING

> Many are the boys, in every seaport, who are drawn
> away, as by an almost irresistible attraction, from
> their work and schools, and hang about the docks and
> yards of vessels with a fondness which, it is plain, will
> have its way. No sooner, however, has the young
> sailor begun his new life in earnest, than all this fine
> drapery falls off, and he learns that it is work after all.
> —Richard Henry Dana
> *Two Years Before the Mast*

Cargo operations complete, the ship lies quiet for the first time in many hours. The shore staff are gone, leaving you with a desk heaped full of memos, magazines, and unopened mail. The short stay in port was hectic but you enjoyed it both because it marked the end of one voyage and the beginning of another. Perhaps it is just because your work has these beginnings and endings, rather than going on interminably as jobs ashore seem to do, that you stay at sea.

The telephone interrupts your reverie.

"The pilot is on the bridge, Captain."

Another voyage has begun.

PLANNING THE UNDOCKING

Take the same care when briefing the undocking pilot as was taken with the pilot who docked the ship; exchange the same information and data card. Be sure to inform the pilot of the status of the anchor in addition to all the other items outlined in previous chapters, especially if they are backed out of the hawsepipe or if one was left on the bottom after docking. It is surprising how often the docking pilot finds out that there are two shots of chain in the water after letting go the last line.

As you did before docking, get out on the wing and feel the wind, check its direction by looking up at the stack gases, and look over the side to check the current. No matter how many instruments you might have to supply such information, it's still important that you use your own senses and get a feel for existing conditions before planning this or any other maneuver.

Too often, the less experienced shiphandler looks upon undocking as a relatively simple operation and does not properly plan the evolution. The ship is usually undocking stern first from a berth, so she steers poorly if at all. Since she is starting from alongside, the shiphandler has fewer options available that make use of the wind and current as the ship begins backing from the berth. During a docking, wind and current are felt when the stern is in clear water and the angle of approach can be adjusted to make use of these forces. This is not the case when undocking.

Even the most careful plans may have to be altered after the lines are let go since it is difficult to determine which of several conflicting forces will most affect the ship leaving the berth. Often the shiphandler lets go expecting to be set off the pier by wind, only to remain hard alongside due to subsurface current. If this occurs, take time to replan the undocking before touching the telegraph. The ship isn't going anywhere—*more accidents occur because of inappropriate action than delayed action.*

DRAFT AND TRIM IN BALLAST

The directional stability and handling characteristics of a loaded ship were discussed in previous chapters, so it is assumed that the ship is now in ballast and light. Ideally, she is ballasted to at least a moderate draft to submerge the propeller, rudder, and bow thruster, and to reduce windage. Give her a few feet of drag. The amount of trim by the stern depends on the handling characteristics of the ship, but it is better to have a bit too much drag than not enough. Try to at least get the stern well down if stress or loading conditions limit ballasting since:

1. The ship has excellent directional stability with good drag.
2. The propeller and rudder are then most effective. With a deeper draft aft the ship steers better, requires less distance to stop, twists less when the engine is put astern, and requires less rudder to counter the torque of the propeller when going astern.
3. It is preferable that the bow also be ballasted to at least a moderate draft to reduce windage and submerge the bow thruster so it is effective.

If a choice must be made, however, between getting the bow down or a proper draft aft, choose the latter. It can be a challenge to hold a light bow into the wind until headway develops, but it can be done using a tug or the anchor. In most situations, the advantages of having the stern down outweigh this disadvantage.

SINGLING UP

After undocking ships for many years, pilots and seafarers alike tend to become complacent about singling up mooring lines. Too often it becomes a habit to single up at a particular berth in the same manner with every ship.

"Two and one forward and a stern line aft, Mate," and without further thought the docking master heads for the coffee maker.

Singling up is *usually* a routine operation until the night when from a warm, quiet wheelhouse you underestimate the force of the wind or current. It took several lines to hold the ship alongside. Yet, when singling up, the ship is left hanging off a few parts stretched fiddlestring tight. Walk out on the wing, feel and see the conditions, and really think about how many and which lines should be taken in.

Ideally the lines are taken in systematically while the ship is held in position without overloading the remaining parts. Which lines should be left until last? This depends on the existing conditions, hence no rule of thumb can suffice. Basically, it is preferable to leave short lines until last, i.e., a short headline and spring forward, a short stern line and breast line aft. *Run a bight or two in place of a single line if the wind and/or current are strong.* It requires only one winch to heave that bight aboard when taking in the last lines, but the bight provides twice as many parts to hang on while waiting to let go. Use tug assistance to hold the ship alongside and reduce the strain on remaining lines while singling up.

Short lines hold the ship alongside more effectively and still keep her from moving forward or aft, and they can also be brought aboard quickly—especially important aft since the propeller should be cleared as soon as possible so the engine can be used.

As ships get larger, winches are geared down to handle the higher loads and thus are slower. It is therefore important that the crew be informed if the last lines must come aboard particularly fast. The mate can leave the shortest line until last, and lead it to the winch before letting go to get the propeller clear quickly.

USING QUICKWATER WHEN UNDOCKING

The ship's quickwater can be an effective tool during the undocking, especially when backing from a wharf or pier, since the ship is passing through the quickwater as she moves astern.

Leaving a starboard side berth the quickwater forces the stern away from the dock or wharf, then moves the ship laterally and, when there is a good flow striking the hull forward of the pivot point, checks up the swing of the bow toward the pier. The more restricted the flow of quickwater along the inboard side of the ship, whether due to shoaling under the berth or to the pier or wharf having a solid face, the more effect it has on the ship.

Quickwater has less effect when leaving from a port side berth since it is inherently less strong on the port side of the ship and is acting in more open water due to the ship's angle to the pier as she starts to back. Quickwater has a minimal effect but does reduce that angle to the berth as it strikes the forepart of the hull.

With some planning, the quickwater can be used to neatly move a ship with the minimum of bells and rudder orders. For example, a ship can be started astern until the stern begins to lift off the pier. The engine is then stopped and the ship drifts astern while the quickwater moves forward to strike the hull ahead of the pivot point. The swing of the bow toward the pier is checked and the ship backs straight astern, clearing the berth in a neat and seamanlike manner. Quickwater is discussed further in Chapter 5.

UNDOCKING FROM A WHARF

Take advantage of any current from ahead when undocking from a wharf. Deliberately get that current inside the ship and create the situation you have been avoiding while the ship was berthed. The current moves the bow off the wharf as you use the engine and rudder to lift the stern without developing any head or sternway over the ground. (Fig. 6-1) The ship moves laterally off the berth.

A certain feel is needed when adjusting engine revolutions so the ship makes no headway but sets away from the berth in the current. Use sufficient engine revolutions to keep the ship abeam of a selected point on the wharf while walking her laterally away from the berth. When wind and space limitations make tug assistance necessary, the tug is backed as required to maintain the ship's angle to the wharf while *the current takes her off the berth.*

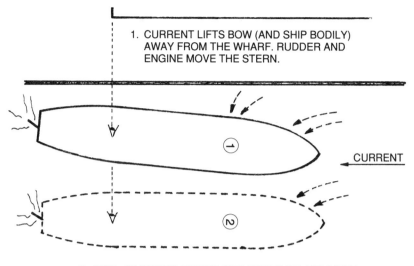

1. CURRENT LIFTS BOW (AND SHIP BODILY) AWAY FROM THE WHARF. RUDDER AND ENGINE MOVE THE STERN.

CURRENT

2. RPMs ADJUSTED SO THE SHIP MAKES NO HEADWAY OVER THE BOTTOM WHILE MOVING LATERALLY.

Fig. 6-1. Undocking—current from ahead.

Greater lateral force and control are needed when ships are berthed close ahead and astern, or a wind blowing on the wharf overcomes the current. Either use a second tug or back the bow tug while the ship's engine turns ahead with more power and hard over rudder. (Fig. 6-2) In the latter case, the tug and engine work against each other to prevent headreaching while moving the ship off the dock laterally. The ship maintains an angle to the wharf so the current can assist the tug and engine in moving the ship off the dock. A more detailed discussion of this technique is found later in this chapter.

When the current is from astern, the ship is undocked in much the same manner as she was docked under the same conditions. Work the bow toward the wharf using the tug, engine, and mooring lines, and then back into the stream. If a vessel is berthed astern, use the engines as necessary to match the current as the ship works laterally off the wharf. Again, maintain a speed through the water that matches the drift of the current so the ship moves laterally over the ground.

A steam turbine powered ship can easily maintain the required speed. Communicate with the engine room by telephone rather than telegraph to obtain specific revolutions instead of using standard maneuvering speeds.

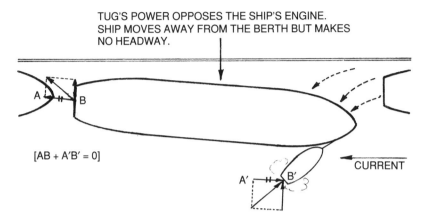

Fig. 6-2. Moving the ship laterally off a berth (one tug).

A motor ship requires more attention since a high speed diesel has a dead slow that often exceeds the required speed. The engine must be stopped intermittently to make good the needed speed, a maneuver that requires some practice. A variable pitch propelled motor ship has an advantage in this situation since the pitch can be reduced to exactly match the drift of the current.

To take a ship off a clear wharf at slack water, put her bow at a small angle to the berth and steam ahead. Use the rudder with care, lifting the stern while maintaining the ship's angle to the wharf. If the wharf is not clear ahead, the ship is either worked off using the engine in opposition to a tug, or the bow is pushed in toward the pier and the ship backs off as described later for a port side undocking from a pier.

BACKING FROM A SLIP

This common undocking situation has as many variations as there are piers. All have some basic similarities though, and the shiphandler uses a knowledge of seamanship to adjust methods to suit the local conditions.

A ship berthed *starboard side to* needs no angle when backing from a pier, since the torque of the propeller and the quickwater move her stern to port, clear of the dock. It may be necessary to use the bow thruster or tug to check up the resultant starboard swing of the bow so it clears the stringpiece, or to intermittently come ahead with hard over rudder to steady up the ship before continuing to back. If the ship is to

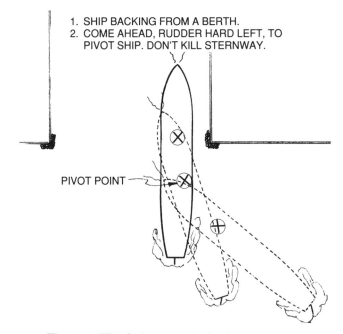

1. SHIP BACKING FROM A BERTH.
2. COME AHEAD, RUDDER HARD LEFT, TO
   PIVOT SHIP. DON'T KILL STERNWAY.

PIVOT POINT

Fig. 6-3. Think "pivot point" when turning.

back to starboard after clearing the slip, go astern until the *pivot point is well clear of the pier* and then come ahead with hard port rudder to walk the stern to starboard as the bow swings clear. (Fig. 6-3) If the turn is begun before the pivot point clears the pier, that part of the ship aft of the pivot point will close on the pier as the stern moves to starboard. This is so whether the ship is turned with the engine alone or with tug assistance, as a tug does not lift the ship bodily—it pivots the hull about the pivot point—a point that shifts aft to about midships as the tug pushes or pulls on the bow.

Before backing from a *port side* docking, work the bow in and get the ship at a good angle with the stern well off the pier. This can be done by:

1. Pushing with the bow tug.
2. Heaving on the headline while holding the forward spring.
3. Backing a stern tug, if used.
4. Coming ahead dead slow against the spring line with the rudder hard over toward the deck.

It is becoming less practical to work against mooring lines as ships increase in size and power. Diesel-propelled ships often have a dead slow

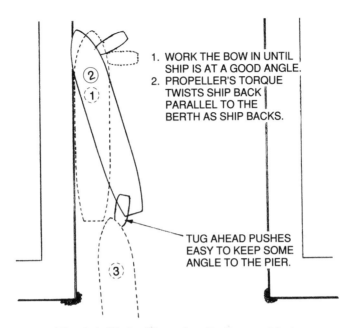

1. WORK THE BOW IN UNTIL SHIP IS AT A GOOD ANGLE.
2. PROPELLER'S TORQUE TWISTS SHIP BACK PARALLEL TO THE BERTH AS SHIP BACKS.

TUG AHEAD PUSHES EASY TO KEEP SOME ANGLE TO THE PIER.

Fig. 6-4. Undocking—berthed port side to.

speed of 6 to 8 knots and are especially difficult to undock by working against ship's lines.

The torque of a propeller going astern walks the stern to port so the ship comes back parallel to the berth as sternway develops. She then comes easily out of the berth and is turned as required once the pivot point clears the pier. (Fig. 6-4)

Whether backing from a port or starboard side berth, the bow tug either backs along with the ship, using a stern line as required, or falls around and follows the ship while hanging on a single line. When there is sufficient room between the hull and berth, a tug line trailing stem to stem can work against either side of the ship to lift the bow and steer the ship as she backs from the slip. (Fig. 6-5)

It would seem quite simple to back from a slip when a strong wind is blowing off the pier but this is not always the case. When the ship is dead in the water the wind tends to move her bodily off the pier, this effect being modified by a large stack or forward or after house which causes the bow or stern to come away more quickly. As the ship develops sternway, she often backs into the wind so the stern usually moves toward the berth, overcoming the torque of the propeller during star-

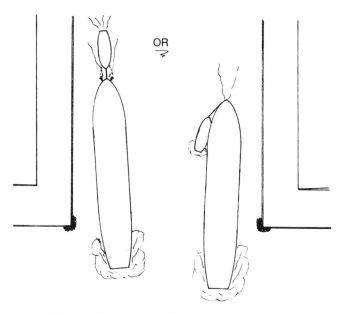

Fig. 6-5. Tug working at the bow—backing from a berth.

board side undocking or accentuating the twisting effect in a port side undocking.

A wind blowing on the pier holds the ship alongside. While more esoteric maneuvers can be used—the ship can be pulled off the deck with an anchor deployed during docking, or a lashed-up tug can be used—more common options available for undocking in this situation include:

1. Sliding along the stringpiece until the stern clears the outboard corner of the pier and the ship is turned fair in the channel. This is the safest maneuver when there is no tug assistance since the ship is alongside at all times until clear and thus can not be blown against the pier and damaged. She may lose some paint while sliding along but this is inconsequential since "paint comes in buckets while steel comes in shipyards."
2. Putting the ship at a good angle to the berth by working against the spring line and then backing clear. However, the entire ship body, or more likely the ship's bow, may be blown back down on the pier and damaged when undocking in this manner.
3. Breasting the ship off with one or two tugs.

The ship's behavior once she develops sternway is primarily a factor of her superstructure and freeboard. She may set back on the pier bodily, or the bow only may set down toward the pier as the ship backs into the wind. The shiphandler must be prepared for either situation unless the ship is being slid along the stringpiece.

Another situation develops when the shed doors on the pier are closed. An eddy often forms as the wind reflects off the closed doors and the ship is set off the dock rather than on it. This simplifies the undocking. Since the ship will lie some distance off the stringpiece rather than hard against it in this situation, the shiphandler is aware of the condition and can plan accordingly.

In any case, the mariner again uses the wind rather than reacts to it. Anticipate wind effects and adjust the ship's angle to the berth so the wind helps her maintain a desired heading. A shiphandler who waits until these effects occur and then responds to them soon feels like a cat chasing its tail.

COMING AHEAD FROM A SLIP

This straightforward and simple maneuver can generally be performed with minimum assistance. In a clear slip it's often possible to depart without tug assistance unless there is a strong wind or current holding the ship on the berth. Even under these conditions a ship can sail without a tug if there is good maneuvering room off the end of the pier.

Undocking when the wind is off the dock is a simple maneuver, the ship steaming clear until the stern has room to swing and then turning fair in the channel. A tug may be required if the channel off the pier is not wide enough to permit turning unassisted. The anchor or spring line can also be used to work the ship around the end of the pier as described in previous chapters.

A wind blowing on the berth presents some problems to a ship docked stern in. Usually a tug is used to lift the bow while the rudder and engine move the stern away from the stringpiece. The ship may depart without a tug though, even in a moderate wind, if the job is planned to make use of existing conditions. Let go all lines and steam the ship at slow speed up the stringpiece keeping the rudder about 10 degrees toward the pier to hold the ship lightly alongside. If the ship were to come off the pier and then blow back down again she could be damaged. As the pivot point clears the end of the pier, increase the revolutions and rudder angle, turning the ship across the end of the pier and lifting the stern clear.

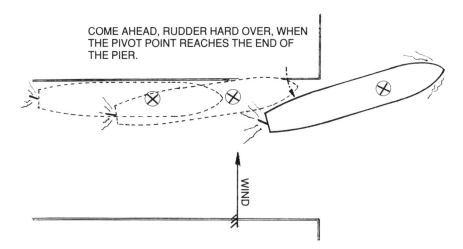

COME AHEAD, RUDDER HARD OVER, WHEN
THE PIVOT POINT REACHES THE END OF
THE PIER.

WIND

Fig. 6-6. Undocking bow out from a slip.

The ship must have enough speed to overcome leeway when she clears
the end of the stringpiece—2 to 3 knots usually being sufficient. The
stern lifts neatly away from the stringpiece as the ship clears the berth
and turns to head fair in the channel. (Fig. 6-6)

The only safe maneuver when the ship is stern in and has to turn
away from the pier with limited maneuvering room is to wait for a tug.
There are maneuvers that can be used but they depend on so many
things going well that the risk of accident is excessive.

COMING OFF PARALLEL TO A BERTH

Often a ship must come off a berth while remaining parallel to the
stringpiece, such as when she is berthed in a narrow slip, or docked
starboard side to with a ship astern, or berthed at a wharf with ships
close ahead and astern. There are several ways to accomplish this:

1. Use a second tug made fast aft to lift and control the stern during the undocking.
2. Lash up the bow tug facing aft and use that tug against the
   ship's engines as discussed in Chapter 3.
3. Make the bow tug fast in the usual manner and back that tug
   to lift the bow while the ship's engine is coming ahead with the
   rudder hard over toward the dock to lift the stern. Sufficient
   engine revolutions must be used to counter the tug's power as
   they work against each other, so the ship maintains her position

Fig. 6-7. "Rule number one, gentlemen. Always back *away* from danger."

over the bottom, i.e., relative to the berth, but moves laterally
away from the stringpiece. (Fig. 6-2)

These techniques can be used alone or in combination with other
previously discussed methods for undocking to turn a ship around in a
limited space, or to accomplish work with one tug that might ordinarily
require two. Such options augment the more common backing and
pushing work with tugs.

BACKING A SHIP TOWARD A HAZARD

Given a choice, a shiphandler never presents the stern of a ship to
danger—never backs toward a shoal or another ship if there is any
option. It is preferable to back into clear water even if this means turning
the long way around to go to sea.

A ship can go bow first into a bank or shallows without damage, but
put her rudder into the bank and she will probably be spending time in
a shipyard. Back toward another ship and have an engine failure (an
event sufficiently common with motor ships that it should be planned
for), and certain embarrassment will result. Back toward open water,

though, and have an engine failure, and you just back a little further than planned before getting an anchor down and the ship stopped.

Make it a rule—when handling a ship, back toward open water.

LEFT HAND AND VARIABLE PITCH PROPELLERS

Keep in mind that the maneuvers described herein are for a ship fitted with a right hand or clockwise turning propeller. The rare ship having a left hand turning fixed propeller is handled in a manner opposite to that described, i.e., a starboard side undocking (or docking) of a ship fitted with a left hand turning propeller is done in the manner previously described for a port side undocking (or docking).

Variable pitch ships often have right hand turning propellers. These propellers turn in the same direction whether the ship is going ahead or astern and only the pitch is reversed to back down. The propeller is therefore turning clockwise when going astern, just like a conventional fixed pitch left hand propeller, so such ships are handled like vessels with left hand turning propellers when docking and undocking. Variable pitch propelled ships should be standardized, all being fitted with left hand turning propellers so they back like other ships that the shiphandler is accustomed to handling. There is no standard at present, so the shiphandler must check the direction of rotation of every variable pitch fitted ship before planning the docking or undocking.

TURNING TO SEA

Turning in relatively open water is a straightforward job so long as the shiphandler minimizes the ship's speed. The basic behavior of ships when going astern, and during the backing and filling maneuver, are discussed in Chapter 1. There are, however, additional points to consider if the ship is to be turned in a restricted area.

It is possible to both turn a ship around and control her position in a channel or turning basin while she has sternway. While moving astern, the ship can be steered using the engine ahead, shifting the rudder to direct the propeller's flow in the needed direction much like a thruster. The flow acting on the ship's stern is the resultant of both the astern and athwartship vectors of this flow. While moving astern remember:

1. To reduce or kill sternway, put the rudder amidships and direct this flow aft.

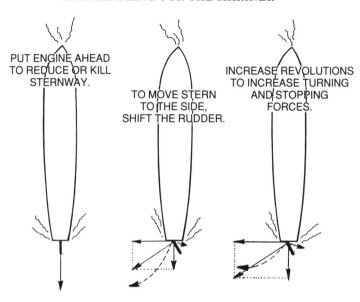

Fig. 6-8. Turning a ship with sternway.

2. To continue moving astern while going to starboard or port, put the rudder to the side opposite that to which you wish the stern to move, i.e., to move the stern to starboard put the rudder to port and the engine ahead.

3. To change the magnitude of this turning and stopping force, increase or decrease the engine revolutions.

Think of these changes as one maneuver, much as you increase, decrease, or stop a bow thruster, rather than as several separate and distinct maneuvers. (Fig. 6-8)

The shiphandler who finds the ship carrying her sternway longer than desired often increases engine revolutions but leaves the rudder hard over. The rudder should be put amidships to direct the increased flow from the propeller directly astern. After the speed has decreased sufficiently, the rudder is shifted back to the right or left to renew the stern's swing.

Face in the direction of ship movement—if going astern, face aft, it's where the action is. This simple change of position does much to improve the mariner's shiphandling technique; seagoing professionals, mates, and masters spend so much time looking ahead at sea that they tend, out of habit, to handle ships in confined water while watching only the bow.

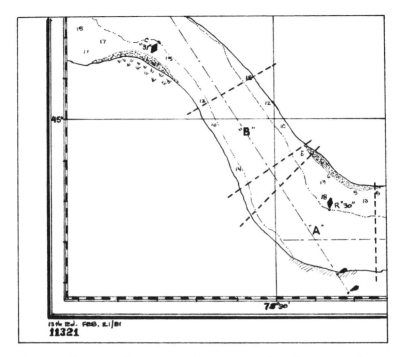

Fig. 6-9. Common bottom configuration in bends and reaches.

If the ship is to be turned in a basin:

1. Turn in the direction that keeps the stern in the best water.
2. Take nearly all sternway off the ship before starting to swing her.
3. All factors being equal, turn the ship to the right to take advantage of the ship's better turning characteristics backing and filling in that direction.
4. Position the ship's pivot point so the stern swings clear.
5. Fix the diameter of the basin in your mind before starting to turn.
6. When possible, put the end of the ship to be swung in the area of maximum favorable current.
7. Put the ship at the end of the basin from which the current is flowing when starting the maneuver.

Discuss the depth and profile of the basin with the pilot, as the location of any shoaling depends on local conditions. Lacking better information you can estimate the location of shoaling based upon the basin's proximity to turns in the channel. (Fig. 6-9) The deepest water in a basin at location "A" will usually be in the bend away from the point,

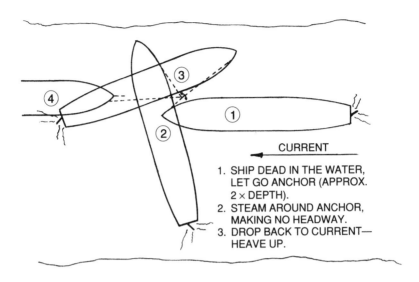

CURRENT

1. SHIP DEAD IN THE WATER,
   LET GO ANCHOR (APPROX.
   2 × DEPTH).
2. STEAM AROUND ANCHOR,
   MAKING NO HEADWAY.
3. DROP BACK TO CURRENT—
   HEAVE UP.

Fig. 6-10. Turning short on an anchor.

and the stern should be swung in that direction. Above or below the turn, at location "B," the deepest water lies on the side nearest the path of the ebb tide as it flows from one bend to the next. Midway between the turns the deepest water would generally be in midchannel so the ship can probably turn in the most convenient direction. *Do not present the stern to potential dangers.*

It may be impressive to watch a ship performing several maneuvers simultaneously *in the basin* as she is both stopped and swung but, if the ship is not nearly stopped before being turned, there is little margin for errors in judgment or for any unknown current. Reduce the ship's sternway, then turn her.

The stem can be put in the mud and the ship pivoted around on the bow if the current strikes the quarter in a favorable direction. The anchor can be used in the same manner, either alone or in conjunction with the bank, to swing the ship. (Fig. 6-10)

Watch natural ranges ashore, both ahead and astern to determine if the ship is being set along the axis of the channel, and abeam to check that the ship does not develop unwanted headway or sternway over the bottom as the tugs and engine are used. Don't be in a hurry to come ahead with the engine after the midpoint of the turn is passed—wait until the turn is nearly completed before starting to come ahead over the bottom.

While swinging, the banks ahead and astern appear closer from the bridge than they actually are so it is important that you fix in your mind the basin's dimensions before starting the maneuver. When the banks start to appear close, remind yourself of the clearance that you know is available, and you will avoid the apprehension that causes unnecessary maneuvering.

DISMISSING THE TUGS

Dismiss the stern tug as soon as her work is done. Do not carry the stern tug along after clearing the slip since, as previously discussed, she is only a hindrance.

Keep the forward tug as long as it might possibly be of assistance. Even if the ship has a bow thruster, a tug that has been used coming into the slip should be kept fast until the ship is headed fair, clear of all obstructions and any traffic that might be a problem. You have paid for the tug's services, so make her earn her money. The bow thruster may quit or refuse to stop when used, or a problem may arise that requires more effective power than the bow thruster can develop as the ship's speed increases.

When dismissing the tug, lower her lines with a messenger. Don't drop them from the ship's deck since a line in the water may foul the tug's screw or your own. Dropping the line also makes unnecessary work for the tug's crew since the line could have been lowered on deck rather than having to be dragged wet from the water. Listen for the tug's signal, often a long blast on her whistle followed by two short blasts, so she can be let go promptly as the ship starts to come ahead. Keep at least two crew members and a mate standing by a tug at all times, even if she is to be held for some period after clearing the berth.

The ship now turned and headed fair, the docking master wishes all a good voyage and climbs down the ladder to the waiting tug below.

CHAPTER SEVEN

DEPARTURE

> Captain N. B. Palmer was a rough old sailor. He was
> determined to see me get along, and helped me more
> than any other man to know my duty as an officer and
> to fit me for a Master.
> —Captain Charles Porter Low
> *Recollections*

*Downbound and light, she made good time despite the flood tide. The old
man, tired from the short, hectic stay in port, left his chair only to glance
occasionally at the chart on the wheelhouse log desk. He had little
inclination to make conversation with the pilot, now ten minutes into a
monologue to which only the third mate was really listening.*

*Fresh coffee in hand, the mate returned to the log desk. She noted the
time on the chart as the ship swung onto the next range, comparing the
course that the pilot had given to the helmsman with the previously inked
and labeled courses on the chart.*

"Right to one, five, four."

*Checking the swing, the A.B. on the wheel repeated the new course,
"One, five, four, Sir."*

"Very well, steady so."

*"Trouble is, Mate, they always have to be looking for problems, and
if there aren't any they create some. It's part of life today but it sure is
hurting the marine industry."*

*The mate had heard all this before, and always some mysterious
"they" were causing the problems.*

"Who are 'they,' Pilot?" she queried.

*"Industry groups, government agencies, the Coast Guard—and why
do we have a military service regulating and policing professionals in a
commercial industry anyway? The Air Force doesn't regulate the airlines!"*

*The captain sat back in his chair and took all this in. He had heard
many such discussions recently and, while the Coast Guard was often
the target of the seafarer's frustrations, the problem obviously went
beyond that agency. What the mariner basically objected to was the*

124

preponderance of often irrelevant regulations that interfered with his work, and the exclusion of the active marine professional from the process that developed those regulations. Some representation from the active seagoing community, at both the national and international levels, was long overdue. The captain appreciated and shared these concerns.

"There is a lot of expertise on the water today, Mate, and the standards in the industry suffer when active professionals are excluded from discussions of matters affecting the marine industry."

Picking up the phone to instruct the standby to rig the pilot ladder, the third mate nodded her agreement.

"You're right, Pilot, we're letting the tail wag the dog in our industry."

"It's a good way of life, Mate, and we can't let others use politics to downgrade it. We have to become more involved in matters affecting our profession."

DROPPING THE PILOT

Well before arriving at the pilot station, the master and the mate on watch discuss inbound and outbound traffic with the pilot. All ships are identified by name and their intentions clarified so there is a smooth transition of the conn from pilot to master. It's easy for the pilot to discuss any potential problem situations with the other ships before he leaves since he has radio contact with both the other pilots and the pilot station. They know the destinations, drafts, nationalities, and intentions of the ships moving in the area, and are able to assist the master in making safe meeting arrangements before the pilot disembarks.

Until the master is fully confident that there will be no problems as the ship departs from the port area, *he should not release the pilot.* Being a responsible professional, the pilot has no objection to performing this last service before leaving and the master must not hesitate to require it.

DEPARTURE SPEED

A lee is made and the pilot boards his boat to go ashore. The ship returns to her heading and proceeds to the departure point at a speed that matches the flow of outbound traffic. Moving at that speed obviously reduces by half the amount of traffic that must be dealt with since now only crossing and meeting ships present any potential problems. Time saved does not justify excessive speed, and any fool can engage in false heroics with a ship that belongs to someone else.

Fig. 7-1. "Cap', could you slow her down a bit while I board the pilot boat?"

Speed is also limited by depth of water. Trying to push a ship at a speed faster than proper for the depth of water causes excessive squat and suction and, since the flow of water to the rudder is restricted by the underkeel clearance, the ship becomes hard to steer. Increased difficulty in steering and the pronounced vibration that can be felt throughout the ship are certain indications of excessive speed.

This remains true until the ship leaves shallow water conditions, not just while the ship is in a harbor or channel. As the ship reaches deeper water, her speed should be increased incrementally, rather than being brought to sea speed upon departure. This is increasingly important as ships get larger, not only because of the inherently greater drafts of VLCCs, but because of the higher horsepower and tendency of the larger hull to develop harmonic vibrations under shallow water conditions. As ship size increases, the master must adjust shiphandling habits.

Make every effort to move with the flow of traffic whether there is a formal traffic separation scheme or not. If a problem develops, do not hesitate to stop the ship and let the situation clear itself up. Since the master and mates have developed their shiphandling skills, maneuvering while maintaining heading and position should present no problem. Too often, the less experienced shiphandler tends to increase speed to "get away from a potentially dangerous situation"—the experienced

Fig. 7-2. "Ya see, Mister Mate, if you come up to sea speed too soon she may vibrate a little."

master or pilot uses the opposite tactic and slows or stops the ship. The other ships are moving ahead to create the potentially dangerous close quarters situation. If you stop, you avoid reaching the problem area until the situation is resolved. Stopping, not rushing on, is the action of the professional.

MANEUVERING WITH OTHER SHIPS

Make your actions known to other ships by whistle signals and by use of the VHF radio. Make any changes in course or speed large and obvious. By making larger than required changes in your heading, especially at night, you are effectively talking to that other ship with your lights—showing her your sidelight—and there can be no doubt about your intentions. Refer to the section in Chapter 1 concerning the proper use of VHF radio, and especially keep in mind that ships of other nationalities do not arrange passing situations, but primarily discuss alterations in heading. If no one on either meeting ship speaks English fluently, there is a chance for misunderstanding when you discuss a port to port passing since this may be interpreted by the other vessel as a request for an *alteration of course* to port.

To effectively maneuver a ship and continually assess traffic, the conning master or mate must be relieved of other navigational and administrative tasks. The pilot develops an intimate knowledge of local waters and is able to navigate mainly by eye, so full attention can be given to traffic and shiphandling. The shipmaster visits many ports and cannot possibly develop the pilot's working knowledge of any particular port; another person is therefore needed to do the navigating so the master can give sufficient attention to maneuvering the ship.

It's true that the master alone can do other work when traffic is light and conditions good, but as soon as any one task requires more than passing attention it is necessary to compromise the major duties of assessment and shiphandling unless additional help is available on the bridge. It is not suggested that the merchant ship resort to having a horde of people on the bridge performing nonessential and redundant tasks, as is too often found on naval vessels (and perhaps the latter will find they can operate more effectively if their number is significantly reduced), but there should be one additional person to compensate for the local knowledge that disappeared when the pilot went down the ladder.

The mate on watch continues to carry out the tasks that were being done while the pilot was aboard, while the additional mate plots traffic as necessary and navigates. The information obtained is passed to the master, who needs only to check the work often enough to be sure that it is being done correctly. The additional officer should be the chief mate when possible, since he is generally the most experienced as well as being the one who will most benefit from the opportunity to be involved as the ship enters and leaves port. Too often the mariner spends several years as chief mate, shuffling papers in the ship's office during arrivals and departures, only to be promoted to master and thrust back into the world of navigation and shiphandling. By assisting the master, the chief mate is gaining the knowledge required for that most responsible of positions, and acquiring the skills required to be an effective shipmaster and shiphandler.

The plethora of bridge equipment has not relieved the master of any traditional tasks, and in fact often creates distractions for the other officers so that essential tasks required by good seamanship are overlooked. Any impression that this equipment makes it possible to conn a ship with a bridge team that is one third smaller than the master-pilot-mate team is illusory—bring an additional officer to the bridge until the ship is at sea, clear of navigational hazards and traffic, so the master can in fact be the shiphandler rather than the navigator.

COURSE CARD AND PASSAGE PLANNING

The passage outbound should be as carefully planned as the passage in, with a chart in the wheelhouse available for consultation, courses inked in with pertinent information labeled, and a course card made up by the master.

The course card minimizes distractions and allows the master to remain at the centerline window to conn the ship. The pilot is able to draw the chart of the port from memory yet carries a course card; how can the master effectively conn the ship without one? The card should contain the reaches or ranges in order, with the course, length of the reach, and turning point at the end of each reach noted. This information can be put on a three-by-five card and kept in the shirt pocket, eliminating the need for repeated trips to the chartroom to pick off each course. The shiphandler can then spend that time watching the tug and tow which may be crossing the bow, while being more certain as the ship is brought to each new heading that there will be no errors in course.

The course card should be made up for the entire run from the dock to sea, not just for the portion of the passage after the pilot has disembarked. This effort will be especially appreciated should a rain squall or fog set in midway to sea since the master will need only to glance at the course card to check the heading as the ship feels her way.

Too often the term "passage planning" conjures up the vision of mates laying out pages of detailed courses, distance, navigation aids, and estimated runs at various speeds. This is fine for voyage planning, but a form-based passage plan alone is not suitable for navigating in restricted pilot waters. Indeed, a shiphandler working from pages of detailed information alone, without marked up charts and a proper course card, is much like an actor reading from a script *during* a performance. This is distracting. It tends to put mental limits on the mariner when situations arise that are not provided for in the original plan. Put complete information directly on the chart and course card prior to arrival or departure to eliminate the chance of error inherent in transferring information from the plan to the chart to the quarter-master while actually conning the ship in traffic and restricted waters. A passage inked in advance on the chart with turning bearings, courses,

Fig. 7-3. The pilot departs off Cape Henry. From an oil painting by
Captain Brian Hope.

and distances noted, together with the pocket course card, are very much
a part of any proper passage plan.

With a proper plan, properly marked chart, a course card, and
effective bridge resource management, the mariner can give the maximum attention to handling the ship. A more complete discussion of the
course card and passage plan can be found in Chapter 12, and excellent
texts on passage planning and bridge resource management are included in the Bibliography.

ABILITY TO MANEUVER

Do not be too quick to change to heavy oil when handling a motor ship
that can maneuver only on light diesel fuel, or to bring a steam turbine
ship to sea speed when this means that you cannot then reduce speed
without delay. The pilot station is the wrong place to increase to sea
speed, or to be unable to stop or go astern on short notice, since at that
point ships are converging from all directions rather than moving in a
predictable manner within a fairway or traffic scheme. The inbound
ships are anxious to get into port, are preparing to take the pilot, and
probably are in the highest risk location of the entire passage. Perhaps
the haste to increase speed is understandable, since those aboard want
to get the ship to sea where the routine will settle down and life will
return to normal, but wait a little longer until traffic is astern.

Yes, contrary to the landsman's opinion, the seaman does consider
life *at sea* normal!

CHAPTER EIGHT

ANCHORING AND
SHIPHANDLING WITH ANCHORS

> I had no means of knowing that what had happened to
> me was a manifestation of the sixth sense possessed by
> every born seaman. You can train a man in navigation,
> seamanship, celestial observation and the computing of
> tide, current, speed, wind, and drift, and yet he will
> never be a sailor unless, at the moment of truth when
> he is forced into a corner from which there is no way
> out except by instant intuitive action, he unerringly
> makes the right move.
>
> —Jan de Hartog
> *The Captain*

Too often a mate is promoted to a position for which, through no fault of his own, he is not ready. The principal cause of this is inadequate on-board experience, especially "hands-on" experience for junior officers under the supervision of more experienced officers. This lack of experience is especially significant in the area of shiphandling, including the conning of a ship in restricted waters and the use of anchors, although it is important that such experience be gained in all the shipboard skills. In an industry that operates in an environment alien to the novice, it's imperative that knowledge be passed from one generation of seamen to the next if professional standards are to be maintained. The fine training schools and maritime academies that serve the seafaring community offer an excellent theoretical beginning, but it is only that—a beginning. There is much that can be passed to a new officer only by example or instruction.

Pride in profession, appreciation of the relative importance of various tasks, and acquisition of that intangible that separates the exceptional seafarer from the average—sea sense—can only be gleaned by observation of others experienced in working at sea.

The planning and effort required to give junior officers on-board experience is as important as any other shipboard task and deserves the same attention from the seasoned master, mate, or chief. Hands-on-training assures both better operating ships and a continuation of seafaring tra-

ditions and skills. Let the chief mate conn the ship and pick up the pilot; have the second mate plan a cargo loading under the supervision of the mate; and give the third mate a chance to handle the ship during Williamson turns and other maneuvers at sea. Insist that these and other tasks be carried out properly. To assure that high standards of seagoing life are maintained, it is necessary that the master be a stern taskmaster and demand that those working for him perform to the highest standards.

In no area is hands-on experience more important than in shiphandling. It is possible to watch a shiphandler work for years and still not acquire a feeling for that art. Arrive at the pilot station a bit early and give the mates an opportunity to perform the maneuvers described in Chapter 1. Let those officers put the ship to anchor. While maneuvering, explain why you choose a particular heading to allow for wind and current. When one of these mates later has to alter course on the mid-watch for a fishing boat not seen until close at hand and is able to maneuver without hesitation or mistake, the effort put into training will suddenly be worthwhile.

As a young mate, didn't you appreciate the master or chief mate who took time to pass along a hint or to recount a sea story with a lesson at coffee time? You have the skills now, and a pride in what you do—it is your turn to pass them along!

ANCHORS FOR ANCHORING

The master's most common shiphandling task may be simply putting a ship to anchor. The skills involved are so basic, so essential, that no mariner is qualified for command until he can put a ship to anchor safely, expediently, and with confidence under all conditions.

On almost every voyage a master anchors for some reason. Done well, the task is completed without fuss or confusion. Done poorly, it becomes an unnecessarily complicated and dangerous evolution as the ship works against nature and the anchor, rust and mud flying, the chain straining and jumping across the wildcat. The skills of the master or officer at the conn make the difference and, fortunately, anchoring skills are easily mastered with practice and planning.

At first glance there seem to be many different, unrelated ways to anchor but that really isn't the case. True, a ship might use one anchor or two, placed in line or spread, from bow or stern, with equal or unequal amounts of chain stretched out or underfoot, but in every case the task is basically the same. A ship approaches an anchorage, maneuvers as closely as possible to the desired final heading, slows or stops, and drops the anchor or anchors to the bottom.

On the other hand, there is no one anchoring technique "for all seasons" because there are an infinite number of combinations of weather, ship types, anchorage locations, and other factors to consider; so it is both impossible and unnecessary to try to discuss every conceivable anchoring method as a distinct and different evolution. Instead, this text discusses only the most common anchoring situations and basic anchoring techniques which any reasonably skilled shiphandler can then adapt to most anchoring situations.

KNOW YOUR SHIP

It is impossible to plan an approach properly without some knowledge of your ship's maneuvering characteristics. Perform as much of the master's trials recommended in Chapter 1 as possible now, if you haven't already done so. The hands-on experience of maneuvering the ship during these trials gives the shiphandler a feel for the ship's response to rudder and engine and confidence in his skill and his ship's ability to complete the maneuvers safely within the confines of a particular anchorage. Ships are too valuable to maneuver by a wing and a prayer, and it's essential to have this knowledge and experience before having to anchor in a difficult situation.

Knowing the ship's maneuvering characteristics means understanding both what a ship can do and what it cannot do. Knowing when *not* to anchor is probably more important than how to anchor. When the anchorage is crowded or the weather adverse so the ship cannot be safely anchored, consider all alternatives including ordering a tug to assist, and if the job can't be done safely, lay off and wait for conditions to improve.

Remember too that maneuvering characteristics are not static and a particular loading condition such as a very light draft, or greater than normal drag, or reduced underkeel clearance, may significantly alter a ship's normal behavior. Some ship types are more affected by these changes than others: a high-sided ship or a heavily loaded ship may handle much differently in strong winds than in light airs, and a loaded tanker is a considerably different ship from a tanker in ballast. Ships change, conditions change, and the weather changes, so don't fall into the trap of trying to do the job the same way every time. Each anchoring is a new task: plan accordingly.

A bow thruster significantly changes a ship's handling characteristics during maneuvers at slow speed in an anchorage. Maneuvering is simplified if the thruster is used to turn a ship to her final heading, set up to back, position and hold the bow, and perform the other shiphandling tasks as the ship goes to anchor. Most ships do not have bow thrusters, though, and thrusters aren't really effective unless ships are moving at speeds of 2 knots or less, so the assumption is made in this chapter that no thruster is available.

AGAIN, PLAN AHEAD, THINK AHEAD

Here again, the same basic principles for successful shiphandling and maneuvering apply. Plan the overall maneuver prior to arrival using information from the charts, pilots, and your local knowledge about the port based on past experience. Apply your understanding of basic shiphandling principles and your appreciation for your ship's maneuvering characteristics learned during the master's trials. Reduce speed early. Adjust the initial plan to use existing conditions and forces to advantage to assist the ship's rudder and engine in maneuvering, then think ahead of the ship, adjusting the original plan as events develop, planning several steps ahead of the ship's maneuvers. Plan the anchoring as a series of simple steps, and always *think ahead, think ahead, think ahead*.

Consider anchoring in two phases because anchoring is an exercise in both basic seamanship and shiphandling. Decide how the ship will be anchored, and then how she must be handled to accomplish that task. Any good seamanship book discusses the first phase fully, so there is no point in repeating that discussion. The assumption is made here that the reader is a knowledgeable mariner who is aware of the seamanship aspects of anchoring and has already correctly planned that part of the evolution, so this chapter will stress primarily the second, shiphandling phase of anchoring.

ANCHOR IN STEPS

Keep the shiphandling phase of anchoring simple. Look at anchoring as a series of four steps: approach, placement, laying out, and fetching up. Plan each step separately as a series of small basic tasks rather than trying to plan the entire anchoring as one long, complex evolution and think ahead of the ship so each step leads more smoothly to the next.

A ship might need to enter an anchorage, reduce speed, back and fill around to the final heading, maneuver to the selected anchoring location, stop, and then move slowly astern, all as part of what might appear at first to be a complex approach and anchoring evolution. In fact, reducing speed is one separate, basic task, as is backing and filling, and stopping while controlling the ship's head, and most of these individual tasks have already been discussed in some context in this book. Consider each task separately, as you proceed step by step to anchor, and even relatively complex, challenging anchoring jobs become simply a series of small jobs that most mariners have mastered.

PLANNING

Every mariner studies the charts, sailing directions, predicted weather conditions and, as the ship gets closer to the anchorage, the radar presentation of the anchorage, looking for several types of information, including:

1. Direction and strength of wind and current.
2. Depth of water.
3. Type of bottom.
4. Location of lee shore, shoals, or other hazards.
5. Maneuvering room for approach.
6. Number and location of ships already at anchor.
7. Conditions affecting visibility, weather, and currents.
8. Local customs and practices of the port.
9. Swinging room after anchoring.

Unfortunately, mariners too often weigh these factors only to decide on the best location for anchoring, the amount of chain, and the number and placement of anchors. They forget that shiphandling is an inherent part of anchoring and that *this same information* must also be used to plan the shiphandling phase of the anchoring evolution. Look at the situation again and plan each step of the task using existing conditions to advantage, to help rather than hinder the work as much as possible.

It is as important to have an *alternative "bail out" plan* in mind as it is to have a primary plan of action, before entering the anchorage, in case things don't work out as expected. Generally, such a plan consists of leaving the anchorage until conditions improve or, if it is too late or impossible to leave, putting down an anchor and riding to a short stay while you sort things out. Remember, having those two anchors hanging at the bow is like having two tugs standing by forward ready to hold your ship and prevent accidents. Bailout plans vary widely depending on conditions, and alternatives are discussed in appropriate sections of this chapter.

Keep in mind too that *any plan must be flexible* since all too often another ship will be anchored in your selected spot or in the way of your approach. The plan is only a starting point: Use your shiphandling skills to adjust to existing conditions as they develop.

Let's look at some of the factors to be considered when a ship is going to anchor.

WIND AND CURRENT EFFECTS

Wind and current determine the preferred direction for approaching the anchorage, the final heading after anchoring, and to some extent the ship's behavior while maneuvering in the anchorage.

Set and leeway increase and the ship's turning circle becomes elliptical because of the wind and current, the longer axis of the ellipse lying in the direction of the wind and current. The effects of wind and current on navigation and shiphandling *increase dramatically as a ship's speed decreases*. The mariner, accustomed to navigating at full sea speed where set and leeway are much less significant, has to plan more carefully and make greater allowances for wind and current effects while moving through an anchorage at reduced speeds.

Don't fight the wind and current. Review previous discussions on their effects as a ship slows, stops, and then moves astern, and plan the maneuver to use these external forces, not just to compensate for them. Current can be a problem, setting a vessel toward other ships and shoals, but it can also move a ship away from hazards. Wind causes leeway but it can also assist the shiphandler, helping to turn a ship around short, for example, as a ship with sternway backs into the wind. *Think ahead* and use these external forces to advantage.

Plan to pass downstream and to leeward of ships, buoys, and hazards to navigation, or, if that isn't practical, *allow plenty of sea room* and several degrees for set and leeway to be sure to pass well clear. The two or three degrees allowed for set and leeway at sea just isn't enough in an anchorage; think in fives and tens, when maneuvering at slow speeds.

Don't, under any circumstances, pass close upstream or to windward of buoys, obstacles, or ships at anchor. It is a most helpless feeling to be passing close across the bow of a ship at anchor as the current sets you swiftly toward her stem. There is little that can be done in that situation except come full ahead, put the rudder hard over to try to move your ship's stern away from the other vessel, and pray you pass clear—and that maneuver isn't very effective if you are in real danger of colliding.

And how far is far enough to pass clear? That depends on current and wind strength, and the speed at which the ship is moving. In any case, particularly at the very low speeds at which a ship is usually moving in an anchorage, it is probably farther than you might expect. The *100 foot rule* discussed on page 100 applies in this situation just as elsewhere, when calculating the effect of both wind and current and estimating the distance a ship will move in a specific period of time. By using that rule, and the length of your ship as the basic unit of distance, you can easily estimate a safe passing distance. For example:

A ship moving at 3 knots is moving ahead at approximately 300 feet per minute. A 600-foot-long ship will take two minutes to move ahead one ship length and pass clear of a fixed point. A 2-knot current on the beam will set that same ship 400 feet, or two-thirds of a ship length, during that time.

The distance of one ship length that looked quite sufficient when approaching an anchorage is not a safe clearance for a 600-foot-long ship to pass clear of another ship at anchor at that speed in this situation when there is a strong current or wind on the beam. If you are the master standing on the bridge, maneuvering under these circumstances, the approximately 200-foot clearance after passing in this example will be too close for comfort.

The term "sail area" gains new meaning when maneuvering high freeboard and light draft ships in a strong wind in an anchorage. Passenger ships, containerships, car and gas carriers, and other similar ship types present a significantly larger profile to the wind relative to their draft and make much more leeway than average ships as they move slowly through an anchorage. It is even more important that these types of ships don't attempt to pass close ahead, to windward or upstream, of other ships and obstacles.

Both ships with large sail areas and common ship types at light drafts, moving at slow speeds in an anchorage, may be difficult to turn to windward when strong winds retard the bow's upwind movement. It is often better to back and fill the "long way around" to a new course, backing the ship's stern into the wind, if the bow won't come through a strong wind directly to the desired heading. Too often, the master stubbornly fights the wind, repeatedly working the engine full ahead and full astern to bring the bow through the wind, forgetting that the longest way around is sometimes the quickest and safest when maneuvering in adverse conditions. (Fig. 8-1)

There will be times when winds and currents are so strong that even an expert shiphandler cannot maneuver to the final heading before letting go, yet it is under these very same conditions that a master most wants to be on that heading to minimize the strain on ground tackle and ship's gear. Put down one anchor and a shot or two of chain and turn on the anchor under these conditions, as described further on in this chapter, or call for a tug, or stand off until conditions moderate. Consider these alternatives well before arrival at the anchorage, not when the situation arises, so contingencies can be arranged in advance.

DEPTH OF WATER

Shallow water affects the ship's maneuverability. As the depth decreases, the ship's tactical diameter increases and she becomes more directionally stable. The ship may need as much as twice the room for large course changes in shallow water as she would in deep water, so it becomes increasingly important to approach a shallow water anchorage at slow speed, in a position to back and fill to assist in turning the ship as required. Remember also that the ship will twist somewhat more in shallow water while going astern during a maneuver. Mentally review the section on shallow water effects while going astern during that maneuver. Review the section on shallow water effects on pages 17 and 18, and Fig. 1-7 on page 17, for a more detailed discussion of these changes.

Deep water also affects anchoring because the anchor has to be put down differently in an unusually deep anchorage. In depths greater than about 100 feet the brake may not be able to stop the chain if the anchor is let go from the hawse, because the chain's weight and the momentum developed as the anchor and chain free-fall that distance exceed the capacity of the brake. The anchor should be walked out in such deep anchorages by engaging the wildcat and backing the chain out of the locker using the windlass, lowering the anchor nearly to the bottom

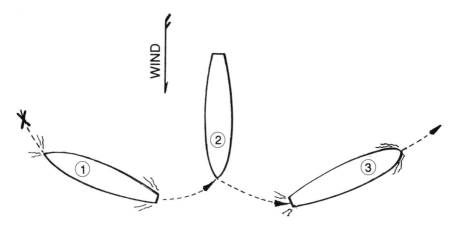

Fig. 8-1. Turn the long way around in strong winds.

before disengaging the wildcat, and letting the anchor fall free the last few fathoms to the bottom. During these operations the shiphandler must hold the ship in position for an extended period of time, even in strong winds and currents, a task made easier if the ship can first be brought to her final heading.

MANEUVERING ROOM

The number and location of ships at anchor, nearby shoals, a lee shore, and other hazards to navigation limit maneuvering room and make it more difficult for a ship to enter, maneuver in, and depart from an anchorage. The shiphandler has to make plans that match the ship's maneuvering characteristics to the available space in an anchorage, adjusting his game plan to the size of the playing field.

Consider all options before entering so your ship and crew are prepared for whatever is required; once again, *don't hesitate to maneuver on the anchor if there isn't enough space to turn or back and fill unassisted.* A tug can be ordered to assist your ship when maneuvering room is limited, but a shiphandler who is reasonably skilled in anchor work can usually turn and position the ship without a tug.

On occasion, there just isn't enough sea room in a crowded or small anchorage to turn to the final heading before letting go, and there will be no option but to let go, heading with or across the wind and current as discussed later in this chapter. Adjust anchoring plans to the real world when you arrive and find the anchorage smaller or more crowded than expected: use your shiphandling skills to adapt the ship's maneuvering characteristics to the maneuvering room in the anchorage or—if there just isn't enough room—don't go. Even the handiest ship may, under some circumstances, have to anchor elsewhere or stand off and wait for conditions to change.

Maneuvering room is as much a consideration when leaving an anchorage as it is when arriving. There may not be enough maneuvering room to turn and depart from an anchorage, even though there was sufficient room when your ship arrived. Other ships may anchor after yours, or your ship may swing to a new heading so there is no longer sufficient room to turn and depart. The same techniques that are used to maneuver at arrival—including backing and filling, using wind and current to advantage, heaving short and steaming around on the anchor, or turning with a tug—can be used to turn a ship departing a small anchorage.

BRIEFING OFFICERS

Discuss the anchoring plan, including the intended approach and the location for letting go, with the mate on the bow, the mate on the bridge, and, if uncommon maneuvering is involved, the engineer on watch, to be sure they all know their responsibilities as the ship is put to anchor. Be sure the mate knows:

1. Which anchor or anchors to use.
2. Whether the ship will turn to the final heading before letting go.
3. How much chain will be put out initially.
4. Direction, ahead or astern, and approximate speed of the ship over the bottom when the anchor is let go.
5. Whether the ship will be turned on the anchor.
6. Whether the anchor should be held at short stay for maneuvering.
7. If more than one anchor is used, how those anchors will be laid out.
8. Final amount of chain to be used.

This briefing is important because neither you nor the mate nor the engineer needs any surprises. A neat, seamanlike maneuver will be spoiled if the mate slacks out too much chain when you intend to maneuver on the anchor or turn short in a crowded anchorage, or holds the chain too soon so the anchor drags and the ship is set beyond the planned anchoring spot. Planning completed, it's time to go to anchor, so let's look at the most common method for anchoring a ship.

NAVIGATE BY EYE

Study the charts and publications carefully, well before arrival, and commit important information to memory. Select some prominent landmarks, aids, and ranges to lead the ship to her selected anchorage and prepare a pocket course card showing these leading marks as well as the approximate courses to the anchorage. Depending on the situation, the pocket card might have the courses and aids listed on one side, as described in Chapter 12, and a sketch of the anchorage showing the intended track and prominent aids and hazards on the other.

Navigate by eye as the ship approaches the anchorage, conning the ship to anchor using landmarks and aids that form natural ranges and leading marks. The mate will navigate as usual, as a backup to keep the master or conning officer informed of the ship's progress, using charts on which the intended courses are laid down in advance.

Visual navigation is preferable when going to anchor because the ship will usually be following a circuitous route rather than a straight track line, backing and filling and turning as needed to round up into the wind and current. If visible marks and aids are not used, you have to continuously interrupt your shiphandling work to refer to the ship's charts.

Accurate navigation is fine and important but it can, at times, be overdone. Pilots routinely anchor while navigating by eye, and calmly and quietly place the anchor at least as precisely as a team of navigators shouting bearings and distances to go and distracting the shiphandler from the important work of maneuvering the ship to anchor. In most cases, a few well-chosen leading marks and an abeam reference visible to the shiphandler, together with a minimum of fixes and some shiphandling skills, are more than sufficient to position the ship as accurately as the often redundant distance circles and continuous cross bearings that are too often relied upon while going to anchor. Quite simply, it is a matter of professionalism.

FINAL HEADING

The term "final heading" has been used several times in discussing anchoring plans, but just what does the term mean and why is it important? The final heading is the direction in which a ship will lie when at anchor heading into the resultant of all external forces, primarily the wind and current acting on her superstructure and underwater hull, after the anchor has fetched up and the ship has swung around to bring all those forces into equilibrium.

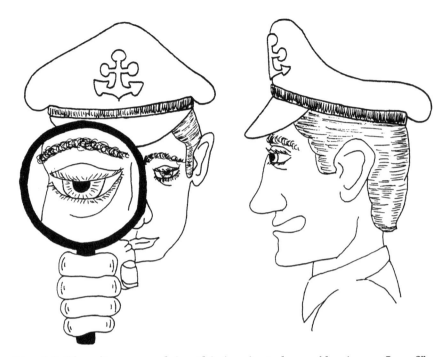

Fig. 8-2. "Aren't you overdoing this 'navigate by eye' business, Jerry?"

There are several reasons why it's better to let go when the ship is on her final heading, and the advantages of doing so more than compensate for any additional time spent maneuvering to that heading. When the anchor is let go on the final heading:

1. The chain will lead clear of the hull as it's slacked out.
2. Wear and strain on the chain, stem, windlass, and the mate's paint budget are minimized.
3. The chain is laid out along the bottom neatly and quickly.
4. The ship can be positioned among other ships and obstructions without concern about swinging clear after the anchor fetches up since your vessel is already on the same heading as those ships.

The more restricted or crowded the anchorage, or the stronger the wind or current, the more important it is to anchor on this heading. *In some instances it is essential to anchor on the preferred heading.* Large bulbous bows can be damaged by a chain leading under and around the bulb with a heavy strain and, even more importantly, the chain itself may be damaged in such circumstances. Naval vessels often have sensitive sonar domes and other equipment protruding from the bow that can be easily damaged by the chain. Heavy winds, swell, and strong currents exacerbate the problem as the chain works and surges more heavily against the wildcat, and the stem, bulb, and any protruding ship's gear.

Obviously, it isn't always possible to maneuver to this final heading before letting go, especially when the anchorage is small or crowded, or the wind or current is quite strong or from the wrong direction, or visibility is restricted. It isn't always necessary to do so either, since a ship may anchor on any heading in light airs or slack water; in a calm, every ship in the anchorage probably lies at a different heading anyway. A real professional, though, tries to bring the ship to her final heading before letting go in even a light breeze or weak current and, in practice, a reasonably skilled shiphandler is usually successful in doing so. There are methods for anchoring to minimize the strain and problems when it is impossible to let go to the final heading, and they are discussed later in this chapter.

How is the final heading determined? Look at other ships and boats anchored in the area that are already lying to the wind and current or estimate the heading if there are no ships in an anchorage. Sea sense and some experience with a particular ship are invaluable in the latter case since the final heading is affected by the ship's draft, her freeboard, the strength of the wind and current, and the location of the ship's superstructure and deck load, if any. In practice, this presents little problem since the ship only needs to be on the approximate heading before letting go; having the wind and current a few degrees on one bow or the other, rather than dead ahead, won't significantly affect the ship or strain her gear.

A master could also compute the final heading by vector analysis, but the calculation would be complicated and impractical in day-to-day work, and there would be no point in doing so when such exact information is not needed anyway. A practiced seaman's eye, current tables, the knowledge that *a 1-knot current has approximately the same effect as a 30-knot wind over a given surface area,* and some seafaring experience are really all that are needed to determine this heading with reasonable accuracy.

ANCHORING OFF THE FINAL HEADING

Under some circumstances, it may be necessary to anchor heading across or away from the resultant of wind and current. In a light breeze or weak current this presents no problem since the ship can turn to her final heading after the anchor fetches up. In stronger winds or currents, though, it is usually best to let go an anchor and one to two shots of chain only, an amount equal to about twice the depth of water, *while the ship moves slowly ahead.* The chain is held while the ship makes a controlled turn on her anchor to the final heading, in the least possible space, as the anchor alternately digs in and breaks free with little strain on the vessel and her gear.

When letting go *on or near the reciprocal of the final heading,* start the ship turning to starboard and let go the starboard anchor, to take advantage of the twisting effect if the engine is needed astern to assist in turning the ship.

When letting go *with the final heading on the port or starboard side,* turn up into the wind or current toward the final heading and use the upstream or windward anchor so the bow comes up into those forces and the chain leads clear of the hull. In both cases, turning in this fashion minimizes strain on the gear and ship while the wind and current assist the ship in turning. (Fig. 8-3)

Come ahead with the rudder hard over in the direction in which the ship is to turn, backing and filling if required, as the ship swings around on this slowly dragging anchor to the final heading. Stop the engine when the ship is on or near her final heading. Ease the anchor's brake and slack the chain to bring the ship to anchor as the wind and current check the ship's headway and then move her astern. Don't just open the brake wide as the ship falls back before the wind and current, ease it so the chain is laid out slowly or the wind and current will take charge and bring the ship up hard against the chain and gear, possibly damaging the ground tackle or pulling the anchor free.

This technique for anchoring off the final heading is especially useful when turning in a strong current such as is found on the Mississippi River and other estuaries or in a strong wind or heavy swell that would put heavy strain on the ground tackle.

BASIC ANCHORING

Anchoring is almost always a "plain vanilla" routine. The ship enters the anchorage, turns as nearly as possible to the final heading, and backs down until she starts moving slowly astern over the bottom. One anchor is let go and the chain is slacked until the desired amount is in the water. The engine is then kicked ahead, if necessary, until the ship loses nearly all sternway, the brake is tightened, and the anchor fetches

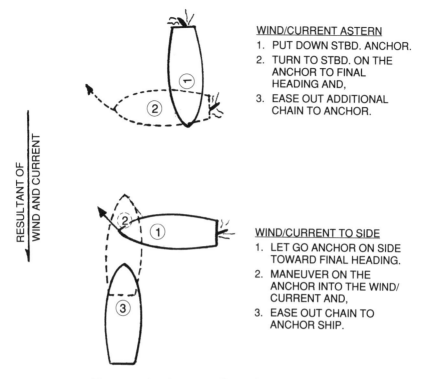

WIND/CURRENT ASTERN
1. PUT DOWN STBD. ANCHOR.
2. TURN TO STBD. ON THE ANCHOR TO FINAL HEADING AND,
3. EASE OUT ADDITIONAL CHAIN TO ANCHOR.

WIND/CURRENT TO SIDE
1. LET GO ANCHOR ON SIDE TOWARD FINAL HEADING.
2. MANEUVER ON THE ANCHOR INTO THE WIND/CURRENT AND,
3. EASE OUT CHAIN TO ANCHOR SHIP.

RESULTANT OF WIND AND CURRENT

Fig. 8-3. Anchoring off the final heading.

up. Port after port, voyage after voyage, the ship usually will anchor in this simple manner, so, for the sake of clarity, we'll discuss this routine in some detail and then briefly mention some of the less common alternative methods for anchoring.

THE APPROACH

The master or conning officer approaches along the planned track, navigating by eye using leading ranges and selected aids as previously discussed and progressively reducing speed. Less speed means more time—time to plan, time to respond, and time to stop the ship if a problem arises—and when speed is reduced, the engine can be used ahead and astern as needed to maneuver without concern about being over speed when the final anchoring location is reached.

Detect your ship's movement over the bottom using the apparent motion between other ships or objects in the anchorage and more distant references afloat and ashore. Closer ships appear to move across, in front of, background references because of the differences in perspective between closer and more distant objects. The apparent movement of references ahead and astern of your ship indicates lateral motion while references abeam or nearly abeam show headway or sternway. Your ship's movement can be detected by eye with surprising accuracy, using this method, long before any change in position is shown by traditional methods of navigation. Use this technique by day and by night, during each step of the anchoring evolution, especially when moving at very slow speeds and when backing down and laying out the chain.

When should a ship start to turn in the anchorage? The master or officer conning knows the ship's tactical diameter at slow speeds from the master's trials and, allowing for any possible set and leeway, estimates by eye and in some cases by fixes, the point to start the turn or turns. It is best to simplify maneuvering by making any large changes in heading well before reaching the location where you plan to anchor since you then only need to stop the vessel prior to letting go. This isn't essential, and in a restricted or crowded anchorage it isn't always possible, but it sure makes the task easier.

As a rule of thumb, a ship turning at a constant engine speed in deep water, that is, water more than one and a half times the ship's draft, will be about three to three and a half ship lengths ahead of her starting point and about one and a half ship lengths to port or starboard after turning 90 degrees, and about one ship length ahead of her starting point and three and a half ship lengths to port or starboard after turning 180 degrees. *These distances are significantly reduced in an accelerating turn using increased revolutions.* In shallower water, the turning circle will increase until, when the water depth is nearly the same as the ship's draft, the distances required to turn are approximately doubled. These distances are not exact, but they are close enough for day-to-day work, especially if you make any needed small adjustments to the estimates to allow for maneuvering characteristics of a particular ship and for the wind and current that make the ship's turning circle more elliptical as previously discussed. (Fig. 8-4)

The following hints should prove useful in maneuvering into, around, and out of an anchorage.

1. Sea room permitting, a large course change as the ship swings around to her final heading, as described in Chapter 1, will significantly reduce headway as the ship approaches an anchorage.

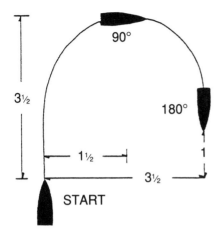

Conditions: rudder hard over, engine speed constant, water depth over 1.5 times ship's draft.

Results: (1) 90° from track, 3½ ship lengths ahead, and 1½ ship lengths to port or starboard of start point; (2) 180° from track, 1 ship length ahead, and 3½ ship lengths to port or starboard of start point.

As water depth decreases, distances increase. When depth almost equals draft, the distances are doubled.

Fig. 8-4. Approximate turning circles in deep water.

2. Turns to starboard are preferable to turns to port, to take advantage of the twisting effect as the engine is backed to reduce headway and stop the ship.

3. A kick ahead will accelerate the rate of turn, reducing the turning circle without a significant increase in speed. Be careful, though, that speed isn't significantly increased by *successive* kicks ahead, as it might be impossible to stop the ship at the selected anchoring location.

4. Backing and filling near the anchoring area, as described in Chapter 1, is usually preferable to successive kicks ahead when about to anchor, as the ship can be turned and simultaneously slowed and stopped.

From the trial maneuvers, the master knows approximately how many ship lengths the vessel will advance after the engine is put astern and thus at what point the ship must go astern to be dead in the water at the selected anchorage. For safety's sake, back down at least once *before* reaching that point to check the ship's speed, using the location of the ship's quickwater as described in Chapter 4. (Fig. 4-2) Too often, a master reduces to what, after several days at sea speed, seems like a slow speed in an anchorage, only to find that the ship is actually moving much faster than anticipated when he backs down to let go.

Put the engine astern *well before* reaching the selected anchoring location when anchoring at night, or in a crowded or restricted anchorage, when speed is both more difficult to estimate and more critical, and back until the ship is dead in the water. There is then no doubt about the ship's speed: it is zero. Come ahead again, slowly move the last few ship lengths, and let go.

PLACING THE ANCHOR

The ship slowly moves the last few hundred feet to the selected anchorage, on the final heading if possible, using the leading marks and ranges to navigate by eye while the mate checks the ship's position. Convert distance to the selected anchoring location from yards or fractions of a mile to ship lengths or feet, units of measure the shiphandler navigating by eye can use most effectively to estimate stopping and turning distances during the last few ship lengths of the approach.

The anchor drops from the bow, not the bridge. It is the bow's location that matters when letting go. Too often shiphandlers overlook this simple fact and estimate distances from the bridge to the shore and other ships. This can cause significant errors when anchoring VLCCs or other large, bridge aft ships in restricted or crowded anchorages where the stern may be as much as a quarter-mile from the anchor, or when anchoring car carriers or other bridge forward ships when the shiphandler is nearer the anchor but 700 to 800 feet from the stern. Put the bow, not the bridge, where you want the anchor to lie before letting go.

Do not routinely anchor in the middle of an open anchorage, so far from other ships and obstructions that you swing clear by several ship lengths no matter how the wind and current might turn your ship. It is unseamanlike to waste space in the anchorage; it causes problems for other ships anchoring after yours and it also causes problems for you, since other vessels are forced to anchor closer to your ship than might be safe because they have to use whatever space you leave. It is also unnecessary because most ships swing to new headings at the same time, staying clear of each other, unless their draft, freeboard, or size are so different that some swing before the others. So there is no need to, at all times, be able to swing clear over an arc of 360 degrees.

Anchor only as far from other ships and obstructions as necessary for your own ship's safety and put the anchor closer to ships ahead than astern. Your ship lies back from the anchor and the ship ahead and, as the ships turn to current or wind, the ship ahead swings away from you. In print, that may sound like common sense, but it is amazing how often experienced masters and pilots put the anchor in the center of an open area and find they are anchored too close to ships astern when the chain stretches out. This can be an even greater problem when the tide or wind changes and the ship astern becomes the ship ahead. Place the anchor closer to the ship ahead, not in the center of an open area, when letting go. (Fig. 8-5)

Think ahead of the ship as you place the anchor. Set up to back and maintain control at all times when the engine is going astern. When anchoring a ship fitted with a right hand turning fixed propeller, under most conditions, *on or near the final heading*, kick the engine ahead with the rudder hard left to start the bow swinging to port and then put the engine astern. Back until the quickwater reaches amidships and then continue backing until the ship starts moving astern. Ideally, *when anchoring close to the final heading,* the bow should steady up as the engine goes astern if the starboard anchor is to be dropped, or begin swinging slowly to starboard if the port anchor is to be used. When anchoring *at some large angle away from the final heading*, the bow should be swinging away from the anchor, as the chain pays out, as previously described in the section "Final Heading."

Masters too often stop the engine when the quickwater reaches amidships because the flow of water moving up the ship's sides creates the illusion that the ship is moving astern when actually she is then just dead in the water. The chain will only pile up on the bottom and stop running out if the anchor is let go without some sternway. Continue backing until the quickwater is forward of amidships so the ship is moving astern, open the brake, and let go.

LAYING OUT THE CHAIN

The brake is tightened and eased as necessary to control the chain as the ship moves slowly astern, laying the chain evenly over the bottom rather than in a pile that could foul the anchor or damage the gear as the ship falls back, until the chain is brought up tight against the anchor with a heavy strain.

The mate on the bow must keep the bridge informed of the lead and weight on the chain at this point. The mate is the master's eyes as he maneuvers to move the ship slowly astern at the best speed and heading, keeping a light strain on the chain at all times so it is laid along the bottom clear of the stem and bulbous bow. The mate notifies the bridge as soon as the ordered length of chain is out so the engine can be put ahead to reduce sternway, if necessary, before the anchor fetches up hard. Everyone gets back to bed much sooner if the mate keeps the

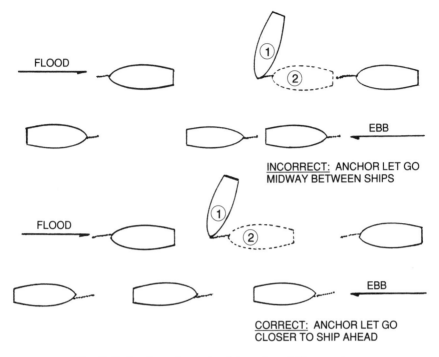

FLOOD

EBB

INCORRECT: ANCHOR LET GO
MIDWAY BETWEEN SHIPS

FLOOD

EBB

CORRECT: ANCHOR LET GO
CLOSER TO SHIP AHEAD

Fig. 8-5. Anchor closer to ships ahead than astern.

bridge well informed without having to be repeatedly asked how the chain is leading.

Tighten the brake enough to check the chain and control it but don't set the brake so tight that the chain is held and the anchor flukes dig in prematurely. When the flukes dig in too soon, before the shank is nearly parallel to the bottom, the anchor may break free again—so balled with mud that it can't dig in when the full scope of chain is out. This is less of a problem when the anchor is intentionally dragged, because it is less likely to have dug in so fully that it comes free with mud and rock jammed between the flukes and shank.

Keep in mind that it is movement over the bottom that's important when letting go, not speed through the water. When drifting with a strong current from ahead, the ship will have sufficient sternway over the bottom to lay out the chain when the quickwater reaches amidships, since she would then be moving over the bottom at the speed of the current. Obviously, if there is a 1-knot current from ahead and you back until the water is midships, you will be making 1 knot astern over the bottom and the chain will lay out nicely.

The aforementioned apparent motion of ships at anchor relative to background references afloat and ashore is the best indication of ship's movement once the ship starts moving astern. The quickwater forward of midships only tells you the ship has sternway, while the Doppler log often becomes useless once the quickwater moves up under the hull. Watch the movement of vessels and objects against the background shoreline and move the ship slowly astern over the bottom.

DIGGING IN

Tighten the brake when the required amount of chain is out and, if the ship still has significant sternway, put the engine ahead one last time so the chain isn't parted due to excessive sternway as the anchor fetches up. You might use hard-over rudder while kicking the engine ahead at this point, if required, to bring the ship closer to her final heading and to keep the anchor chain clear of the stem, bulb, and any underwater gear. Remember that the rudder directs propeller thrust, and the stopping effect as the engine turns ahead is much greater if the rudder is amidships.

The engine is used ahead only long enough to *reduce* sternway. Don't stop the ship completely. Hold the chain and let the ship move slowly back against the anchor as the catenary caused by the chain's weight absorbs most of the force of the remaining sternway. The ship must have a bit of sternway to work against the anchor and dig the flukes well in to the bottom. Back the engine again, if the ship inadvertently stops too quickly, so the anchor is well dug in before the engines are rung off.

SWINGING ROOM AT ANCHOR

Obviously, masters prefer to anchor far enough from other ships and obstacles, space permitting, to swing clear on both the present heading and all other possible headings on which the ship might later lie at a safe distance from other ships.

But how far are you from ships ahead and astern? In a crowded anchorage, especially after days in the open ocean, other ships *always look closer* than they actually are due both to your height of eye and to the lack of visual references with which the distance between ships can be compared. Even experienced pilots are often surprised when, after anchoring a ship in what appeared to be close quarters, they get into a launch to go ashore and, from a more distant vantage point close to the water, look back to find that the ships actually are quite far apart. Unfortunately, the master and deck officers are rarely able to view their vessel from a launch, but they can walk down to the main deck where the true distance between ships becomes immediately apparent. Try this the next time you are concerned about the distance between anchored ships.

It is sometimes difficult to actually measure the distance to other vessels anchored close to your ship. Radar, while excellent in open anchorages, is often less effective for measuring absolute distance between closely anchored ships because it measures distance from your radar mast to some not always definable point on the other ship, to an accuracy of fractions of a mile, not yards or meters. Stacks and ship's gear also obstruct the radar and ships anchored in those blind areas are not visible to the radar at all. Radar is usually more helpful to detect changes in distance, such as when one ship or the other drags closer or farther away, than it is to measure absolute distance between anchored ships.

Estimate distance from other ships by eye using your ship's length as a reference and measure the distance from other ships ahead and astern to your bow or stern, not to your location on the bridge.

Some pilots swear they can estimate distance more accurately by bending over and looking between their legs. Pilots and seamen often joke about this technique but, quite frankly, it seems to work. It's probably better to try it without an audience, though, as shipmates may think you a bit strange, standing bent over looking between your legs at ships forward and aft, but it helps—so bend over and look.

It may be necessary for a ship lying at anchor in a crowded anchorage to maneuver on the anchor using the engine, rudder, or bow thruster if available, to swing clear of other ships as she turns to a new tide or a shift in the wind. Calculate tide and current changes and watch the weather and other ships closely. Have the engine and thruster ready well before the calculated change and, in a particularly restricted anchorage, have a tug ordered and standing by to assist in turning. Don't wait until the other ships start swinging to make these preparations.

The master may also decide to put down two anchors in a small anchorage to limit the ship's swing. Mooring to two anchors may be the best action under some circumstances and common methods for doing so are discussed later in this chapter.

It may not always be possible to moor to two anchors in a crowded anchorage if other ships close by are riding to one anchor. They will move in a wider circle and your ship, restricted by the second anchor, may not swing clear. Either use one anchor, or be ready to maneuver or to heave up the second anchor if other ships start swinging toward you in such circumstances. Local practice is important, since all ships will generally follow the custom of the port when anchoring or mooring so that all ships swing together.

Fig. 8-6. "He says things look better that way."

MOORING AND ANCHORING WITH TWO ANCHORS

Any number of seamanship books present the reasons for mooring and anchoring to two anchors, so this text will briefly discuss only the shiphandling aspects of these evolutions.

The *running moor* is a maneuver for putting down two anchors in line while the ship has headway. The ship is brought to her final heading, stemming the current and wind, and the first anchor is let go. That chain is slacked as the ship continues moving slowly ahead to drop a second anchor. The first chain is then heaved in as the second chain is slacked so the ship drops back to ride between both anchors. The two anchors can be laid along the axis of a channel or in line with a current so the ship rides between and swings within nearly her own length to each turn of the tide.

The running moor is sometimes called the *"flying moor."* The name is colorful, traditional, and unfortunately misleading since it conveys an image of an action-packed, high-speed anchoring maneuver under something less than perfect control. No competent shiphandler does a flying anything and the term should be avoided. Walking moor might be a better name!

The ship can also anchor to two anchors laid out ahead in a maneuver similar to a running moor, as described in the section on five- and seven-point moorings in Chapter 9, perpendicular to the wind and current using the same or different lengths of chain to minimize yawing, increase holding power, or hold a ship's head to a swell to reduce rolling while working cargo. A similar method for anchoring to two anchors, for ships fitted with bow thrusters, is described in the section "Mediterranean Moor" in Chapter 9.

A standing moor or ordinary moor is similar to the running moor except the ship comes to her final heading, backs until she has sternway, drops her first anchor, and slacks the chain as she maneuvers astern to let go the second anchor. The first chain is then heaved in while the second is slacked until the ship rides between the two anchors. The standing moor is more commonly used to lay anchors in line with a current since the shiphandler has less control of a ship when going astern, while the running moor with steerage- and headway is more often used to lay anchors perpendicular to wind and current.

Seamen are often reluctant to use two anchors for mooring or anchoring because of problems clearing round turns in the chain, so you

Fig. 8-7. "I thought shiphandlers never did a flying anything."

may go to sea for years without mooring in this manner. Round turns are caused by the ship repeatedly swinging to the current and wind in the same direction, clockwise or counterclockwise, wrapping the chains around each other so it becomes impossible to heave the anchors home. With a modicum of seamanship and shiphandling skills these turns can be prevented by turning the ship *in the opposite direction at each turn of the tide or change in the wind.* (Fig. 8-8)

Turn the ship by putting the rudder hard over and kicking the engine ahead as needed, or have a tug push on the quarter or tow the stern around on a hawser. Start the ship swinging in the preferred direction, putting the current or wind on the proper side so it too pushes the ship around alternately clockwise and then counterclockwise on successive tides. Seamanship texts also discuss canting the ship using hard over rudder, but the ship's engine or a tug is usually more reliable and effective in turning today's larger, more diverse ship types, which may not respond to the rudder alone.

Mooring to two anchors may be the best way to anchor under some circumstances, in spite of potential problems with round turns in the chain, and every seaman should know how to prevent round turns and how to clear them if they do occur.

STERN ANCHORS
By Captain Warren G. Leback, Master Mariner

Stern anchors are most commonly found aboard the great number of naval landing and assault vessels built during and since World War II. These anchors give an added measure of vessel control, prevent broaching due to wind, swell, tide, and current, and are used to kedge off a beach.

Stern anchors probably came into use shortly after man put to sea. Kedge (stern) anchors were used to hold a ship of the line in position to provide a steady platform when bombarding shore batteries or opposing fleets in numerous naval battles during the sixteenth through the

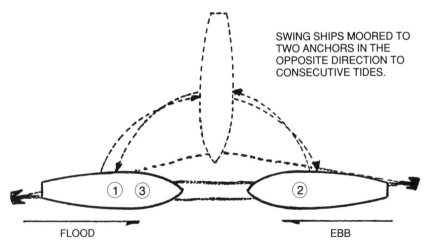

SWING SHIPS MOORED TO TWO ANCHORS IN THE OPPOSITE DIRECTION TO CONSECUTIVE TIDES.

FLOOD   EBB

Fig. 8-8. Prevent round turns when moored.

eighteenth centuries. One of the more memorable naval engagements in which stern anchors were used was the Battle of the Nile where Admiral Nelson's Mediterranean fleet caught the French fleet at anchor in Akubir Bay. Nelson divided his fleet into two columns, ran down both sides of the French fleet and, using kedge anchors, positioned his vessels so they could pour deadly broadsides into the opposing fleet. The outcome changed Napoleon's plans to advance into the Middle East.

Unfortunately, few merchant vessels other than those designed for specific trade routes are presently fitted with stern anchors, so only a limited number of masters and deck officers have had an opportunity to use them. As with any gear that receives only limited use, there are numerous theories about the use of stern anchors—some correct and many incorrect.

A few steamship companies, including Grace Line, Inc., and El Paso LNG Company, have fitted their vessels with stern anchors. Grace Line fitted their four *Santa Lucia* class vessels, their C-2s, and their C-2 combination passenger/cargo vessels with stern anchors. The anchors were used to keep the ships in position while lying at anchor at a number of open roadsteads along the west coast of South America.

El Paso LNG Company fitted their nine liquefied natural gas vessels with stern anchors. These anchors are to be used in the event of either a rudder or engine failure to slow the ship and give directional control and to make it possible to anchor these large ships in the Chesapeake Bay and the narrow channels of the Savannah River. They are of sufficient weight and are equipped with the amount of chain needed to hold the 950-foot ships in the strong flood and ebb tides found in these areas.

When using a stern anchor:

1. The master must have confidence in his shiphandling ability and understand the stern anchor's uses and limitations.
2. The mooring maneuver must be carefully planned in advance and put on the chart with three predetermined reference bearings laid down.
3. The maneuver must be reviewed with the other officers so they are thoroughly familiar with the plan and its alternatives.
4. The steering gear and engine must be used judiciously, especially once the stern anchor is let go.
5. Throughout the maneuver the master must think ahead of the vessel and adjust for changes in wind and current.

There is a significant risk of damaging the rudder and propeller with the stern anchor and its chain because of the stern anchor's location. Be certain all sternway is off the ship before letting the stern anchor go. Limit sternway when heaving up so the chain leads aft with a light strain at all times—*the ship must not overrun the stern anchor*—and wait until the anchor is in sight and clear before putting any headway on the ship.

In an open roadstead both bow anchors and the stern anchor are laid out in a "Y" pattern to form a three-point moor. The maneuver is straightforward. After all planning and preparations for mooring have been completed:

1. The ship begins her approach at the minimum speed required for steerageway.
2. The moor is made, searoom permitting, with the bow to seaward. Approach from sea to the left of the intended moor to take advantage of the ship's ability to back and fill to the right. Make the approach as wide as searoom allows.
3. Come up to point "A" as shown in Figure 8-9 so the three predetermined bearings intersect.
4. Proceed down the reciprocal of bearing line "B" with the port anchor backed out and ready to let go. Back down as the ship nears the drop point, take all headway off the ship, and let go the port anchor.
5. Back the ship slowly back along the reciprocal of bearing line "B" and turn her to bearing line "D."
6. Come ahead and proceed slowly down the reciprocal of bearing line "D" while keeping the port chain slack until the drop point for the starboard anchor is reached. Take off all headway and let go the starboard anchor.
7. Back the ship to point "A" while controlling the ship with both anchors, then continue backing along bearing line "C" to the drop point for the stern anchor.
8. Make sure all sternway is off the vessel so the ship cannot override the anchor and chain, and let go the stern anchor.
9. Heave the bow anchors while slacking the chain aft until the ship is riding to all three anchors and the three-point moor is complete.

To unmoor, slack the bow chains and heave the vessel astern using the stern anchor. Bear in mind that you must pay out the bow chains

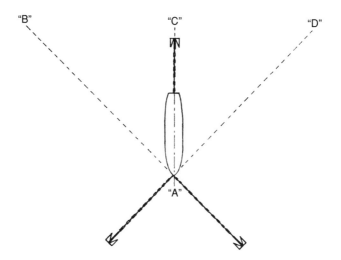

Fig. 8-9. Mooring with a stern anchor.

slowly to control the vessel. (Remember, you must not overrun the stern anchor.) Wait until the stern anchor clears the water and is in sight before moving the ship ahead. Heave both bow chains simultaneously until point "A" is reached, and disengage the starboard chain. Continue to heave on the port chain until the ship reaches a position approximately halfway between point "A" and the port anchor drop point. Lock in the starboard anchor again. Resume heaving; by the time the port anchor is aweigh you will have a slight strain on the starboard chain so the vessel will not sag down on the beach.

The same sequence of maneuvers, performed while the ship is stemming the current, is used to anchor a ship fitted with a stern anchor in a river or restricted anchorage. One bow anchor may be sufficient in some cases, but the maneuver is still performed in basically the same manner.

THE ANCHOR AS A SHIPHANDLING TOOL

The anchor is rarely used when handling a ship, and now usually seems to be thought of as a tool of last resort to be used only in emergency situations. This is unfortunate since a ship can be maneuvered using an anchor in ways not possible with only the engine, rudder, and tugs. The anchor is called the "poor man's tugboat" for good reason—it is often more effective than a tug.

Fig. 8-10. "I got ten shots out, Cap', and she seems to be taking a strain."

When handling a ship with an anchor, it is essential that the mate assigned to let go the anchor be well versed in the use of anchors and be thoroughly trained in handling ground tackle, letting go the anchor properly, and putting out the correct amount of chain. The importance of having a man on the bow who can handle the anchor and be relied upon to put out the correct amount of chain cannot be overstressed.

Perhaps the most fundamental misunderstanding about shiphandling with an anchor is the belief that a ship sheers in the direction of the anchor that is put down. This is not so. Sheering is not a significant consideration when selecting the anchor to be used. The bow of a ship with headway *is steadied by the anchor regardless of which anchor is used,* and is not pulled in any particular direction. The hawsepipe, and hence the lead of the chain, is so close to the centerline of the ship as the anchor drags that only a minimal pivoting moment develops. (Fig. 8-11)

The pivoting effect can become significant, however, if a large turn is deliberately initiated using the engine and rudder after the anchor begins to drag. The pivoting moment increases as the direction of the anchor's retarding force and the ship's forward momentum shift in opposite directions away from the vessel's centerline and each other, as shown in position 2 of Figure 8-11.

This delayed pivoting effect occurs only after the ship develops a significant swing, and requires deliberate action by the shiphandler who must start the ship swinging. The resultant reduction in the diameter of the ship's turning circle is one of the desirable effects of anchor use when maneuvering. The sheering or pivoting to one side is neither an immediate nor an inevitable result of dropping a particular anchor. It does not occur without deliberate action and, for practical purposes, the magnitude of this pivoting force is equal for a turn to port or starboard regardless of which anchor is put down.

There is some disagreement among mariners over which anchor to drop. (Fig. 8-12) Some shiphandlers contend that the lee anchor, or inboard anchor when docking, should be used because it leads under and against the hull and therefore will hold better in a beam wind. They also claim that using this anchor puts less stress on the windlass brake due to the friction between the chain and the hull. Others feel that the windward anchor, or offshore anchor when docking, should be used since that anchor leads clear of the hull and requires more chain before it digs in and holds. *The latter choice is recommended because:*

1. INITIAL TURNING MOMENT G'–A' IS INSIGNIFICANT AS ANCHOR DRAGS ON SHORT SCOPE OF CHAIN.
2. IF VESSEL DELIBERATELY SWUNG, THE TURNING MOMENT G'–B' INCREASES AND SHIP PIVOTS AGAINST THE ANCHOR.

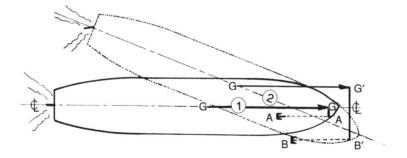

Fig. 8-11. Pivoting effect of a dragging anchor.

1. The anchor should not hold.
2. The chance of damaging the hull with the anchor is minimized if the windward (or offshore when docking) anchor is used since the chain tends away from and clear of the hull.
3. It is easier to work the ship up to the dock when using the off-shore anchor since it does not tend to fetch up as it would when the ship works across and over an inboard anchor.
4. The outboard anchor can be left in the water ready to heave the ship back off the berth, and can be heaved up without damaging the chain, hull, or antifouling coating.
5. Heaving the chain hard against the hull may damage the chain and the ship's hull.

By using the outboard or windward anchor there is less chance that the anchor will hold even if a little too much chain is inadvertently put in the water. It is always possible to slack more chain, but a good docking will come to a halt if the anchor fetches up and the ship has to stop to heave the chain back in.

When the chain is heaved against the hull, each link bears against and is bent around the relatively small radius of the hull in the area of the bow, whether it leads across the stem, under the foot, or around a bulbous bow, and the chain is therefore subject to damage. The presence of a bulb is reason enough to avoid using the inboard or lee anchor.

The ease with which the offshore anchor can be heaved up is an important consideration if the anchor must be heaved home after

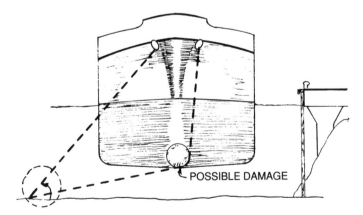

POSSIBLE DAMAGE

Fig. 8-12. Lead of inshore anchor versus offshore anchor.

Fig. 8-13. "I think we should have used the offshore anchor."

docking. The offshore anchor comes up easier because of the more direct lead from hawsepipe to anchor, and without causing any of the afore-mentioned damage.

Some mariners are concerned that it might be difficult to stop the chain after letting go because of the ship's motion over the bottom. This concern is especially prevalent when handling larger ships. This is not a problem. *Static friction is three times greater than dynamic friction for an asbestos brake band bearing on the windlass's drum.* The brake has three times as much holding power when the wildcat is stopped as when it is turning. The chain only runs out, after the anchor strikes bottom, until it goes slack. The brake is then set up. The anchor digs in as the chain again comes tight and then is pulled free from the bottom before static friction is overcome, dragging along as the flukes ball up with mud. Additional chain can then be slacked to achieve the desired effect.

SHIPHANDLING WITH ANCHORS—HOW MUCH CHAIN?

Have the anchors manned and ready to let go when maneuvering in restricted waters. Should the anchor be required during a maneuver, let go only enough chain to allow the anchor to first grab and then break loose and drag. The anchor must not dig in and hold.

For the anchor to be most effective, an amount of chain equal to about twice the depth should be put well in the water and the brake screwed up tight. If necessary, the second anchor can also be let go with a like amount of chain. The ship slows and stops as one or both anchors drags along the bottom.

There is a common misconception, especially in an emergency, that a large amount of chain should run out so the anchor digs in and stops the ship. To stop a vessel in this manner would require the relatively small brake on the windlass to overcome the inertia of the entire moving mass of your ship. It will never happen! The brake will probably burn out and all the chain will run out while the ship continues moving ahead. If the brake does hold, the chain often parts as it comes tight. It is most unlikely that a chain would be able to withstand the shock load and almost instantaneously stop a moving ship, as it would be required to do if the anchor is allowed to dig in hard. Instead we want the anchor to break out and relieve the strain on the chain before its breaking point is reached.

What a helpless feeling one has as the ship heads toward a bank with no engine to slow her headway while the mate on the bow lets the chain run out to the bitter end in a cloud of dirt and rust! A deeply laden chemical tanker was transiting the Panama Canal a few years ago when the ship's wheel was put the wrong way by the helmsman. The ship dove for the bank and anchors were ordered let go, only to have the chain continue to run as shot after shot passed over the wildcat. The chain did finally stop running and the ship came to a stop—but only when she was hard against the bank at Contractor's Hill. A ship's windlass just doesn't have a large enough brake to stop a loaded ship.

The proper use of anchors is in danger of becoming a lost art. Be sure all deck officers understand what they are to do with the anchors, and especially how much chain to slack out, before they go forward to stand by. Too few mates do!

DOCKING WITH AN ANCHOR

Most dockings can be done using an anchor rather than a tug, although the tug generally is more convenient.

When using an anchor as an aid in docking, sufficient chain is put out to eliminate headway when the engine is at dead slow or slow speeds.

How much chain is required? That can only be determined by increasing the length of the chain a few links at a time until the desired effect is obtained, since there are several factors affecting the ship and anchor, and their net effect cannot be predicted. When the ship is held in position both laterally and fore and aft, with the engines coming ahead slowly, you have put out the proper amount of chain.

Drop the anchor well before arriving at the berth and drag it into position. Done properly, the anchor takes nearly all headway off the ship since an amount of chain has been slacked that is sufficient to slow the ship when the engine is stopped, and the ship will make no headway until the engine revolutions are increased to at least slow ahead. Spend sufficient time adjusting the length of the chain, putting out a few links at a time until you feel you have total control over the ship. It is obvious to the shiphandler when the proper amount of chain is out: the ship makes no headway at lower engine revolutions, as you work her around the anchor with the rudder, and slowly develops headway when revolutions are increased.

Since the ship slows and stops with her engine stopped, as the anchor drags along the bottom, no twisting occurs and the ship remains shaped up for the berth.

There is no reason that the engine cannot be put astern if needed, although this is not usually necessary.

When docking *with an anchor down:* (Fig. 8-14)

1. The ship is eased straight ahead toward her berth—adjusting engine revolutions to maintain the desired speed and using the rudder to maintain heading.
2. Reduce engine revolutions so the ship loses headway and,
3. Use the rudder to change her angle of approach by moving the stern towards or away from the berth.
4. After her heading is altered, increase engine revolutions to move the ship ahead, bringing the bow nearer the berth.
5. Reduce revolutions again so the ship loses headway and the bow moves no farther ahead. Let the engine work slowly ahead and use the rudder to bring the stern laterally toward the pier or wharf.

In effect the bow and stern are moved separately as the ship is docked while excellent control is maintained over the forward and lateral motion. Revolutions are adjusted so the anchor either holds or drags and the ship

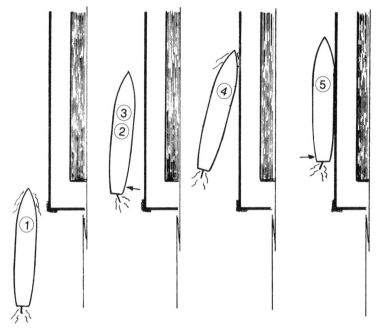

Fig. 8-14. Docking with an anchor.

is moved nearly sideways or directly ahead as desired with a surprising degree of control. The key to docking with the anchor is slacking sufficient chain so the ship remains in position at low revolutions but moves ahead as the revolutions are increased.

HOLDING A VESSEL WITH THE ANCHOR

Often a ship must proceed at a slow speed with a strong wind on the beam, or maintain her position in a channel because of restricted visibility or the late arrival of a tug. The anchor greatly simplifies this work, no matter how large the ship. The technique varies a bit with larger ships because of the increase in mass, but ships a thousand feet long are worked against an anchor without difficulty.

A heavy rain squall, with strong winds and blinding rain, strikes the vessel proceeding up a narrow channel. The rain reduces both visibility and the radar's effectiveness, so the master and pilot are unable to distinguish the aids or the bank on either side, and the ship is unable to proceed. This can be a moment of great stress—or the anchor can be put down until conditions improve.

An anchor is let go and a shot of chain put well in the water. The brake is set up while the engine is used ahead only to maintain the vessel's heading, the ship slowly losing headway due to the dragging anchor. When the ship is dead in the water her engine is put slow or half ahead and she works against the anchor, additional chain being slacked as required until the ship just holds her position while the quartermaster steers by compass to maintain the heading, since no landmarks are visible. Those on the bridge can now relax, adjusting the engine revolutions occasionally to allow for changes in the wind while the ship, which had been setting sideways out of the channel and not answering her helm, steadies up nicely with the anchor down.

If a single anchor is not sufficient, a second anchor can be put down in a similar manner. It is best to put that anchor down while the ship still has some headway, so the chain is laid out properly and the anchor's flukes fall flat, assuring that the flukes do not set against the hull. The amount of chain needed for one or two anchors depends on the profile of the hull and superstructure, i.e., the ship's "sail area," the type of bottom, and the strength of the wind. Initially a shot is put in the water and additional chain is slacked until the anchor takes charge of the bow, although the steadying effect of the anchor is felt immediately after the anchor begins to drag.

Use only a minimum amount of chain until the ship has lost nearly all her way, since the holding effect of the anchor increases as speed is lost. You don't want so much chain out that the anchor fetches up as the ship loses headway.

ANCHORS TO ASSIST STEERING

When meeting another ship in a channel so narrow that there is danger of sheering as the quarter feels the bank, or when negotiating a turn smaller than the ship's tactical diameters, or when proceeding at slow speeds in a strong wind so it is difficult to steer the ship—use your anchor. The anchor steadies the bow laterally and retards the ship's headway despite higher engine revolutions—or conversely, higher revolutions can be used to increase the rudder's effectiveness without increasing headway.

Less chain is used so the ship maintains some headway as the anchor drags along the bottom. Let go well before the critical point in the maneuver so the anchor has time to ball up with mud and you have time to adjust the amount of chain and achieve the desired effect. The length of chain is increased a few links at a time until this balance is found. The amount of chain is not critical so long as so much chain is not put out that the anchor fetches up.

Once the anchor becomes effective, the ship turns in a much smaller diameter and is easily controlled. The pivot point shifts forward so that the ship pivots around a point nearer her bow. Advance is reduced, becoming a factor of the scope of chain and revolutions used during the turn, i.e., the degree to which the anchor is allowed to drag.

Since the pivot point is farther forward, the stern initially swings in a wider area than it would without the anchor, but the overall turning diameter is greatly reduced. Steering becomes more precise and the ship more controllable due both to the restricted movement of the bow and the greater flow over the rudder for a given speed made good over the bottom.

ANCHORS TO BREAK A SHEER

Should the ship take a sheer, the anchor can be used to regain control and prevent collision or grounding. It is important, though, that the anchor not dig in when used at such a time, so minimize the amount of chain slacked. If the anchor were to fetch up, the already present sheer would be accentuated because the pivot point then shifts ahead to the hawsepipe, and the suction of the quarter, in combination with the rotational momentum already developed, takes charge.

When the anchor is dragging properly the bow immediately steadies up and the rudder becomes more effective, the stern lifts away from the bank, and the sheer is broken. The anchor has both checked the swing of the bow and retarded the ahead movement of the ship, while the engine continues to come ahead forcing a maximum flow over the rudder to quickly increase its effectiveness. Needless to say, the shiphandler has also increased the engine speed to full ahead to break the sheer. (Fig. 8-15)

This same effect is used to assist a ship in negotiating a bend with a radius that is less than the ship's normal turning radius.

EMERGENCY USE OF THE ANCHOR

Today, the anchor is most often used for emergencies and it is an extremely effective tool for preventing groundings and accidents when the engine or steering is lost. Because the ship continues along her track slowly losing

1. SUCTION ON THE QUARTER CAUSES SHEER.
2. ANCHOR IS PUT DOWN AND BOW STEADIES UP.
3. RUDDER BECOMES MORE EFFECTIVE SO STERN LIFTS FROM THE BANK.
4. SHEER IS BROKEN AND SHIP PROCEEDS SAFELY.

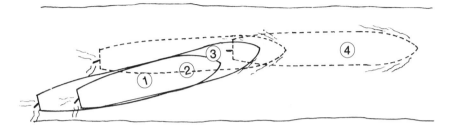

Fig. 8-15. Anchor used to break a sheer.

headway after the anchor is down, she can be brought to a controlled stop under most circumstances if there is sufficient sea room ahead.

Two anchors can be used to increase the stopping force in an emergency but neither anchor should be allowed to fetch up for the reasons explained earlier. If a stern anchor is available it is manned in narrow channels and used in the same manner as, and in conjunction with, the bow anchors. The stern anchor is especially effective for stopping a ship in a short distance while maintaining her heading, and holding the ship laterally after headway is lost. Obviously though, if it is necessary to work the ship around a bend or change her heading while stopping, the stern anchor would not be an appropriate tool. For further discussion on the use of stern anchors, see the section of Chapter 8 entitled "Stern Anchors."

Some steering control can be maintained despite a loss of rudder power by making use of the ship's natural behavior in conjunction with the anchor:

1. The ship can be turned to the right by backing the engine and taking advantage of the tendency to twist in that direction.
2. The ship can be turned to the left by utilizing bank suction on the starboard quarter.
3. A conventional ship will turn into the wind when she has headway, or lie at some large angle to the wind when dead in the water.
4. If a ship develops sternway she tends to back into the wind, after which the anchor can be put down so the ship backs nearly straight.

A recent grounding of a VLCC might have been prevented had the master made use of this tendency of a ship to back into the eye of the wind: the ship would usually back *into* the same wind which in this case blew her onto the beach.

If dragging anchors cannot stop the ship before grounding, and if the bottom is soft so there is no chance of damaging the hull when the ship goes aground, slack more chain when one to two ships lengths from the shoal so the anchor or anchors are laid out and ready to pull the ship back off. This decision has to be made only by the master at the moment of crisis, but it is an option that is available. The shiphandler's responses to such situations are more effective *if possible emergencies are considered before they arise and actions preplanned.* When things go wrong, they go wrong in a hurry and reaction time is brief; by planning for such contingencies the response can be instinctive and immediate.

Putting the engine full astern is often the worst response if steering is lost. The properly used anchor will stop a ship in a reasonable distance, and backing should be minimized in such situations because of the ship's tendency to twist and behave with less predictability.

Anchors are also the mariner's most effective tool when the engine is lost. The rudder can be used so a ship can be steered and drifted until she is nearly dead in the water. Do not be too quick to get the anchors down in this case, since once the anchor takes charge much of the rudder's effectiveness is lost due to the stabilizing effect of the dragging anchor. When possible, wait until the ship loses steerageway or until a straight reach lies ahead before letting the anchor go to stop the ship.

Due to the stress of the moment, and despite the shiphandler's acquired ability to function under pressure and make immediate decisions for which he alone holds total responsibility, the master may hesitate to use the anchors in an emergency situation. This hesitation is born of lack of confidence. From time to time, get to the pilot station early and put an anchor underfoot so that you can perform the maneuvers that have been discussed. Let the other mates try them as well. Confidence comes with practice.

LYING ALONGSIDE A BANK

At times it is necessary to anchor a ship in a narrow channel and be confident that she will not swing with the tide or lie across the channel and impede the movement of other vessels. If the bank has a steep

CURRENT

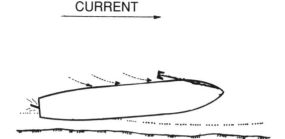

Fig. 8-16. Lying alongside a bank.

gradient and is of a soft material such as mud or clay, the ship can be put alongside and held with the anchor regardless of the direction of the wind and current.

If the current is from astern the ship is brought to the starboard side of the channel and speed reduced to bare steerageway. Drop the outboard or port anchor and slack the chain until the same control is gained as in previous maneuvers. Do not put out so much chain that the ship stops before she is alongside the bank. If the anchor fetches up too soon, the current from astern takes charge and causes the ship to get crosswise in the channel. Ease the ship ahead against the anchor and, as the ship nears the bank, put the rudder to port. Reduce RPM or stop the engine and lay the ship easily alongside at a slight angle to the bank. The stern lies against the bank and the anchor holds the bow off as the current from aft strikes the hull on the port side. (Fig. 8-16)

Should the current change direction, come ahead with a few revolutions and put the rudder hard to starboard to lift the stern. Let the ship fall back with the current, kicking the engine ahead as necessary to keep the stern off the bank until the ship is riding to her anchor. The eddy current between the bank and the hull then usually holds the ship a short distance off the bank so she lies nicely until the next change in the current. The ship is later put alongside as the tide turns and floods again, the procedure being repeated as necessary for as long as the ship needs to remain at anchor.

GOING ASTERN WITH AN ANCHOR

A ship being maneuvered astern for any distance can use an anchor underfoot to steady the bow and make the ship back almost directly

Fig. 8-17. Moving a ship astern with an anchor.

astern. The anchor replaces a bow tug and the engine is used to move the ship astern, either unassisted or with a tug on a hawser astern to tow the ship.

Skill is required when using the engine alone in this manner, since the ship pivots to some degree when the engine turns astern even though the anchor is steadying the bow. As the ship backs with the anchor down the resultant motion is almost directly astern, the stern walking to port at a much lesser rate than it would when backing without the anchor underfoot. (Fig. 8-17) When the stern does begin moving to port, the engine is stopped and kicked ahead with hard over rudder to bring the ship back to the desired heading and then the backing maneuver is resumed.

However, should the anchor be allowed to fetch up so all astern motion is lost, the ship walks only to port. It's therefore important that only the minimum chain required to steady the bow is used.

When using an anchor in this manner *in a strong wind,* a tug must also be used aft on a hawser. The anchor holds the bow up to the wind while the tug both pulls the ship astern and holds the stern up to the wind. In this case, slack the chain until the bow no longer falls off as the tug pulls astern and to windward. Due to the heavy strain on the anchor, the ship's engine is needed to assist the tug during the maneuver. It will probably be necessary to increase the amount of chain used once the ship begins moving astern under these conditions, since the anchor balls up with mud and loses some holding power. When the bow starts to feel the wind, slack chain—if the anchor fetches up, increase revolutions astern to work it free. The tug continues to pull throughout the maneuver, since it is primarily holding the stern to windward while assisting the engine to move the ship aft.

CHAPTER NINE

SPECIAL MANEUVERS

> Captain Ironsides was as cool as a cucumber. He
> moved his ship about with geometric precision . . . the
> ship seemed to perform a slow, formal dance to the
> accompaniment of whistles and kettledrums; every
> move followed a rigid pattern.
>
> —Jan de Hartog
> *The Distant Shore*

The morning is wet and still. A light mist born of chill night air still lingering within the jungle's ferns and coconut palms rises vaporlike up the sides of the cone-shaped hills. Even the hard case seaman lingers on deck to enjoy this morning as his containership eases slowly toward Gatun Locks and begins her crossing from the Atlantic to Pacific. The Panama Canal severs the Isthmus of Panama, forever changing the patterns of world commerce but altering not one bit the tropic splendor of this land.

Thousands of ships each year parade up, over, and then down the far side of the spine of Central America, yet so professionally do the pilots and others involved with this enterprise work that the innately impressive operation seems routine, almost mundane, to casual observers. To seamen though, whether old hands or first trippers, the Panama Canal is fascinating. Ships anchor, berth, meet in narrow channels, lock up and down, and maneuver in wind, tropic rain squall, fog, and spill current with and without tugs; the canal is a microcosm of the shiphandler's world.

The pilot watches from the starboard wing, radio in hand, preparing to put this ship smoothly into the lock with but 2 feet of clearance on each side. His skills and confidence are a product of hundreds, even thousands, of transits.

"South four, this is Gatun east side. We have your ship scheduled for twelve wires, and will be back for her in about ten minutes."

"Roger."

A laconic reply, but all that is needed.

173

Time is paramount if the canal is to operate safely and efficiently so the ship continues to ease steadily toward the lock, moving at the pace of a slow walk to arrive at the center wall simultaneously with the locomotives returning down the mile long track from the ship ahead. Few words are spoken. The silent lockage is a characteristic of the Panama Canal transit of which the pilots are justly proud.

Heaving lines drop from the ship to the small skiff lying off the now horizontal arrow at the north end of the center wall—the Pacific lies just eight hours away.

CANALS AND LOCKS

Mariners routinely handle ships in canals and locks throughout their careers at sea, be they the locks at the entrance to the tidal basin in Bombay or Buenos Aires, or those at the Panama or Welland Canal. Each passage is unique since specific approach and lockage techniques vary to suit the conditions of a particular port or waterway. By understanding the problems and methods common to most of these facilities though, the mariner can develop an appreciation of their operation.

Most seafarers transit the Panama Canal at some point, so this waterway will serve as a basis for discussing shiphandling at all such installations. This canal presents a composite of conditions found in most lock-type canals: fresh- and saltwater sections, single and multiple locks carrying ships both up and down, and a restricted channel with all its inherent shiphandling problems.

A passage through locks can be divided into four segments: the approach, entrance, fill, and departure. During the lockage a ship is affected by the same laws of hydrodynamics and the same effects of wind and current as a docking vessel, and also the combined effects of the spill and turbidity currents found to some degree at all locks. It is a common misconception that there are no currents in the Panama Canal, or at other 'lock-type canals. There are, in fact, strong currents, which can reach a velocity of 3 to 4 knots at the lock's entrance or jaws.

A huge amount of water flows from a lock chamber as its level is lowered, forming a *spill current* that follows a predictable pattern for which the pilot must compensate during the approach. (Fig. 9-1) The spill current is primarily a surface current and its effect varies with the ship's draft.

Many locks connect two bodies of water of different density. For example, the last or sea-end lock at the Panama Canal moves the ship

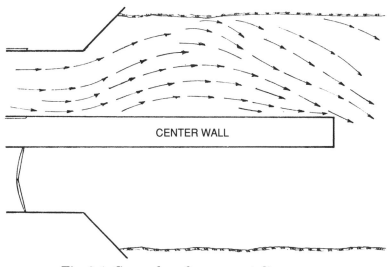

Fig. 9-1. General surface current diagram.

from the canal's fresh water lake and locks to the Atlantic or Pacific
Ocean salt water. A complex *density current* forms when those lock
gates are opened and the heavier water on one side of the gates mixes
with and displaces the less dense water on the other side. While the
surface pattern of the turbidity current is similar to that of the spill
current, below the surface the heavier water forms a current flowing in
the opposite direction, *toward and under the lighter fresh water*, affecting the ship in varying degrees and directions depending on her draft
and the period of time that the masses of the water have been mixing.
In the Panama Canal specifically, the more dense salt water outside the
entrance to the first lock (the "sea entrance") begins to displace the
lighter fresh water in the chamber as soon as the gates are opened. As
the fresh water is displaced it flows out of the chamber in a strong
surface current reaching down to a depth of 20 to 25 feet.

Because of these currents, the pilot may have the gates kept closed
until the ship is almost to the jaws or entrance of the lock and until the
bow wires are aboard the ship and fast. At other times this current will
be allowed to dissipate before a large Panamax-class ship approaches
the locks.

At the Panama Canal ships follow an "S" pattern as they approach
the locks to compensate for this complex current pattern. (Fig. 9-2)
Compare Figure 9-1 with Figure 9-2 and it is obvious why ships ap-

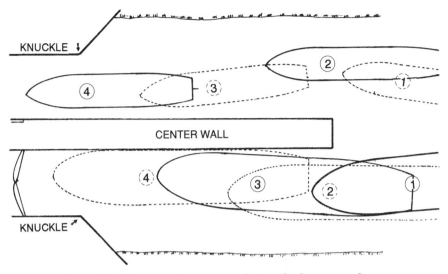

Fig. 9-2. Allowing for current during lock approach.

proach in this manner. The current flows strongly for about thirty minutes after the water stops spilling from the chamber, the gates are opened, and the spill current and density current combine to affect the approaching ship.

The distance between the ship and the center approach wall varies depending on the ship size, the current strength, and the ship's draft. Smaller ships approach the center wall in the area of the jaws, or the entrance locks, and then bring the stern in toward the wall as the bow enters the locks and the locomotives are made fast. Larger or more deeply laden ships are kept closer to the center wall during the approach as shown in Figure 9-2 and, in the case of Panamax ships, the bow or the entire ship is brought hard up against the center wall prior to the time the ship reaches the entrance to the lock chamber.

Speed of approach is very important because the engine will have to be kicked ahead to alter the ship's heading as the ship nears the jaws. So long as speed is reduced to a minimum during the approach (usually 1 to 2 knots is satisfactory), the engine can be used as needed without developing excessive speed at the entrance. Speed is critical at the Panama Canal since the locomotives move at a maximum towing speed of 3 knots and thus cannot put wires aboard a ship that exceeds that speed.

At the locks a ship must have only an officer and crewmembers forward and aft to operate the line handling winches, and supply two mooring lines at the bow and stern in case it is necessary to tie up at some point. The canal seamen supply all other gear. Other canals, such as the Welland Canal and Saint Lawrence Seaway, require the ship to supply all gear and to handle her own lines. Local rules must be carefully read to determine the requirements of a particular waterway.

Communication is by walkie-talkie with hand signals to back up the radio in case of failure. The ship's whistle is also utilized to communicate a danger signal to the lockmaster and locomotives should some problem develop.

Anchors are kept ready for letting go, but must be stowed in the hawsepipe, rather than backed out, so the wires and messengers will not be fouled on the flukes.

Tugs are used in the same manner as discussed in previous chapters to assist larger ships during the approach. The bow, or the entire midbody of large, deeply loaded ships, is held against the fendering on the center wall by the tugs and locomotives during the latter stages of the approach. This minimizes the risk that the current will force the ship's bow into the knuckle, as pilots call the corner where the side approach wall meets the side wall of the lock chamber. (See Fig. 9-2) The tugs are kept working, using the tug signals discussed earlier in this text, to adjust the tug's power, and push to hull against the center wall until the bow is well into the chamber.

Interestingly, there are significant differences between the methods used by very experienced pilots putting the same Panamax-class ships into the locks.

Some pilots put the entire ship against the wall. They hold her flat alongside with the locomotives and tugs until the forward sections of the parallel midbody pass inside the locks. The theory is that by keeping the ship alongside the wall, the hull is as far as possible from the knuckle. More important, because the ship is tight alongside, there is no way for the current to get between the ship and the wall to force the ship away from the center wall.

Other pilots believe this is quite wrong. They hold the *bow* alongside but allow the stern to stay a few feet from the wall while they slide the ship into the locks. This group believes the ship actually stays alongside easier if it is angled toward the wall. If the bow does get off the wall, it can be easily brought back alongside because water can flow freely astern rather than being trapped between the hull and the wall. This seems to be borne out by the fact that only one tug is needed to keep the ship alongside during the operations and even that tug usually comes ahead only at a slow speed rather than being used full ahead as is needed using the first method.

The second method is used by a growing number of pilots who find they have less problem keeping the bow clear of the side wall if the stern is not hard alongside. The point, though, is that both methods work well. Which is best? The method the pilot feels most comfortable with or, as a pilot might say, "what works for you." There are obviously wrong ways to do a job but, since thousands of Panamax ships have been put safely into locks for the better part of a century using either method, it is really only a matter of personal preference. Keep this in mind the next time someone insists there is only one way to do a job. T'ain't so, as the aforementioned variations in working by some of the finest shiphandlers in the world clearly demonstrate. Again, it is only important to understand shiphandling techniques and principles of hydrodynamics, plan ahead, use external forces to advantage, and to do the job in the manner with which you are most comfortable.

The lockage procedure is the same regardless of whether the pilot puts only the ship's bow or the entire midbody alongside. Wires are taken from the locomotives as the ship passes along the center wall, the number of wires depending on the displacement and length of the ship as determined using an empirical formula developed over nearly a century of operation. Sidewall wires are taken aboard during the entrance stage of the lockage and, when aboard, are used to center the ship and assist her in moving into the chamber. The engine is used throughout the approach to move the ship and to position the stern.

Larger ships must be driven into the lock, often at full ahead. Their beam and draft so fills the cross-sectional area of the chamber that the water cannot flow out as it is displaced by the entering ship and a piston effect is created.

Using the wires from the locomotive's two constant tension winches, and the braking and towing effect derived from the undercarriage drive that meshes into the drive rack, up to 70,000 pounds of pull is exerted on the ship by each locomotive. The rack is located between the locomotive tracks that parallel the chamber. The "mules" are positioned ahead of the ship's chock to center and tow the ship, or abeam or abaft the chock to center or brake the ship as necessary, depending on the instructions received from the pilot over the walkie-talkie. A set of idler wheels under the locomotive locks into the cambered sides of the drive rack to assure that the locomotive is not pulled into the chamber.

All locomotives are shifted to a braking position abaft the chocks as the ship nears the gate ahead and she is stopped in the chamber to await flooding or filling. Due to the aforementioned piston effect, large ships practically stop themselves after the engine and locomotives are stopped. Often a ship's master is needlessly concerned that the ship is going to strike the gates ahead, not realizing that the vessel actually tends to stop on her own. In the Saint Lawrence Seaway and other locks without locomotives, the vessel is stopped using the engine and piston effect alone, an effect that increases rapidly as the blockage factor approaches unity.

The entrance phase complete, all locomotives shorten up their wires to get the best lead to hold the ship centered as the chamber fills. The immense gate valves are opened, the water flowing down the length of the center and side walls and through lateral culverts beneath the ship. The design and construction of this engineering masterpiece makes interesting reading and several recommended titles can be found in the Bibliography. The ship is usually held in the center of the chamber in the Panama Canal while the water level is raised or lowered. In other waterways that use ship's lines or wires rather than shore-based locomotives the ship is kept hard alongside the wall during the fill or spill.

Up and down lockages differ greatly. The ship lies quietly during a down lockage as the placid water drains out from under her. During an up lockage though, the ship surges heavily as the water comes into the chamber at a high rate, either from the bottom or side depending on the design of the lock. Filling from the bottom is preferable because the movement of the water is then primarily vertical and the ship is less likely to be forced into the wall. The positioning of the vessel, centered or alongside the wall, is peculiar to the lock system but in all cases the ship must be held in that position throughout the fill and not allowed to develop any athwartship movement. A ship held alongside by proper fendering will not be damaged, nor can there be any damage to a ship held in the center of the chamber. When a ship starts to move about in the chamber though, the forces acting on her sides become unbalanced and she begins to surge, developing momentum and probably being damaged as she comes alongside one wall or the other.

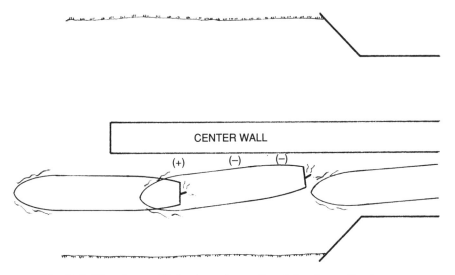

Fig. 9-3. Keeping sufficient angle as the ship clears the jaws.

The fill or spill is completed and the massive gates swing open as the ship moves ahead using her engine and the towing locomotives. A large ship is further assisted out to the locks by putting water into the chamber behind her; she is "flushed out" of the chamber. The displaced water does not then have to flow through the restricted area between the ship and the lock walls and floor as the ship departs the chamber— instead a head of water is created behind the ship to assist her in leaving.

As the ship clears the jaws (Fig. 9-3) she is put at an angle with the bow away from the center wall. This angle helps to compensate for the imbalance of pressures as the ship passes along the center wall after clearing the chamber. The wall affects the ship in the same manner as the close bank described in Chapter 2. By keeping sufficient angle, maintaining a balance between the turning couple created by the rudder and the suction effects on her quarter as she moves along the wall, the ship is slowly steamed from the locks. Alternatively, some pilots choose to put the ship against the center wall fendering and slide along until the ship is clear, especially when moving larger ships which will usually be drawn onto the center wall anyway. The previously discussed currents at the *seaward ends* of the locks assist a departing ship to clear the center wall and the ship can basically be steamed straight from the last or sea end chamber.

Since the ship obeys the same physical laws, and is handled in the same manner as for any other narrow channel during her passage across Gatun Lake and through the narrow and rock-edged channel of Gaillard Cut, any discussion of that phase of the transit would be redundant. Suffice it to say that this transit offers an excellent opportunity for the mariner to observe ship behavior when maneuvering and when meeting other ships in confined waters.

SINGLE-POINT MOORINGS

Few ports in the world can accommodate deeply loaded VLCCs and ULCCs, so offshore oil terminals such as the LOOP terminal in the Gulf of Mexico are being constructed as a practical and efficient alternative. Being a relatively recent innovation, these terminals have been visited by only a small number of seafarers to date and only a few mariners have brought a ship into such a facility.

The LOOP terminal is typical of offshore ports using single-point moorings. The facilities at LOOP lie in water ranging from 100 to 125 feet in depth, approximately 19 miles off the Louisiana coast. The designated port area is reached via a defined fairway under the guidance of a pilot/mooring master.

After completion of a prearrival inspection to assure that a visiting VLCC or ULCC meets the statutory requirements for tank vessels, she is brought into the terminal area in which three SPMs and the pumping platform are located. The ship is turned to the heading at which she will lie after mooring is completed and brought up to the buoy.

Unless the ship has been at anchor in the vicinity of the port area, the best indication of the required approach heading is the direction in which the floating cargo hoses trail from the buoy. Coming from the anchorage, the ship approaches on the heading at which she was lying while at anchor; the ship does not know whether she is swinging on the buoy or the anchor and will lie at the same heading in either case. If coming from sea, approach straight up the hoses since they at least lie to a resultant of the surface current and the prevailing wind. It would be advantageous to have a current meter at a mid-draft depth of 40 feet on the buoy anchor chain to supply subsurface current information, and such equipment should be installed on all SPMs in the future.

Since tugs are not generally used, the ship must approach on a heading which balances the forces of wind and current or she will be set

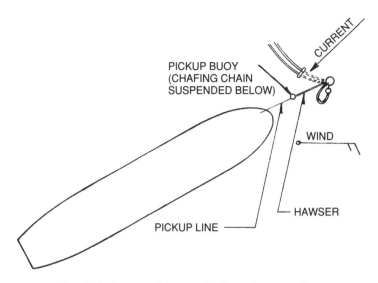

Fig. 9-4. Approaching a single-point mooring.

away from the buoy before the mooring lines and chafing chains are
brought aboard. (Fig. 9-4) The relative effects of the wind and current
depend not only on their absolute forces and direction relative to the
ship's heading but also on the ship's draft. Refer again to the discussion
in Chapter 5 on wind versus current forces. It would seem that, because
of the VLCC's greater draft, the current would usually overcome the
wind, but this is not the case. VLCCs have a great deal of sail area and
even a 15-knot wind significantly affects the approach heading—that
heading is a resultant of the wind and current in all but the lightest
breeze.

The heading is adjusted during the final stages of the approach when
effects of the outside forces increase *geometrically* as the ship's headway
decreases to the less than 1-knot speed that is necessary to safely
complete this evolution. Once the proper approach heading is found, the
ship maintains that heading without a large amount of rudder and will
not set laterally away from the buoy; the buoy remains at the same
relative bearing fine on the port bow. This feel that the ship is "in a
groove" is one of the best indications that the proper heading has been
found. Instrumentation, especially a Doppler log reading speed over the
ground laterally and fore and aft, is especially helpful at this point, since
a heading which eliminates all sideward motion over the ground can quickly be determined as well as speed over the ground towards the buoy.

There is greater room for error in determining the approach heading if tugs are available, but the technique for approaching and mooring remains the same.

Speed of approach is important of course, and by using methods discussed in previous chapters to slow the ship the approach can be completed efficiently while assuring that speed is reduced to minimum steerageway for the last few shiplengths of the maneuver. Most important is the significant reduction of headway during large changes in course typical with ships of this size; if the ship has to change heading during the approach, she can proceed at a greater speed prior to the course alteration. Plan one large change of heading during the last stage of the approach rather than using a series of small alterations in course as would normally be done when approaching a berth. The ship can then approach at 3 to 4 knots until the course change, rather than approaching at 1 to 2 knots on her final heading, and the last 2 miles can be covered in about one hour rather than the two or more hours that would be required at 1 knot. Since the approach with a VLCC is made over a distance measured in miles rather than feet, these considerations are significant.

The ship is steadied on her final heading well before reaching the buoy, since there usually are no tugs to check any residual swing after

Fig. 9-5. SPM pickup rope and chafing chain.

the ship loses headway/steerageway. Despite their 75- to 80-foot drafts, VLCCs and ULCCs generally steer very well at minimal speeds with the engine stopped, so this final approach can be made at very slow speeds. During the final 600 feet of the approach the crew heaves the pickup line aboard under the direction of the assistant mooring master, the ship proceeding with only minimum headway so she can be stopped when 100 feet from the buoy. The pickup line brings the chafing chain aboard to be made fast with either a chain stopper or Smit bracket. (Fig. 9-5) The chain stopper, which resembles the traditional riding pawl assembly used for the ship's anchor, is preferable to the Smit bracket since there are no connecting links and shackles to handle and the mooring can thus be completed faster and more safely.

The pickup hawsers are not to be used to heave the 350,000- to 600,000-ton ships to the SPM. The ship must be steamed to the buoy while these lines are used only to bring the chafing chain aboard.

Two service craft are generally used to assist during the mooring, one moving the hoses off to the ship's port hand and clear and the other

Fig. 9-6. "The toughest part of putting a VLCC to a mooring is remembering that the guys on the bow may be in a different time zone."

bringing the mooring lines to the ship to be brought aboard. The hoses and buoy are kept on the ship's port bow so the ship can pass clear without damaging the installation if there is any error in estimating the stopping distance required. The port bow is chosen because the ship's bow swings to starboard away from the hose and buoy if the engine is put astern. Do not have the boat pull the hoses clear to port until the ship has nearly reached them, since the hose string is used to determine the approach heading.

A second pilot or assistant mooring master must be on the bow as the ship approaches the SPM. When within a few hundred feet of the bow, the buoy is no longer visible from the bridge and the assistant mooring master then conns the ship, giving helm and engine orders via the walkie-talkie to the mooring master. For this reason, the man on the bow should also be a pilot qualified to handle ships of this size.

Communication is by UHF walkie-talkie with VHF backup. The ship supplies two 20-fathom messengers to bring the buoy pickup lines aboard and any of the international standard mooring systems such as:

1. Bow chain stoppers (Fig. 9-7) designed to accept the 76.1 mm (3 inch) section of chafing chain. (This is the preferred mooring system.)
2. Smit brackets built to OCIMF standard dimensions.
3. Mooring bitts suitably positioned and of adequate strength.

In all cases the ship must have two closed chocks leading fair to the mooring equipment that are suitable for the 76.1 mm (3 inch) chafing chain.

A mooring line must be ready aft to be used by the workboat as required to hold the ship off the SPM during discharge. Constant attention is required during the discharge operation to be sure the ship does not ride up on the hoses and buoy. It is usually necessary to use the ship's engine astern at 8 to 10 revolutions or a line boat pulling astern to prevent this. Because the wind and current are usually at some angle to each other, the ship sails up to and across the buoy, much as she tacks back and forth across her anchor in an anchorage.

Despite her deep draft, a loaded VLCC is as much affected by the wind as a smaller ship, since she presents a sail area of the same proportion to the below water hull as any other vessel.

When the mooring is completed, the hoses are picked up from the water and bolted up, using ship's gear under the supervision of the assis-

Fig. 9-7. Chain stoppers for mooring a VLCC at a single-point mooring.

tant mooring master. The equipment used for the actual oil transfer operation is beyond the scope of this text.

Except in the worst of weather, it is possible for the ship to make up and to stay at an SPM. The primary limiting factor is the sea state during the makeup as even moderate seas make it impossible for the line boats to handle the hoses.

So long as speed is kept down to bare steerageway during the final approach, and the ship is put on a heading close to that at which she will lie after mooring, the maneuver to make up at an SPM is a safe and straightforward task. (Fig. 9-8)

SHIP TO SHIP LIGHTERING
*By Captain William Deaton, Lightering Master, and
Captain Marshall Irwin, Lightering Master*

A great deal of offshore ship to ship lightering is being done throughout the world, especially off the coast of the United States where the shallow

Fig. 9-8. Completed mooring at an SPM. Courtesy LOOP, Incorporated.

ports and the lack of offshore facilities make lightering necessary so oil can be imported in very large crude carriers. Offshore lightering is less efficient than transfer via conventional multiple- or single-point mooring facilities, but it is a workable substitute with which the mariner should be familiar. For clarity, the abbreviation VLCC as used throughout this section includes both the very large crude carrier and her still larger relative, the ultra large crude carrier.

Certain preparations are necessary prior to putting a smaller "offtaker" (a smaller ship that accepts the oil from the VLCC) alongside a VLCC. Under supervision of the lightering or mooring master, fenders are rigged on the port side of the offtaker. These fenders are placed on the offtaker even though it would be more expedient to rig them on the VLCC, which will be receiving a number of ships as her cargo is discharged. By having the fenders on the smaller ship when she comes alongside, the shiphandler is able to assure that the offtaker lands on the fenders. If the fenders were on the VLCC it would be possible for the offtaker to land between fenders and damage one or both ships.

Two types of fenders are used while lightering. Four or more large floating "Yokohama" type fenders, specially fitted for lightering, are floated along the parallel midbody of the offtaker, and two smaller "pillow" type fenders are hung off, one at the shoulder forward and the other on the quarter. Typically, the floating fenders are made fast by a wire which leads from a forward bitt on the ship's deck down to the first fender floating along the ship's side. A mooring line joins each fender and another line runs back up to a bitt on the ship's after deck. (Fig. 9-9)

Have all the necessary equipment laid out and ready aboard both ships before the operation begins. Walkie-talkies are used for communication between the mooring masters on the bridges of the two ships and between the bridge, bow, and stern of each vessel. Have several long 3-inch messengers and sufficient heaving lines on hand forward and aft to run the mooring lines.

Mooring lines with synthetic tails are laid out to be taken first from the offtaker and later from the VLCC as the mooring operation is completed. It is important that the wires have synthetic tails or pendants so the ships can break apart quickly in an emergency. The weather can deteriorate with surprising quickness and it may not always be possible to slack off mooring lines so they can be let go. A small crew can handle synthetic tails more easily and the synthetic tails absorb some of the shock of loading if the ships do begin to work against each

Fig. 9-9. Rigging fenders for ship to ship lightering. Courtesy Gulf Oil
and Seward International.

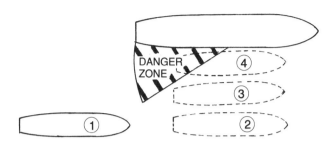

Fig. 9-10. Keep the offtaker's bow clear of the VLCC's quarter while
going alongside.

other after mooring. The tails can be cut to break apart as a last resort
in an emergency.

The mooring master aboard the offtaker has overall command of the
mooring while the second mooring master aboard the VLCC maintains
a steady course and speed as required by the offtaker. The VLCC steams
into the wind and sea at the minimum speed possible, only kicking the
engine ahead to maintain steerageway. This minimizes the hydrodynamic effects between the two ships, especially the effect of the acceler-
ated flow between them that draws the ships together and causes them
to land with excessive force. These are full bodied, relatively low powered merchant vessels and the maneuver for putting these ships together is much different from that described for underway replenishment maneuvers with fine lined, high powered, highly maneuverable
naval vessels. A constant speed and heading are maintained by the
VLCC while the light offtaker comes alongside to make fast. If a cross
swell makes it impossible to head into both sea and swell and keep the
ships from rolling, abort the lightering operation until the cross swell
moderates.

The offtaker approaches the starboard side of the VLCC, remaining
wide until abeam of the flat parallel midbody of the larger vessel. It is
very important that the smaller ship stays clear of the VLCC's quarter,
since suction between the ships in that area will draw the offtaker
rapidly into the larger ship's quarter. (Fig. 9-10) When parallel to the
VLCC's midbody, so both ships are heading into the wind, begin easing
the smaller ship alongside while using the wind as a tug—keep the wind
on the starboard bow to bring the offtaker alongside, or put the wind on

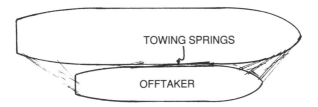

FIRST LINES (FROM OFFTAKER)
- MAIN DECK SPRING
- TWO HEADLINES
- TWO AFTER SPRINGS

Fig. 9-11. General arrangement of lines for lightering.

the port bow if she is closing too rapidly. The wind has a significant effect on the offtaker at this point since she is light prior to loading.

Continue to keep the smaller ship flat to the VLCC as she lands to spread the force of landing over the entire midbody of the offtaker. Land on all the floating fenders simultaneously to create the maximum hydraulic cushion between the ships to check up the lateral motion.

The offtaker first passes a forward spring to the VLCC, followed by two headlines to work against while the remaining lines are run. The course is then changed to put the wind on the offtaker's starboard bow to hold her alongside.

Although the pattern of lines can vary depending on the deck layout of the two ships, the suggested lines are: (Fig. 9-11)

1. Offtaker runs 5 headlines, 2 forward springs, 2 after springs leading from the main deck forward to the VLCC, and 3 sternlines.
2. VLCC runs 3 wire headlines, 2 forward spring wires, and 2 stern wires. Be sure to get 2 good spring lines run from the VLCC's main deck in the area of her manifold, leading aft to the offtaker, to tow the smaller ship during the operation.

Always run all lines regardless of the weather conditions or prognosis at the time, since the running of lines is a time consuming operation which may not be possible later if the weather deteriorates.

If weather permits, anchor the VLCC prior to hooking up hoses. Use minimum revolutions astern to stop the two ships, drifting headway off the ships rather than backing, so that a combination of the momentum of the offtaker plus the quickwater moving up between the ships as the

VLCC goes astern does not force the ships apart and part their lines. Should weather and sea conditions later change, the VLCC heaves up and resumes steaming slowly on a heading that minimizes rolling. Steam at minimum speed throughout the operation if it is not possible to anchor. The rate-of-turn indicator is used to steer at minimum speeds, kicking the engine ahead only to check any swing that develops. By maneuvering in this manner the heading is maintained into the wind and sea while headway remains almost nil. Keep the wind and sea a point on the VLCC's port bow during the transfer so the larger ship can provide a lee for the offtaker.

The ships remain together for the transfer operation unless the sea conditions deteriorate and the ships begin rolling. There is then a danger of parting the ship's lines and hoses. Don't wait until the weather deteriorates so much that lines start to part, as it then becomes too dangerous to let go, and a vessel finds herself in a position of being unable to stay alongside and unable to let go safely. Watch the weather reports and local conditions and break up the operation before conditions deteriorate. (Fig. 9-12)

Keep the lines tight and the deck well lighted throughout the operation as good seamanship dictates for any berthing situation. Retain the ballast aboard the offtaker for as long as possible while oil is being transferred. The sooner the offtaker develops a deeper draft, the sooner the wind's effect on her decreases and the operation stabilizes. Keep sufficient crew on deck. The lines require more attention, and are more difficult to handle, than at a terminal since the drafts of the two ships simultaneously change in opposite directions.

It may be necessary to get underway on short notice to either steam as a unit or break apart, so keep the engine ready to maneuver at all times.

When the transfer has been completed, let go all the VLCC's lines and single up the offtaker's lines to two headlines, a forward spring, a breast line aft, and the after main deck spring which leads forward to the main deck of the VLCC. This line keeps the offtaker from sliding aft under the VLCC's quarter, and is used to work against as the offtaker is broken away from the larger ship, and will be the last line let go. Throw off the headlines, then the lines aft as the bows begin to separate. If there is no wind, heave on the after breast line to bring the bow off, and then work against the main deck spring line to develop a significant angle to the VLCC. Steam slowly away from the larger ship, again

Fig. 9-12. Offtaker *Esso Zurich* lightering *Esso Atlantic*. Courtesy
Exxon Corporation and Black Star Publishing.

keeping the wind on the port or inner bow as the "poor man's tug," to
separate the ships.

If the ships are already underway at the completion of the transfer,
the lines are taken in the same order, but the force of the water passing

between the two ships is used to separate them as you hold the last spring line aft. When there is sufficient angle between the ships let go the last line and depart without increasing speed until the ships are well separated. Avoid increasing the flow between the ships as this would create suction and draw them together again.

Done properly, the offshore lightering operation can be completed safely, although care is required and none of the described precautions should be overlooked. If there is any problem during a ship-to-ship transfer, it is usually the result of complacency that develops after a series of routine lighterings.

FIVE- AND SEVEN-POINT MOORINGS
By Captain Carl R. Dingler, Mooring Master

Five- and seven-point moorings are used primarily on the west coast of the United States. Deep water is available close to shore so moorings can be located 1/2 to 1 mile from the shoreline, making this type of facility attractive and practical. Five or seven mooring buoys are positioned to hold the ship into the prevailing wind and sea and over the 10- to 16-inch submarine hoses. The vessel moors under the direction of a mooring master, using two bow anchors and ship's lines to the buoys lying abeam and astern. Generally, the five-point moorings are used for ships to 35,000 tons while the seven-point moorings accommodate ships to 165,000 tons. Tugs may assist ships over 80,000 tons deadweight when mooring.

Prior to arriving at the mooring the ship prepares the following:

1. Up to fourteen synthetic mooring lines (two lines for each buoy to be used).
2. Both anchors, backed out below the forefoot and ready to drop.
3. Boom or crane and other hose handling gear at the manifold.
4. Good stoppers for all lines with extras for doubling up as needed.
5. Walkie-talkies on the bridge, forward, and aft.

The size of the lines depends on the deadweight of the ship, but they must be a full coil in length so they can be run to the buoys without having to marry more than one line together. Wires may be substituted for mooring lines although the practice of *mixing* lines and wires varies from one terminal to another. If wires are used they must be at least 800 feet in length.

Both anchors must be backed out and ready to let go, clearly marked so they can be placed accurately without the mate on the bow having to guess how much chain is out.

Gear required at the manifold for handling the hoses includes a boom or crane with a safe working load of at least 7 tons to pick up the hose; buoy, hose, and chain bight slip ropes as specified by the port and mooring master; a handy billy; and a boat hook. The boom must be rigged for its full safe working load to handle safely the loads involved when picking up the hoses since a 12-inch hose places a dynamic load of 4.7 tons on the gear, while the load when handling a 16-inch hose is 7.2 tons. Wire runners must be rigged and the gear and runner should be in excellent condition. The ship must supply a wire pendant with a hook if a running block is used so the launch crew does not have to handle the weight of the block when picking up the hoses.

Quarters should be prepared for the mooring master and the launch crew.

The lines and hoses are handled by the ship's crew under the mooring master's direction. Before reaching the berth, the mooring master briefs the ship's master and officers on the mooring procedure and inspects the gear that is going to be used.

There are some significant differences between berthing a ship at a mooring and docking her, and the master must keep this in mind as the mooring master is bringing the ship into the mooring. The vessel approaches on a heading approximately 90 degrees to the axis of the berth along the line on which the anchors will be laid. (Fig. 9-13) Because the mooring lies into the prevailing wind and the sea, the approach is usually made with the wind and sea on the beam. This creates some problems for the mooring master and means that higher speeds than might otherwise be desirable may be required during the approach. The mate stands by the offshore anchor which must be let go immediately at the mooring master's command so it is precisely positioned relative to the mooring. When the anchor is let go, all the required seven to nine shots of chain are allowed to immediately run out. *Do not check the chain,* since this will cause the ship to pivot on the anchor and may also possibly drag the anchor out of position. The ship's handling characteristics change immediately as the anchor is put on the bottom, since just the drag of the chain is sufficient to steady the bow and shift the ship's pivot point forward, altering the ship's behavior relative to the

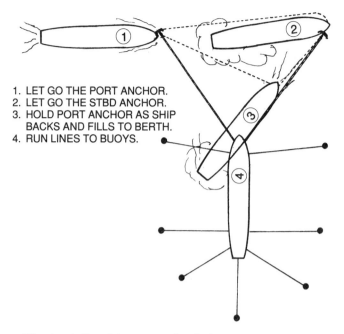

1. LET GO THE PORT ANCHOR.
2. LET GO THE STBD ANCHOR.
3. HOLD PORT ANCHOR AS SHIP
   BACKS AND FILLS TO BERTH.
4. RUN LINES TO BUOYS.

Fig. 9-13. Berthing at multiple-buoy mooring.

wind and her response to the engine and rudder. The mooring master
allows for this during the approach.

The ship carries her headway past the axis of the berth before
stopping and letting go the second anchor. The ship is not backed and
filled into position for dropping the second anchor, she is swung and
maneuvered into position. The amount of swing put on the ship prior to
letting go the second anchor is critical as the stern must be positioned
so the ship's tendency to back to port when going astern into the berth is
allowed for. Let go the second anchor and tighten the brake on the first anchor so it fetches up and takes a strain. The ship goes astern while
the anchors are used to assist in steering the ship into position. *The
stern moves in a direction that is opposite to the side on which the
anchor is held.* Hold the port anchor and the strain on the chain
causes the ship to back to starboard—hold the starboard anchor and
the ship backs to port. If the chain on both anchors is kept slack, the ship
usually walks to port, although the wind will affect the ship to some
extent, as always.

This same technique of laying out and then steering with two anchors
is useful when making a Mediterranean moor.

Slack both chains as required as the ship backs into the mooring and run the ship's lines to the buoys using the line boat. It is essential that everyone involved be safety conscious at this point so no one is hurt while putting out mooring lines. There is a heavy strain on these lines while working into the mooring. The mates must be instructed to alert the bridge before stopping off lines so the ship can be maneuvered to relieve the strain until the lines are on the bitts. This is especially important aft since the crew working on the stern cannot be seen from the bridge. If there is a significant amount of strain double stoppers must be used.

Do not allow the propeller to be turned while the lines are going out except by direct order from the mooring master. Since the mooring master is communicating with the line boat by radio, the boat can tell him when the lines are clear of the screw. The first line is usually a breast line from the main deck on the up current or windward side of the ship, followed by the other lines as directed by the mooring master. The order of the lines depends on the weather and current conditions. When all lines are out a strain is taken on both anchors to position the ship over the submerged hose. The anchors form an equilateral triangle and hold the ship into the predominate weather. (Fig. 9-13)

During the transfer operation, the mooring master works with the crew to keep the ship over the hose or hoses, now connected to the manifold, adjusting for the change in draft as well as for any change in the weather or sea conditions.

Based on his past experience, the mooring master advises the ship's officers concerning weather conditions and the advisability of remaining at the mooring and transferring cargo if the conditions deteriorate—a significant responsibility in view of the time required to break up the mooring as opposed to the possible consequences if the ship remains at the mooring too long. The direction of weather and sea is as important as its state when making the decision—when the weather is from other than ahead the strain on lines becomes heavy, while as long as those forces are from ahead the strain is on the anchors and the ship can remain longer at the mooring. The value of a mariner's experience in situations such as this is not fully appreciated by the landsman, since ashore responsibility is usually shared and the results of a decision are rarely so immediate, be they right or wrong.

Keep the engine ready in case it is necessary to leave the mooring and maintain a full watch both on deck and below. Maintain a continuous watch on the NOAA VHF frequencies since conditions can deteriorate rapidly and sufficient warning is necessary if the ship is to break up the mooring before unsafe conditions develop.

When transfer is completed the hoses are lowered back to the bottom and the lines singled up as the line boat trips the hooks on the mooring buoys. The ship then departs the mooring, the exiting maneuver varying depending on whether the ship is light or loaded.

A loaded ship brings the lines aboard in basically the reverse order from that in which they were run (assuming that the conditions are still the same), until all lines are gone and the propeller is clear. Heave the anchors as the breast lines are let go, using the engine and rudder as necessary to hold the stern in the center of the berth. Come ahead as the anchors come clear and steam away from the buoys.

A light ship takes in the lines in the same manner but uses the anchors to compensate for her light draft while working clear of the berth. Heave the starboard anchor short to two shots in the water and then heave on the port anchor. Work against the starboard anchor while heaving on the port to keep the ship's bow into the wind. The ship must not fall off the wind or she will wind up on the buoys. As soon as the port anchor breaks free the ship is driven out of the berth, dragging both anchors until clear. Heave the port anchor home and then heave up the last two shots of chain on the starboard anchor and proceed to sea.

MEDITERRANEAN MOOR
By Captain Earl R. McMillin, Master Mariner

Until the advent of roll-on vessels the Mediterranean moor was used only in less developed ports with limited facilities. Several RO/RO ships fitted with stern ramps, which commonly dock stern to the berth with anchors laid out ahead, are now in service, so more deck officers need to be familiar with this maneuver.

The procedure for putting a tanker into a five- or seven-point mooring is also the most efficient maneuver for completing the Mediterranean moor. The maneuver is described completely in the previous section and it would be redundant to repeat the steps for making a proper approach, laying out the anchors, and backing into the berth using the anchors to assist in steering. Ideally, the anchors are spread at an angle of 60 degrees so the bow is held in position regardless of wind direction. This may not be possible when maneuvering room is limited. Plan the mooring so the an-

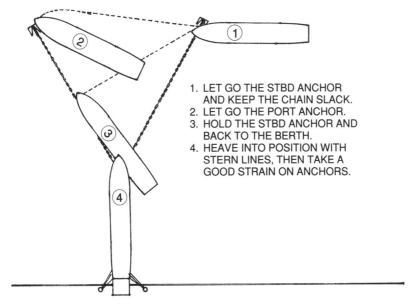

1. LET GO THE STBD ANCHOR AND KEEP THE CHAIN SLACK.
2. LET GO THE PORT ANCHOR.
3. HOLD THE STBD ANCHOR AND BACK TO THE BERTH.
4. HEAVE INTO POSITION WITH STERN LINES, THEN TAKE A GOOD STRAIN ON ANCHORS.

Fig. 9-14. Mediterranean moor.

chors are let go far enough from the berth to give a good scope of chain, and drop them far enough apart so the chain and spread between the anchors form legs of an equilateral triangle. The ship should finally be moored with at least one shot more chain than would be used to anchor in water of the same depth as is found off the berth. (Fig. 9-14)

Unlike the five-point moorings, a cargo berth is rarely built with any regard for prevailing wind and sea conditions, so these forces are more commonly from some direction other than ahead. It is necessary to allow for set and leeway to one side in these conditions, primarily by adjusting the amount of swing that is put on the ship prior to putting down the second anchor, and by holding one anchor or the other as the ship backs to the berth.

Plan the approach and mooring procedure with the mates who will be stationed forward and aft. The mate forward must let go the anchor immediately when ordered so the anchors are properly placed and then control the chain precisely as the ship backs to the wharf. The mate aft must keep the bridge informed of the bearing and distance from the ship's stern to the berth as the ship backs to the pier (and more importantly the rate at which the bearing and distance are changing) since

RO/RO ships usually have the bridge well forward where it is difficult to see the stern.

A line boat should be available so the stern lines can be run to the berth as soon as possible, after which the ship is backed as the mate forward walks the anchor chain out under a light strain and the crew aft heaves on the stern lines. Keep the stern lines clear of the propeller since it must at all times be possible to use the engine to hold the ship in position and then stop her as the stern nears the stringpiece. The vessel is now under total control and can be brought up close to the berth. Don't use the engine to back the last few feet—heave the ship astern so there is no chance of an accident from a delay in engine response.

Use sufficient lines or wires aft so a good strain can be taken on both anchors after the ship is fast. Heave the chains partially out of the water so the ship cannot move astern if there is any later change in sea or wind. The stern is right up to the berth so it must not be possible for the ship to move any further astern after the mooring is complete.

Reliable bow thrusters are available, and all ships fitted with a stern ramp, which will commonly berth stern first, should be fitted with this equipment. A thruster greatly simplifies positioning the bow prior to letting go each anchor, and steering the ship as she backs to the berth. When weather conditions and the layout of the berth require it, the ship fitted with a bow thruster can lay out the anchors without being perpendicular to the berth, moving the bow laterally with the thruster to get into position for letting go the second anchor. Restricted maneuvering room may require this. Heretofore it was necessary at times to wait for favorable conditions prior to berthing stern to a dock. The bow thruster makes it possible to moor Mediterranean fashion in all but the worst conditions and no ship that works cargo over the stern should be built without one.

Departure from the Mediterranean moor varies with weather conditions, of course, but generally the ship takes in lines aft and immediately begins heaving on the windward anchor. Heave short to two shots and then heave on the lee anchor while steaming against the weather anchor. Maintain position and heading so the ship isn't set back against the berth as the anchors come clear of the bottom. Start moving the ship ahead as soon as the lee anchor breaks free, heaving and dragging both anchors until well clear of the berth. Heave the anchors home and proceed to sea.

WILLIAMSON TURNS

The classic Williamson Turn is described in most textbooks on seamanship. The turn works well and is especially useful as ship size increases. Ships with high block coefficients lose headway faster than smaller, finer lined vessels, and a VLCC will typically have lost most of her headway by the time she has reached her reciprocal course at the completion of a Williamson Turn. Little astern maneuvering is then required to stop the ship and pick up a person or object on the water. Because of this, and because of the predictability of the vessel's path, the Williamson Turn is preferable to a round turn or other maneuver for putting a ship on a reciprocal heading.

The path that a ship follows during a Williamson Turn becomes even more predictable if the variables of the maneuver are eliminated. For example, instead of stating that the ship should be steadied up after she has reached a course that is 60 to 65 degrees from the ship's original course, it is preferable to state that the helm should be shifted at some predetermined point and left in that position while the ship checks up and then swings to the reciprocal of her original course. If the classic instructions are followed, the turn is less predictable because the time to check the swing and the amount of rudder used are dependent on the helmsman's or deck officer's experience and judgment. The resulting track can vary greatly.

Further, the classic turn always uses a 60-degree change of heading as a basis for shifting the helm. Ships have changed greatly so neither this nor any other fixed point will suffice for all ships. The Williamson Turn must be performed routinely during an ocean passage as part of the crew emergency training, and the point at which the helm is to be shifted should be determined by trial and error during those exercises. If a deeply loaded, large beam tanker that is directionally unstable were to follow the classic instructions, she would never return to her original track. If the rudder is shifted when that vessel is 60 degrees from the initial heading, she swings well past the desired point since it takes a great deal of time to check the swing of such a ship. The directionally unstable vessel then turns more rapidly toward the reciprocal heading since her turning rate is so much greater.

A particular VLCC returned to her own wake when the rudder was shifted when she was *35 degrees from her initial course.** By experimen-

*Daniel MacElrevey, *El Paso Arzew Maneuvering Trials.*

tation, this point and the amount of rudder needed to steady the ship were defined so all variables were eliminated from the maneuver. In this case the rudder was shifted hard over to check the swing when the ship's heading was 15 degrees from the reciprocal. Similar tests should be done by the master for his particular ship before the need to maneuver in an actual emergency arises.

A Williamson Turn is defined as follows:

> Put the rudder hard over toward the side on which the person has gone overboard and keep it there until the ship is 35 to 50 degrees from the initial heading. (The precise point for a particular vessel is to be predetermined by trial.) Shift the helm hard over in the opposite direction. Keep the rudder in this position while the ship swings all the way around toward the reciprocal of the ship's heading at the time the Williamson Turn began. When the ship's heading is 10 to 15 degrees from the reciprocal of her initial course, at a point predetermined by trial, shift the helm hard over again so the ship steadies up on the desired reciprocal heading. (Fig. 9-15)

Note that only three movements of the rudder are necessary, and that these changes in helm are at defined points that are not dependent on the watch officer's judgement.

The engine speed is not changed during the Williamson Turn, although the engine is put on standby so the engineer on watch can prepare for maneuvering. By maintaining revolutions, the rate of turn is predictable, the ship returns to the desired point in the minimum time, and speed is still sufficiently reduced. The ship is then stopped using maneuvers described in Chapter 1.*

The man-overboard routine for a particular ship and crew are beyond the scope of this book. It is stressed, though, that regardless of the man-overboard maneuver used, *the person or object in the water must be watched at all times*; this is even more important than the correct execution of the Williamson Turn. If sight is lost of a person in the water it is extremely difficult to locate the person again in any but perfect conditions. By throwing a life ring and other available objects into the water as close to the person or object as possible, with a light, dye marker, smoke flare, or other aid attached, the task of locating that person is greatly simplified. It is important that a light be put into the water at night. There

---

*Brian Hope, *El Paso Consolidated Maneuvering Trials*.

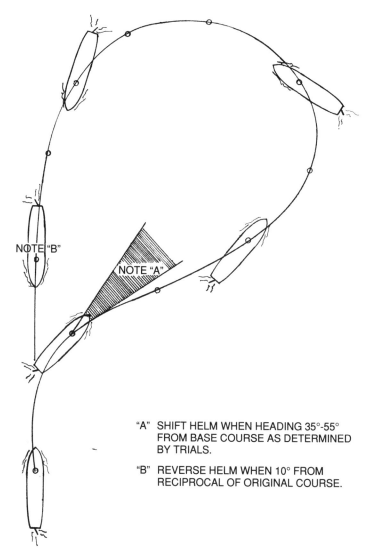

"A" SHIFT HELM WHEN HEADING 35°-55°
     FROM BASE COURSE AS DETERMINED
     BY TRIALS.

"B" REVERSE HELM WHEN 10° FROM
     RECIPROCAL OF ORIGINAL COURSE.

Fig. 9-15. "Three helm order" Williamson Turn.

is no substitute for repeated man-overboard drills, and during drills it becomes obvious just how difficult it is to see a person or object in the water.

Using the described Williamson Turn, a VLCC returned to the
original location in eleven minutes and was making 4 knots when the
reciprocal course was reached, although the engine remained at full
revolutions throughout the maneuver, which began when the ship was

making 19 knots. The ship was easily brought dead in the water at the desired point so that a boat could be launched.*

TWIN-SCREW SHIPS

There is a misconception that twin-screw ships inherently handle better than single-screw ships. This is not necessarily so.

The type of propulsion and the number, configuration, and location of the rudder or rudders affect the maneuverability of twin-screw ships and some twin-screw ships handle more poorly than single-screw ships in routine operating situations. Older turbine driven twin-screw ships with single rudders usually handle like water-soaked logs. Most modern diesel propelled twin-screw vessels with either conventional propellers or controllable pitch propellers, bow and stern thrusters and, in most cases twin rudders, are excellent handling ships.

Today, the twin-screw configuration is found primarily on passenger vessels where it is used both to minimize vibration while operating with higher horsepowers and greater speeds, and to facilitate maneuvering in the smaller harbors increasingly frequented by cruise ships looking for new and less spoiled ports.

Diesel and turbine propelled twin-screw ships exhibit the same engine response characteristics, for the same reasons, described for single-screw diesel and turbine ships in earlier chapters of this book. Diesel ships respond more quickly to engine orders, so the effect of "kicking" a diesel propelled twin-screw ship ahead for a short period of time to move the stern laterally without gaining headway is significantly greater. Because of this faster response, diesel propelled twin-screw ships also react more quickly than turbine ships when a master or pilot *twists* or turns the vessel within her own length using one engine ahead and the other astern or *walks a ship sideways* by using the rudder in opposition to that twisting effect.

Twin-screw, twin-rudder ships are inherently more responsive at slow speeds than ships with single rudders, regardless of engine type, since twin rudders are located aft of the twin propellers and the flow of water from the propellers passes directly over the rudder's surface. Without this flow, the ship's rudder has little effect until the ship gains sufficient headway to create a flow over the surface of the rudder independent of the flow from the propeller.

*Daniel MacElrevey, *El Paso Arzew Maneuvering Trials.*

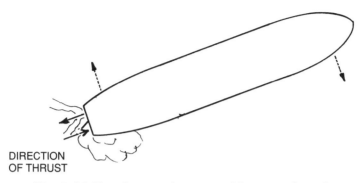

DIRECTION
OF THRUST

Fig. 9-16. Turning a twin-screw ship to starboard.

It should be noted that shiphandlers find twin-screw, single-rudder ships generally steer better at very low speeds when the engines are stopped than when they are coming ahead. When the engines are stopped, the minimal flow past the rudder that does exist is not disturbed by the turning propellers and the inherent directional stability of the spread propellers that counters the turning moment created by the rudder no longer exists. Try stopping the engine if a twin-screw, single-rudder ship with headway is behaving poorly at very slow speeds, instead of working one screw against the other to twist the ship to a new heading.

MANEUVERING TWIN-SCREW SHIPS

If the propeller shafts are well separated, and especially if the ship is diesel rather than turbine propelled, *a twin-screw vessel can be turned in a very small area* by working one propeller ahead and the other astern. By using the port engine ahead and the starboard engine astern, the ship is turned to starboard. By adjusting the revolutions of both the ahead and astern turning engines, increasing and decreasing speeds of either the ahead or astern turning engine as appropriate to cancel any headway or sternway that might develop, the ship can be turned literally within her own length. Because a propeller is more efficient when turning ahead, fewer revolutions are usually needed on the shaft turning in the ahead direction to turn the ship while maintaining its position. (Fig. 9-16)

The twin-screw ship can be moved laterally using the engines in opposing directions ahead and astern to move the stern in the desired direction while a tug or bow thruster is used to move the bow in the same

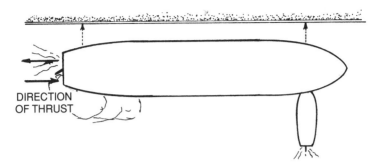

Fig. 9-17. Moving a twin-screw ship laterally.

direction. For example, to move a ship sideways toward a berth, the outboard propeller—the propeller away from the dock or other structure toward which the ship is to be moved—turns astern, while the inboard propeller turns ahead. (Fig. 9-17) The two propellers are then rotating in the same direction (clockwise or counterclockwise) but thrusting in opposite directions (ahead or astern), simultaneously walking and twisting the stern toward the berth without developing any headway or sternway. At the same time, the tug or thruster is used to push the bow toward the berth so the ship moves laterally and bodily toward the berth. Before landing on the pier, the direction of rotation of the propellers is reversed to check the lateral motion of the stern so the ship is laid gently alongside without the assistance of a stern tug.

Obviously, the direction of rotation of the propellers is important during this maneuver. Usually, outboard turning propellers are more effective than inboard turning screws when moving the stern laterally. A ship maneuvering starboard side to a berth uses the starboard screw ahead and the athwartship component of force created by this clockwise turning propeller walks the stern toward the dock. The port screw is used astern and, since the left hand screw turns clockwise when going astern, the athwartship component of that screw's forces also walks the stern to starboard. These forces complement the opposing fore and aft flows from the two propellers, the starboard propeller operating ahead and the port propeller astern in this case, that are minimizing the fore and aft movement of the ship and also driving the stern to starboard toward the dock.

Very good handling, high power, twin-screw, twin-rudder ships such as naval craft, supply and research vessels, and very high powered passenger ships can be *moved laterally without tug assistance or a bow thruster* by using a maneuver that, at first glance, seems to contradict everything said above. Consider again the situation described where the ship is being moved toward a dock on the starboard side. To move these special case, high powered ships with twin rudders toward the dock, the rudder is put hard left to move the stern to starboard, *but* the engines are used in the opposite direction to the example above—in this case of high powered, twin-screw, twin-rudder ships, the port engine turns ahead and the starboard engine turns astern to move the bow to starboard. The rudder and engines are then opposing each other with the net effect of moving the ship laterally to starboard.

Consider the forces at work here. The rudder effect from the wash of the ahead turning engine flowing over the rudders put hard left creates a force that moves the stern to starboard and the bow to port, as is normally the case. At the same time though, the engines are operating in opposing directions, the port engine is turning ahead and the starboard engine astern, in a manner that would normally move the stern to port and the bow to starboard—the opposite direction to that in which the rudder is trying to move the bow and stern. The net effect, in the case of these very responsive ships, is that the rudder overrides the engine forces so the stern moves to starboard, while the rudder and engine forces counter each other to the extent that the bow does not move to port. The ship maintains, or nearly maintains, its heading while the ship moves laterally to the right, toward the dock on the starboard side.

Shiphandlers are again cautioned that this is a special case that is only effective when handling very powerful twin-screw naval vessels, supply boats, and passenger ships with large twin rudders that can develop the strong opposing forces needed to move the ship in this manner. It does not usually work for the common merchant vessel. Most ships would simply respond to the opposing engines, moving the stern toward the side on which the propeller is turning ahead, with the rudder having little effect except to reduce, to some extent, the turning effect created by the engines.

It may be necessary to increase the revolutions of one shaft, when maneuvering twin-screw ships in a shallow channel, to compensate for an unequal flow of water to the screw that is closer to the bank or shoal, or when one propeller is turning in the shallower area through a mud bottom. The twin-screw ship in this situation is more likely to take a sheer than a single-screw ship, due to the proximity of the offset propeller to the shallow area, the restricted flow to the propeller and rudder in the shallower area, plus the usual unbalanced forces experienced around any hull passing close to a bank or shoal. It is also more difficult to recover from that sheer due to the same reduced flow and imbalance of forces. The shiphandler has to take special care and watch more carefully for signs that the ship is taking suction when maneuvering a twin-screw ship in this situation. One such sign would be repeated, large rudder angles as the helmsman tries to maintain a course along a straight reach in the channel. Another sign would be the need for unusually large rudder angles to start a ship swinging in a turn from one reach or straight section of the channel to another.

Another potential problem develops with twin-screw vessels when one engine starts before the other, or when the revolutions are not matched while the ship is steaming. Especially when handling a motor ship, plan to start one engine before the other and plan maneuvers to allow for the resulting ship behavior. Start the second engine after the first is turning ahead and, since you are now set up for the worst case, there will be no problem should either engine not start immediately. This imbalance has less immediate effect while steaming since there is a good flow past the rudder and it is possible to compensate for the sheering that results when an engine doesn't start or the revolutions are not properly matched.

When near a dock or wharf, especially if the berth has a solid face, the inboard screw can be used to advantage to lift the quarter and keep the ship from going alongside prematurely. Put the inboard engine astern when the quarter sets toward the berth. The off center propeller twists the stern away from the berth, and the quickwater moves up the side and lifts the entire ship, just as it does when handling a single-screw ship.

Be especially alert, though, that the ship does not develop any angle to the berth so that the stern is near the stringpiece. Being off center, the propeller is exposed and will certainly be damaged if allowed to touch the face of the berth, which will happen if the stern sets down with any angle. Be sure also that the ship does not develop any angle that places the stern near a bank or shoal, or another ship when going alongside. Lines are easily fouled in the exposed screw and care must be taken when undocking a twin-screw ship that lines are not thrown into the water in the area of the propeller.

An interesting variation that overcomes many of the disadvantages of the twin-screw ship and still allows the use of high horsepower propulsion systems is the triple-screw design used on some recent container-ships. The center shaft is used at maneuvering speeds, allowing the ship to be handled like any other single-screw ship, and the outboard engines and propellers are used only at high speeds when the ship will be in open water where the disadvantages of a twin-screw ship are not important. The best of both worlds is achieved for the naval architect and the mariner.

MOVING UP TO LARGER SHIPS

The handling characteristics of VLCCs and ULCCs are surprisingly similar to those of smaller ships. The *Esso Osaka* tests demonstrated the excellent handling characteristics of very large ships and the conclusions drawn from these tests have been confirmed by pilots and mooring masters who handle these ships. Especially appreciated by masters is the ability of these ships to steer at very low speeds with minimal use of the engine.

Stopping distance changes geometrically as ship size increases, so it is important that the shiphandler think even further ahead when altering speed or maneuvering. These changes are exacerbated by the higher tonnage to horsepower ratios typical of VLCCs. Some typical ratios might be:

$$\text{VLCC} = \frac{380{,}000 \text{ tons displacement}}{40{,}000 \text{ horsepower}} = 9.5$$

$$\text{Bulk Carrier} = \frac{80{,}000 \text{ tons displacement}}{16{,}000 \text{ horsepower}} = 5.0$$

$$\text{Containership} = \frac{65{,}000 \text{ tons displacement}}{60{,}000 \text{ horsepower}} = 1.1$$

Obviously, while the displacement of modern ships is much greater, their horsepower has not increased proportionally. It is no longer practical to rely on engine power alone to stop a ship, but VLCCs and ULCCs can be safely handled in restricted waters by planning ahead and using the techniques previously described to slow a vessel. Too often the nonseafarer makes much of the fact that more searoom is required to *stop* a large ship when, in reality, that ship will usually *alter course* to avoid a close quarters situation, taking advantage of the excellent steering characteristics of VLCCs to compensate for her relatively low backing power.

Fig. 9-18.

The large ship's maneuvering characteristics must be considered when determining moderate speed in restricted visibility or areas of heavy traffic. The COLREGS recognize this fact and stipulate that a ship's maneuverability is a significant factor when determining safe speed at any time. Since the VLCC's most effective response in a close quarters situation is an alteration of course rather than a reduction in speed, the mariner must plan on this alternative when possible. If conditions make a reduction in speed necessary, however, it will be immediately apparent why safe speed for a VLCC in a close quarters situation is significantly less than for smaller ships.

In addition to changes in handling characteristics, a VLCC is affected differently by changes in sea conditions. A smaller ship pounds heavily in a head sea, so the need to reduce speed or alter course in those conditions is obvious. The same head sea will set in the plates at the bow of a VLCC without being felt significantly on the bridge. More deliberate thought is therefore required when handling the larger ship, since it is not possible to conn her in a seaway by feel alone. Because of increased mass and length the panting and slamming stresses as the ship pounds in a head sea are actually much greater, even though the pounding itself may be hardly felt. (Fig. 9-18)

The hogging, sagging, and wracking stresses that are not usually considered at sea aboard smaller ships now become important. A VLCC works dramatically in a seaway as she alternately hangs suspended between two crests at her ends and then is supported by the sea amidship while her ends fall into the trough. Close attention to bending moments and sheer stresses is, of course, required while loading a VLCC, and at sea the mariner aboard a VLCC must reduce speed and/or alter course to reduce severe hogging and sagging stresses that are rarely considered with smaller ships. The mariner must recognize that the same sea state that damages a smaller ship also damages a VLCC, and reduce speed or alter course accordingly to ease the vessel even when these stresses are not obvious from her motion.

Instruments are being tested that may in the future give mariners more absolute information about the forces of the sea acting on a hull, but presently experience is the best guide for the master or deck officer. Sea sense, and the mariner's appreciation of the environment gained over the years spent at sea, become extremely important when making qualitative judgments such as when to ease a VLCC's motion in a seaway.

Shallow water effects are felt as the ship nears land or shoal and, since the VLCC's draft is often twice that of the average ship, these effects are felt sooner and in deeper water. The changes in the ship's directional stability, the larger diameter of her turning circle, and the increased twisting effect are all felt in water that the mariner aboard smaller ships considered open and deep.

The COLREGS define (Rule 3.h.) a vessel as being "constrained by her draft" when, because of her draft in relation to the available depth of water, she "is severely restricted in her ability to deviate from the course she is following." This should be interpreted to include not only restrictions on her track resulting from having to keep sufficient water under her keel to avoid grounding, but also *restrictions due to shallow water effects* which degrade the ship's maneuvering capabilities. There is some uncertainty whether this is the present intent but such interpretation is proper and consistent with today's understanding of hydrodynamics and ship behavior.

In port, the mass and hull form of the VLCC becomes more significant; bottom effects increase as previously discussed, while the ship's reaction time when correcting for the results of such effects is significantly longer. The shiphandler must plan the passage and maneuvers, must think ahead of the ship, with greater attention to these effects. It is stressed though, that there are no mysteries; very large ships obey the same laws of hydrodynamics as other ships and the differences in behavior are differences in magnitude, not character.

Forward speed of a VLCC is more difficult to judge not only because of the greater height of eye from which the shiphandler works, but also due to the subtle differences between proper and improper speeds through the water with a ship of such mass. If the mariner is handicapped by lack of proper instrumentation, there is no option but to err on the safe side when moving a VLCC and the ship must progress at very slow speeds. When estimating safe speed of approach remember that a VLCC moving at less than 2 knots still requires more than a ship length to stop. Fitting large ships with state-of-the-art instrumentation makes it possible to move such ships more expediently as well as more safely.

Due to the greater mass, some adjustment in technique is required:

1. Tugs are less effective.
2. It is impractical to warp a VLCC alongside using ship's lines only.
3. A ship must be stopped further off the pier and pushed alongside due to the need to land flat on the stringpiece or clusters.
4. Minimum lateral speed is important if the ship is to land without damage.
5. Doppler speed indicators showing lateral motion as well as ahead and astern speed are essential if the VLCC is to be docked expeditiously.

The ship must come alongside flat so the forces generated as the ship lands are distributed throughout the length of the midbody and are absorbed by the maximum number of frames. The vessel's great length makes this more difficult, perspective causing the bow to appear much closer to the dock than the stern when actually the two ends are equidistant from the stringpiece. (Fig. 9-19) *Observe the rate of closing* forward and aft, rather than only the apparent distance off, since the relative distances forward and aft will appear to decrease at the same rate, even though the distances themselves do not appear equal when the ship is parallel to the berth.

When the mariner steps aboard a VLCC for the first time there is often some trepidation about handling this different ship. The differ-

Fig. 9-19. Allow for the "railroad track" effect when estimating a VLCC's distance off a berth.

ences are really only of scale and timing—ship behavior is no different and the mariner will quickly adjust work habits to these differences in magnitude. No new skills are required, only greater attention to the advanced planning needed to stay ahead of the ship and greater patience while waiting for her to respond. With a good professional background, a competent shiphandler can handle a VLCC as well as any other type of ship. Too much is made today of qualifying a pilot for every different type of ship that shows up at a pilot station, when it is general experience gained over several years of doing gradually more demanding work that prepares a shiphandler for a particular task, not two hours of observation time aboard a "new" class of ship.

REPLENISHMENT AT SEA

A small but significant number of ships engage in replenishment operations at sea and this number can be expected to increase if the trend toward greater use of merchant ships to support naval operations continues. Transfer by helicopter will be considered separately and only ship-to-ship transfer of equipment, oil, and stores will be considered herein.

For clarity, the ship that maintains course and speed during the maneuver is designated the "large ship," because this ship is usually the physically larger of the two vessels involved. The second vessel is the "maneuvering ship."

Initial planning between the two vessels is done by radio. A base course and speed is determined to put the sea two points on the bow of the "large vessel" that will be away from the operation, to make a lee and minimize rolling and yawing. The steering gear must be tested and inspected carefully prior to commencement of the operation, and a seaman trained in shifting from bridge to local trick wheel steering must be stationed in the steering gear flat. The "A" frame or other rig is set up and all accessory gear is laid out. Sufficient crewmembers are assigned to the deck and bridge, and a good helmsman—preferably experienced in steering during ship-to-ship transfer operations—is assigned to the wheel.

Usually the larger, or, in the case of naval vessels, the supplying merchant ship, maintains the base course and speed throughout the evolution, and all maneuvering is done by the approaching ship. In a heavy sea, it may be prudent to have the larger ship maintain course and speed, and put the sea in the prescribed position, no matter which ship is doing the supplying, to assure the best lee for the transfer operation.

When within ½ mile of the large or steadied up vessel, the maneuvering ship comes to a heading that parallels the large ship's wake. Speed is adjusted to be about 3 to 5 knots greater than the speed of the large ship and the approach is begun. Note that more speed is appropriate for this operation than for offshore lightering, when the maneuvering ship actually goes alongside the large ship. There is interaction between ships throughout the maneuver, but it is greatest as the bow of the maneuvering ship passes the larger ship's quarter. This "danger zone" (Fig. 9-20) should be passed through before the speed of the maneuvering ship is reduced to the final base speed to minimize the passage and assure good rudder control while in it. High powered naval vessels will often approach at much higher speeds and back down just before coming abeam, but this is not a prudent approach when two merchant ships are involved. It is not practical for merchant ships to back down since the effect on steering will be significant and their backing power is not sufficient to slow a ship from the higher speeds used by the handier naval vessels. A lower powered merchant ship continues at a speed greater than that of the steadied up ship until past the danger zone and then reduces engine speed and slowly loses headway until she is moving at the base speed.

One hundred feet is generally a proper separation distance between ships, although some rigs used for transfer require less separation. Don't allow the ships to be pulled together by constant tension winches during the transfer operation. The maneuvering ship heads a few degrees away from the larger ship to compensate for the pull of these winches and also for the suction effect between the two moving ships.

When in position abeam, the ships pass a *distance line* forward, marked at intervals to assist in maintaining the required separation distance, and then pass the highline and other rigging required for the replenishment operation. Course is adjusted by giving the helmsman headings to steer rather than using helm orders, to assure that all changes are minimal so the ships don't develop any radical swing while alongside. The continued intership attraction while in this position, caused by the reduced pressure as the water flows between the two ships, presents no problem as long as the specified distance and slight angle is maintained between the ships. If the ships get closer to one another they could be drawn together. The mariner can do little to counter intership suction if the two ships are allowed to get too close, since this

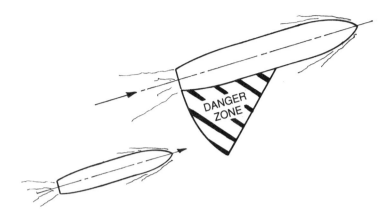

Fig. 9-20. Area to be avoided during approach.

precludes the maneuvering ship getting sufficient angle away from the larger ship to overcome the suction.

While alongside, the maneuvering ship adjusts speed a few revolutions at a time to match her speed with that of the larger ship. Do not make any large changes in revolutions (such as would result from using the telegraph to change speeds). Use abeam bearings and watch the distance line to maintain the ship's position during the transfer.

To depart, open the angle at the bow slightly and let the maneuvering ship come slowly away from the larger ship, *increasing revolutions only enough to overcome any decrease in speed due to the change in heading and rudder*. Do not pass ahead of the latter ship since any machinery failure would result in almost certain collision as the departing ship veers across the other ship's bow. Don't increase ship's speed through the water until well clear of the larger ship, as this increases the inter-ship suction.

HELICOPTER OPERATIONS

It used to be that a helicopter was used only for emergency evacuation of a sick or injured crewmember. This task was accomplished by hovering over the ship and lowering a litter to the deck. Increasingly, helicopters are being used for crew changes and storing of VLCCs and ULCCs enroute from port to port: the helicopter lands on the ship's deck to make the necessary transfer of stores and crew.

In either case, it is preferable to put the ship on a heading and adjust speed to create a 15 to 25 knot *relative wind* on one bow. This gives the helicopter a headwind, minimizes the turbulence over the deck that would be created by the ship's superstructure if the wind is put dead ahead, and carries the stack gases to one side away from the approaching helicopter. It is stressed that it is the relative wind that is important and a maneuvering board plot should be done if necessary to find the heading that produces the desired relative wind direction and force. Often the necessary heading is not obvious, especially if the true wind is stronger than the desired 25 knots.

Communication should be established with the helicopter on VHF as soon as practical so maneuvers can be agreed upon. The helicopter pilot may recommend course and speed changes. When the ship is rolling more than a few degrees, and the helicopter is to land on deck for the transfer, the master must warn the helicopter off since it is dangerous to land under such conditions. If the helicopter is only to hover, this is not a problem.

Lower the dipole antenna and remove any other obstructions prior to the helicopter's arrival so they do not foul the helicopter's rotor blades during the operation. An unobstructed deck area must be provided, clearly marked with the internationally recognized letter "H" surrounded by a circle to designate the clear area. Have the engine ready to maneuver in case any problems develop during the operation. Hoist a flag forward and another on the flying bridge so the pilot can judge the wind direction and speed during the operation. Light the ship well so all obstructions and the landing area are clearly visible, but use lights shining forward so they don't blind the pilot as he approaches.

Do not touch a basket or litter when it is lowered. Allow the basket to land on deck so the static charge is discharged before anyone handles it. While putting a man or gear into the basket or litter do not secure it to the ship in any way.

CHAPTER TEN

TRAINING

> ... the redeeming and ideal aspect of this breadwinning
> is the attainment and preservation of the highest
> possible skill... It is made up of accumulated tradition,
> kept alive by individual pride, rendered exact by
> professional opinion, and, like the higher arts, it is
> spurred on and sustained by discriminating praise.
>   That is why the attainment of proficiency, the
> pushing of your skill with attention to the most delicate
> shades of excellence, is a matter of vital concern.
> —Joseph Conrad
> *The Mirror of the Sea*

Like other professionals, the novice seaman must learn new concepts, skills, laws, and practices; unlike other professionals, though, a seaman must apply what is learned in a new environment, and become so adept at living and working in that environment that once-alien reactions become intuitive—the mariner develops "sea sense." Training for a maritime career is therefore of greater depth than in many other professions, begins at a more basic level, and must be continued throughout a mariner's career. It is both formal through various private, union, and governmental facilities, and informal through continuous self-study and contact with shipmates, be they peers or senior officers.

Formal training receives the most attention and is handled well in most cases. Equally important informal training unfortunately gets less attention, yet it is through this type of training that a seaman learns priorities and adjusts theory to reality.

Only rudimentary training in shiphandling and piloting is provided at the maritime academies. Significant training in this area begins aboard ship and is received from several sources including:

1. Masters and senior officers, primarily covering at-sea shiphandling and anticollision maneuvering, and maneuvering at the pilot station or anchorage.

2. Pilots and docking masters. Few mariners take the initiative required to tap this source of training, which is unfortunate since pilots are proud of their skills and generally willing to share much information. In reality, pilots primarily train other pilots.
3. Passive observation of shiphandlers at work, a laudable but relatively unproductive exercise similar to learning heart surgery by watching a transplant operation on television.
4. Study of textbooks and video training material, both personal and company supplied.
5. Simulator based training programs and scale model basin training facilities, where a mariner or pilot can obtain a good grasp of shiphandling and bridge operating procedures in both routine and emergency situations.

ON-BOARD TRAINING OF SHIP'S OFFICERS

Every officer is serving aboard a multimillion dollar training aid. The ship, and the company and personal material aboard her, are available to the mariner; it is in the master's and company's interest to encourage use of that training aid. Training opportunities are limited only by master's imagination and initiative, and include:

1. Bridge demonstrations and critiques of situations that arise and actions taken in those situations.
2. Informal coffeetime discussions of professional subjects including shiphandling at sea and in port.
3. Planned training sessions covering anchoring, stopping a ship, conning techniques, making a lee for a pilot, Williamson Turns and man-overboard exercises, and other appropriate shiphandling skills.

Training should start at the most basic level. Masters must insist that deck officers conn the ship to new headings at sea, rather than just giving the helmsman a new course to steer, so that they develop a feel for the ship and the amount of rudder needed to handle her. Deck officers should handle the ship when anchoring or picking up the pilot, while the master observes and corrects the work as necessary. Every mate must be prepared for the duties of the next higher position, especially the chief mate who must do as much shiphandling as possible. A pro-

Fig. 10-1. "Only training and 'hands-on' experience take the mystery out of shiphandling."

motion is not an opportunity to start training. It is a recognition of skills already possessed.

Use all available time in the ship's schedule to train the ship's officers, using the techniques described for instruction in previous chapters. Select scenarios that are commonly encountered and recreate them in an anchorage or open roadstead while waiting for a pilot or berth, allowing each officer to handle the ship and complete the planned maneuver. When routinely maneuvering the ship, explain to the deck officers what you are doing and why—action taken in a particular situation and the reasons for that action are not obvious to the less experienced officers unless you get them involved. Point out how the ship backs into the wind or the bow falls off to starboard as the engine goes astern, since seeing this action once makes a more lasting impression than reading about it a dozen times.

Because of inexperience, too many deck officers suffer from the "don't touch" syndrome. The less experienced officer is not initially comfortable with bridge equipment, so there is a very real hesitancy to use it. It is important that these officers overcome this hesitancy or they can never become proficient. If shipboard training accomplishes nothing else it is irreplaceable if the officer becomes more willing to take action.

Hold a "hands-on" session and encourage each officer to use the bridge equipment—insist that they repeatedly use the telegraph, whistle, put the rudder hard over (yes, at sea speed. . . it will *not* damage anything). Explain that each officer is just to grab on and use the gear repeatedly and to its maximum, then stand back. Go ahead Mate, use the whistle . . . sound it again . . . put the rudder hard over . . . put the engine astern, ahead, astern again. Now that mate has started to be a useful and competent deck officer. Few drills will ever be more productive than these initial hands-on sessions.

There is no magic to shiphandling, just experience, good sense, and confidence in one's skills, and no one can become proficient until they are totally comfortable using bridge equipment and making the ship respond to their demands.

A new 1,000-foot ship went aground a few years ago while maneuvering to avoid fishing craft in the straits of Gibraltar. During the ensuing investigation the master was asked why he repeatedly altered course to avoid one vessel after another rather than slowing or stopping the ship. He replied that he wanted to go astern but hesitated because he didn't feel he could back the ship at the speed she was making without losing control. He wasn't sure how his ship would behave if the telegraph was put astern! A beautiful, new ship would not have settled on the rocks if a short, simple hands-on session had been held aboard ship at some time during the master's twenty years at sea.

Most ships have a video recorder on board, and several good training films on all maritime subjects including shiphandling and ship behavior are available for lease. Maritime academies and union school libraries maintain source lists for such material, which can be obtained by a telephone call if you do not already have addresses of suppliers. Companies leasing or selling these films also advertise in maritime publications, such as the excellent *Safety at Sea* and *Professional Mariner* magazines, which should also be put aboard ship as training material. Obtain training films for use throughout the fleet, in conjunction with training sessions and maneuvers, to get the maximum benefit from an on-board training program.

Some masters combine fire and emergency drills with training sessions, and hold the sessions prior to each drill. By gathering officers and crew in the lounge and discussing a particular subject over coffee (the subject usually being complimentary to the drill although this is not required), the crew and officers develop greater interest in drills and training in general. The crew is soon requesting that specific subjects be discussed and contributing to the discussions. Most of the crew is involved and interested in shiphandling and it should be included in this training program.

Distribute educational material obtained from professional publications to all on board, licensed and unlicensed; your interest is contagious and your satisfaction great.

ON-BOARD TRAINING OF PILOTS

Even with modern simulation, there is still no better, more effective training for apprentice pilots than "hands-on" experience aboard ship. It has become increasingly difficult for ship's officers to develop shiphandling skills aboard larger, fast-turnaround ships with ever smaller crews, but pilots, by the very nature of their work, still have daily access to the ultimate training tool, the ship.

Unfortunately, there is presently a tendency to downgrade the importance of such training in favor of written tests and licensing, classroom time, standardization of training requirements, and simulator training. This only reflects a lack of understanding of piloting since the state of the art of other teaching systems simply has not reached the level of sophistication required to replace shipboard experience.

Apprentice pilots must make full use of the ship, just as ship's officers must use every opportunity to gain information on shiphandling from a pilot. A great deal of money is being spent for pilot association-owned, shore-based training facilities, which is commendable, but the ship itself is not being fully utilized as a training aid. Use the various types of equipment, including radars, *in every possible mode*, to keep skills current. Too many pilots put the radar in the "head up" presentation as soon as they get to the bridge (even before getting a cup of coffee!) because that is the only presentation with which they are comfortable. You can't always effectively watch the relative motion of other ships when the radar is used in the head up presentation and the targets are changing their location on the PPI as you maneuver, yet when feeling your way up a narrow channel in the fog there is less chance of error when operating in the head up mode. There is a proper time for each mode and the ship is a laboratory in which to experiment.

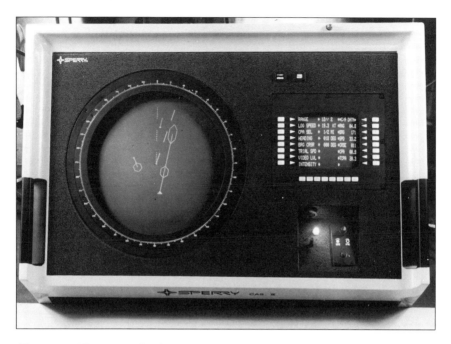

Fig. 10-2. Use new ship's equipment as a training aid continuously to
update shipboard skills.

Question the ship's officers about any new gear found aboard ship.
This is their field of expertise and they are trained in the use of such
equipment. Exchange your knowledge of shiphandling for information
about new ship's equipment.

Work with LORAN-C, ARPA satellite navigation, modern fathome-
ters, and Doppler equipment, and understand the latest types of steering gear so you know them as well as the ship's officers. Overnavigate,
even though the last thing you might need is a fix as you make your
thousandth trip up the river; it sharpens your skills and may save you
from having to rely on a less than competent mate when the fog sets in
on a strange ship.

When training an apprentice *create* opportunities to use tugs or an
anchor in less common situations and insist that the apprentices occasionally navigate by radar on clear days. Require multiple trips under
difficult conditions. Insist that an apprentice make a large number of
night passages and trips on difficult ships to give the broadest possible
base of experience and assure the learning of good work habits. A specific
pilot in the association should be responsible for training, and continu-

Fig. 10-3. "Captain Buck is in charge of pilot training and takes the job very seriously."

ally review and update training requirements to reflect the changes in ship types and local conditions. Training, be it for the ship's officer or the pilot, is too important to be left to happenstance.

There is a great deal of political pressure from within the industry to standardize and formalize pilot training and have pilots work only under a federal license. It is obvious to the working pilot that conditions are too different in each port to adopt standard requirements—that is the very reason that pilotage services are needed as ships move from port to port. There is, however, some basis for criticism at present as some pilot associations have no formal training program, and each pilot follows an informal path to qualify for his various licenses. Other associations have formal training, strictly enforced standards that usually far exceed any statutory requirements, and a system of peer evaluation that again is often more effective than any federally administered licensing scheme. *In self defense* it is time that all pilot associations establish formal training programs and definite standards to qualify an apprentice to serve as full pilot. If the associations don't do this, others will, and the piloting profession and the industry will suffer for it.

SHIPHANDLING SIMULATORS

Teachers have used books, lectures, and written tests to teach the theory of shiphandling and other maritime skills for generations. Countless seafarers learned their trade through this traditional instruction and then went directly aboard ship to apply their classroom knowledge in the real world where most did an excellent job in a profession where skill development was motivated primarily by tradition and professional pride.

This training served the industry well even though it failed to address some serious gaps between theory and application that the mariner was forced to fill by trial and error at sea. These gaps were at times sizable, as most mates standing their first bridge watch alone will attest. Who forgets that first watch when, after dropping the pilot and putting the ship on course to her next port, the master stepped below leaving the new third mate, alone and untested, to deal with navigation and traffic. The young mate, who had read all the books and mastered countless exams quickly learned, during the next few proud but nerve-wracking hours, that a sometimes horrifying gap exists between theory and application. Most of us survive to serve without incident through a career stretching for years and hundreds of thousands of miles at sea, but there is no denying we all would have benefited from some form of training that more closely resembled that first watch at sea or first encounter with some new situation.

With simulation, mates, masters, and apprentice pilots have an opportunity to apply theory to real world situations without being aboard ship, and simulator-based instruction is now part of training in shiphandling and bridge operations at the U.S. Merchant Marine Academy, the state academies, the union schools, private training facilities, and several simulator facilities worldwide.

THE RULES OF THREES

An overview of simulation training as it impacts on shiphandling is presented in this chapter and the practice maneuvers in the book's last pages can be used as part of a simulator-based shiphandling program. More detailed information about a curriculum and teaching techniques are outside the scope of this text and readers should consult specialized texts (see the Bibliography), such as Chapter 8 of *Watchstanding Guide for the Merchant Officer,* for a more detailed discussion on this rapidly developing field. Complete reports of studies and guidelines for simula-

tor-based programs have been produced at the CAORF facility at Kings
Point and are available for review.

Simulator training follows two basic Rules of Threes:

> There are *three components* to a good simulator program—the
> simulator, the instructor, and the curriculum.

> There are *three steps* to effective simulator training—classroom
> presentation of theory in a detailed briefing session, the train-
> ing exercises on the simulator, and an all-important debriefing
> session where performance is reviewed and critiqued.

Together, the three components and the three steps form a teaching
process that changes the very nature of instruction for several facets of
the work done by shipmasters, deck officers, and pilots as well as for
operating tasks performed by professionals in other demanding positions, such as airline pilots and power plant operators.

Simulators are powerful tools for training in the very important
operational work done on the ship's bridge and in the engine room, but
simulation is not a panacea. Mariners are generalists in an era of special-
ization and simulator-based instruction is not, at least at this time, useful
for teaching every type of work which deck officers routinely perform.

SIMULATORS AS INNOVATIVE TRAINING AIDS

Simulators fill a long recognized gap between classroom instruction and
hands-on application of many operating skills including shiphandling,
rules of the road, radar, navigation, watchkeeping and bridge procedures, and bridge resource management. For the first time, with simulation, dynamic real world situations can be created in a controlled
classroom environment where ship's officers and pilots can:

1. *Practice* new techniques and skills with an instructor and peers.
2. *Transfer theory* to real world situations in a classroom environment.
3. Deal with multiple problems *concurrently* rather than sequentially.
4. Learn to *prioritize* those multiple tasks under the same high
   stress, changing conditions faced in actual shipboard operations.

Shiphandling and many other facets of the merchant mariner's and
pilot's work are operating skills. The principles can be learned from
books and lectures, but proficiency comes through practice. Before simu-

lation, there was no way to complete the learning process without actually going aboard ship and working at the job. As stated elsewhere in this text, one does not learn to play the piano by reading about it, and professionals doing operational work do not learn their craft through study and classroom instruction alone. Mariners master their craft by doing it aboard ship but, with simulation, it is now possible to at least practice fundamentals, correct poor work habits, develop procedures, and demonstrate basic proficiency before actually going aboard ship.

This is a major advancement in maritime training. Textbook instruction can be put into practice and, at least as important, skills can be applied in real world situations where several tasks are done simultaneously, not one at a time. Before simulation, shipboard skills were discussed and tested *sequentially,* because there is no way to address several tasks simultaneously on paper or to learn the all-important art of *prioritizing* work. In real life, deck officers and pilots deal with multiple operating tasks *simultaneously* and, through practice, they learn to prioritize instinctively and, most importantly, to shift priorities, in changing routine and emergency situations.

Simulators are bringing a new dynamic into the classroom where experienced mariners or pilots teach skills using books and lectures with the added dimension of real time experience to *actually teach operating skills rather than just explain them*.

TYPES OF SIMULATORS

There are two basic types of simulators—model-based simulators in which pilots and deck officers ride in large scale models while learning and practicing shiphandling, and computer-based simulators using a bridge mock-up and a computer-driven presentation. Computer-based simulators use either an image of the selected geographic area generated completely by the computer with the ship's behavior programmed as an overlay, or a computer-generated image together with points of light projected on that image. Each has advantages and disadvantages and both types, properly operated, are very effective training tools.

SCALE MODEL-BASED SIMULATORS

Scale model-based simulators at facilities in Grenoble, France; the Southampton Institute in the United Kingdom; and the presently closed United States Navy school in Little Creek, Virginia, use large scale models of various ship types to simulate actual ships and shiphandling situ-

Fig. 10-4. A typical scale training model with riding positions for
the instructor and student. Courtesy the Southampton Institute,
Maritime Operations Center. Photo by Steve Park.

ations. The student and shiphandler/instructor ride in the models (Fig.
10-4) on relatively large, specially designed lakes laid out with modeled
channels, docks, locks, canals, mooring buoys, single-point moorings,
and anchorages to recreate a wide range of shiphandling activities.

The model-based simulator gives a dynamic presentation of bottom
and bank effects, wind and sea conditions, and intership effects created
as two ships pass. Scenarios are created to provide a wide range of
shiphandling experiences. (Fig. 10-5) The ship models respond to external wind and current and behave like an actual ship when backed and
turned. Anchor work is practiced in the model-based simulator under

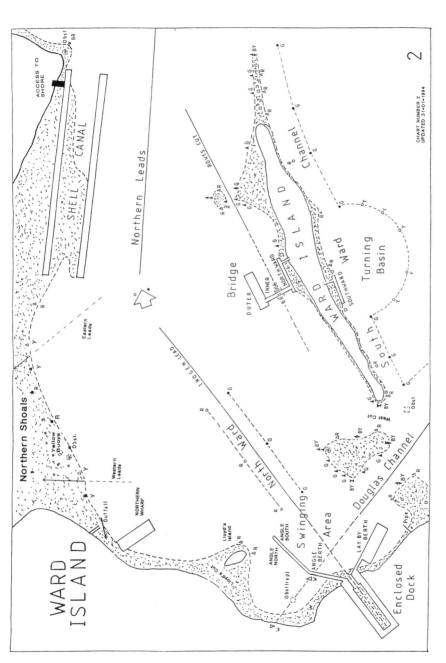

Fig. 10-5. A model-based simulator lake laid out with channels, berths, and other operating areas for several types of training exercises. Courtesy the Southampton Institute, Maritime Operations Center.

normal and emergency situations in a very realistic environment where a real, albeit small, vessel is maneuvered using an actual anchor. These are real floating craft in real water behaving according to the laws of hydrodynamics, so the effect experienced by shiphandlers is correct even though it is scaled down.

Because the simulation is scaled down, neither the external effects nor ship behavior can be in "real time." There is some difference of opinion among experienced shiphandlers who have worked with both computer-driven and model-based simulators as to whether this scaled behavior significantly decreases the effectiveness of this training.

SCALE—IS IT IMPORTANT?

Shiphandlers speak of "having a feel" for a ship—being able to take the correct action at the correct time based on an almost instinctive sense of a particular ship's behavior. The ability to anticipate ship response at this level is gained by actually handling similar ships for several years. It would appear, therefore, that the lack of real time response would be a major disadvantage to any system that is being used to teach shiphandling. In fact, most ship's officers and pilots insist they quickly adjust to this scaled time, so it does not seem to degrade training. Further, any disadvantage that might exist is partially offset by the fact that many effects and situations can be simulated, and actually felt, in a dynamic, scaled down vessel moving through the water, that cannot be recreated as effectively using present computer-driven equipment. There seems to be general agreement, especially among experienced pilots and shiphandlers who have actually spent time on both types of simulators, that scale does not degrade the effectiveness of scale model simulators as learning tools. Computer-driven and scale model simulators each offer advantages and, generally, the more experienced shiphandlers seem to have a greater appreciation of scale-model training.

COMPUTER-BASED SIMULATORS

Computer-based full and part task simulators are proliferating at maritime schools, union schools, and private training facilities world-wide as ship bridge simulation becomes an affordable and effective marine training tool. This growth of marine simulation, and particularly ship bridge simulation, is very much technologically driven as equipment develops to fill a long known need for a means to teach operating

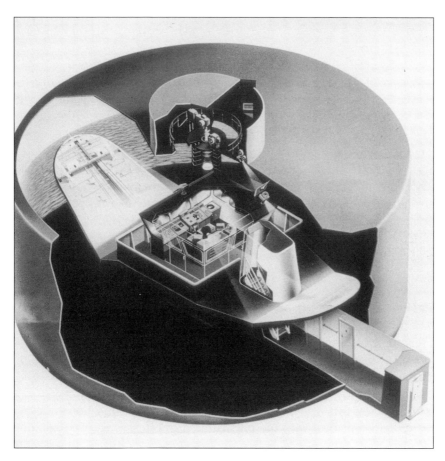

Fig. 10-6. The computer-driven simulator used at the Maritime
Institute of Technology and Graduate Studies showing their unique
projection system. Courtesy International Organization of Masters,
Mates and Pilots.

techniques that, before simulation, could not be taught in a classroom.
(Fig. 10-6) Smaller, faster desktop and mini-computers with greater
memory capacity have made it technically and financially practical to
build equipment that simulates complex hydrodynamic models moving
over realistic visual scenes at a reasonable cost. Early simulation with
rather basic, cartoonlike presentations and simplistic ship models have
evolved into detailed and visually accurate scenes with complex models
and multiple meeting and crossing vessels. Limited ahead-view only
screens have evolved into 240- to 360-degree presentations that usually

provide a view aft so the computer-driven simulation is useful for pilots and deck officers.

There are *two basic levels of computer simulators*, defined by completeness of the simulation and purposes served. *Part task simulators* present a limited number of features, typically one or two systems, and are intended for training in a specific task such as radar, rules of the road, ARPA, or cargo system training, where it is not necessary to use a more expensive, complex full bridge simulation. *Full task simulators,* also referred to as full mission bridge simulators, present a complete environment, such as a complete engine control room or a full ship's bridge complete with navigation equipment, radar, steering stand, communications equipment, engine control, and all the other systems that would be present in a modern wheelhouse. A full task or full mission simulator is designed to create a realistic environment in which the ship's officer or pilot can train and practice the same full range of tasks in a real-time scenario that they would experience aboard ship in routine and emergency bridge watch situations.

Full task simulators, regardless of type and builder, share a common background. All begin with a mathematical model developed from data collected in shallow water tests and sea trials of the class and type of ship being simulated. The hydrodynamicist supplies the ship data to programmers who create a visual presentation that moves across a set of screens recreating vessel motion and the hydrodynamic and environmental effects suitable to the particular training session, limited only by available computer memory and speed. Experienced pilots then spend many hours working with the programmer and hydrodynamicist tailoring the model, modifying the data-based presentation until it "feels" to the shiphandler like the class of ship being modeled. This modification or tailoring of models is controversial and obviously unscientific but, with current simulators and the maneuvering data available to the hydrodynamicist, it seems necessary to blend the experienced mariner's intuitive evaluation with the theoretical model to develop a sufficiently accurate simulation.

Simulators have a mock-up of a generic ship's bridge with some type of front or rear projection visible forward of the bridge upon which the visual scene and the ship's deck are either projected or developed. (Figs. 10-7 and 10-8) It is generally accepted that the simulator's bridge should recreate, to the maximum extent possible, the actual shipboard environment. Most facilities include a chart room, ship's passageways, and the

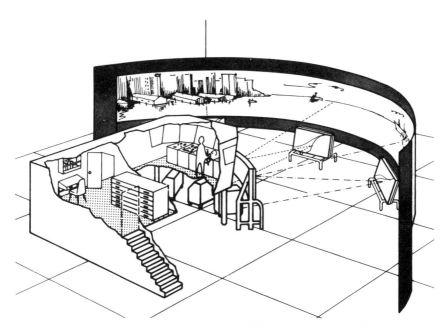

Fig. 10-7. Cutaway drawing showing MarineSafety shiphandling simulator's bridge, chartroom, and wheelhouse, and the "gaming area" projected on 12-by-10 curved screen by three projectors and mirror system under the bridge.

usual navigation equipment, reference books, and instruments found on a typical ship's bridge. The visual presentation should present at least a 240-degree field of visibility, since shiphandlers depend as much on a view aft, or at least abaft the beam, as they do on the view ahead when moving ships in pilot waters and close quarters situations. (Fig. 10-8) A greater arc of visibility is desirable when working in very close quarters situations, and a view astern is now available in a few simulators for training in docking and undocking.

Various ship types are simulated. Depending on the work to be done, the mathematical ship model might be specific, such as when doing port research or training for a new class of ship, or it might only simulate an average ship of a particular size or type for less specific instruction in bridge operations and general shiphandling. Effects inherent to the ship, including steering characteristics, engine response ahead and astern, effects of backing, twisting, trim, draft, and directional stability or instability are all included in the ship's program. Shallow water effects,

Fig. 10-8. Experienced mariners get deeply involved in problems when working on a real time simulator. Courtesy MarineSafety International.

the hydrodynamics of bank and intership action, and external forces such as tugs, wind, and current effects which change as the ship type and loading conditions are altered, are overlaid on that ship's program. The ship and the forces affecting it are overlaid on a representation of the port or open water maneuvering area that includes the visual cues and prominent features used by the shiphandler maneuvering in the port. Conditions of restricted visibility, day and night scenes, the effects of wind forces on water surface, buoy and navigational aids, and the sounds of whistles and buoys are included in the simulation.

Increased computer power makes it possible to simulate more complete vessel behavior in given wind and current conditions and in response to changing bank effects as a ship proceeds along a channel. Intership effects between passing ships are presented with reasonable accuracy although computer-driven simulation is waiting for the next generation of computers to be able to handle the complex calculations needed to reproduce fully the interaction of two ships passing. The most modern simulators are also able to simulate at least the basic effects of dragging and steaming on anchors and the use of an anchor in emergency situations.

The technique used to actually generate this visual presentation is of more importance to the simulator operator than to the student. The simulator user is more interested in:

1. The *accuracy* of the mathematical ship model over a full range of maneuvers ahead and astern.
2. The detail or *fidelity* of the visual presentation.
3. The arc of visibility presented.
4. The accuracy with which the external forces are recreated to simulate the effects of wind, current, bank and shallow water effects, intership action, and the effects of tugs and anchors.
5. The degree to which the simulator recreates the bridge environment.

There is some debate concerning the need for highly specific mathematical ship models and detailed visual scenes, and the impact of added detail on the effectiveness of the simulator as a teaching tool. Academics tend to feel detail is not as important as application while mariners, the users, generally contend that realism is important to make the simulation believable but, as computer power increases and cost declines, the debate will probably become moot. Simulators will provide increasingly accurate reproductions of the ship and the environment in which she operates simply because technology make it possible to do so at ever lower costs.

There are still some areas that are *not* accurately presented through simulation, including the intership effects of two vessels meeting and passing in shallow water and the use of anchors for routine and emergency maneuvers.

Presently, the effects of two ships meeting and passing in shallow water are distorted since the equations and speed of calculation needed to simulate precisely those effects between two ships simultaneously are beyond the computational capabilities of most computers now available at an acceptable cost. In practice, this does not detract significantly from the simulation since the presentation is reasonably close to actual conditions, so that technique, if not the full effect of passing ships, can be practiced. Given the rate at which computer speed and memory capacity is developing, there is little doubt that the next generation of simulators will reproduce those effects accurately.

On the other hand, the effects of dragging and maneuvering on one or two anchors are poorly simulated at best. This is probably the case because programmers and design engineers don't appreciate the important role anchors play in emergency and routine shiphandling and the lack of sufficient real data that can be used for programming. The anchor looks to them like a big parking brake. This shortcoming is significant because the anchor is the primary tool in emergency situations when power or steering is lost and, since simulators are touted as tools for teaching emergency maneuvers, the effects of the anchor must be simulated accurately. The most recent generation of simulators seems capable of doing this to a limited degree, but simulators will not reach their full potential as tools for emergency training until the effects of dragging and working with anchors is fully and accurately documented and simulated.

COMPARISON OF MODEL AND COMPUTER SIMULATORS

There are some advantages and disadvantages to both model- and computer-based simulators, independent of the operational differences between the two types.

Model-based simulators need several acres of natural or man-made lake, so that there are limitations to where this type of facility can be located. A suitable natural or man-made lake and a few acres of open land are needed for the facilities, so the model facility may have to be established in an inconvenient, and possibly expensive, location. Computer-driven simulators can be set up literally anywhere without regard to proximity to water or large areas of open land since only a few reasonably sized rooms are needed for the equipment and bridge mock-up. The facility can be built in a convenient, low cost location although the site cost consideration is at least partially offset by the high cost of purchasing, maintaining, and upgrading the computer-driven simulator and its software.

Model simulators are affected by weather, which can significantly reduce the time this type of simulator is usable. This can be a significant disadvantage in areas with severe winters and a high percentage of rainy days. Computer facilities can be used for training year round independent of weather conditions, although some mariners claim the real life environment of model-based simulators adds to the learning experience.

The very low teacher to student ratio inherent in a model-based simulator, where the instructor rides with only one or two mariners for several days, makes this type of instruction expensive. The teacher to student ratio is only marginally better for computer simulators, so neither type of simulator has a significant advantage in this regard. It seems then that there are no overriding advantages or disadvantages to one system over the other and that each is more effective for teaching particular aspects of shiphandling.

These designs and cost differences tend to balance out, so the real consideration is which type of simulator is most effective for teaching the particular subject matter. Pilots seem to prefer the model simulator that effectively recreates hydrodynamic effects, external forces, anchor work, and ship behavior both ahead and astern in very close waters, since they are more interested in the subtleties of shiphandling and operations in pilot waters. Deck officers seem to prefer computer-driven simulators for their ability to simulate particular ports and a familiar bridgelike setting of a ship underway for training in bridge operations, navigation, rules of the road, and other operations more related to the work of a ship's officer. Perhaps this is to be expected since the two user groups do have different interests.

If a generalization can be made, it is that there are advantages to the ship model simulator for teaching the subtleties of shiphandling, while the computer-driven bridge simulator seems to be better for teaching many of the other aspects of the deck officer's or pilot's work. In any case, advantages of model simulation may be lost if the next generation of computer-driven simulators is able to recreate the effects that are presently simulated most effectively using models. Until that time, the best facilities will probably use both computer-driven and scale model simulators to teach those aspects of shiphandling for which each is most suitable. This is presently done at the Southampton Institute in the United Kingdom.

TOOLS OF SIMULATOR INSTRUCTION

Modern simulators create an environment where performance can be demonstrated, measured, and replayed, so that *recording equipment* of several types is important. The simulator changes the methods used to review and test learning in much the same way it changes the nature of instruction itself, because simulator recordings provide an active, dynamic measure of performance rather than the passive pass-fail written tests used in the traditional classroom.

Typically, the tools used to record both performance and behavior under routine and high stress emergency conditions include:

1. "X-Y" or similar plotters that reproduce a vessel's track and heading.
2. Computer- or printer-generated graphs and tables of vessel speed, engine and helm orders, rate of turn, and associated data related to time.
3. Simulator playback capability, so that situations and performance can be recreated for selected times.
4. Audio recording of pilot's or deck officer's orders and discussions during a simulator run.
5. Video recording of participants' actions and use of equipment.

Use these records of each simulator exercise in a debriefing session to review and compare performance with past sessions and accepted standards. Skills are mastered on a simulator through this process of measured performance, review, and repetition after a debriefing where each recorded session is reviewed by participants and the instructor. Be critical of yourself and open-minded when reviewing records of each exercise so that subsequent simulator sessions do more than reinforce old, often improper work habits.

SIMULATOR VALIDATION

A simulator is of little use if the information presented is not accurate, since incorrect or misleading information is worse than useless: it can be dangerous. The process of evaluating the accuracy of the simulation is known as *validation*. Studies of various means for measuring accuracy of the simulation and validating simulator facilities are ongoing in several countries but, as yet, the criteria are nebulous at best, since the user is trying to catch up with the fast changing technology while, at the same time, deciding where simulators fit into the maritime training picture. Simulator validation is becoming increasingly important as simulators gain acceptance for required training, testing, and licensing, and as companies increase their use of simulators for evaluating mates and masters for promotion and retention.

THE SIMULATOR INSTRUCTOR

The instructor is the second and most important component of the simulator package.

It is far too easy to overlook the instructor's essential role amidst the bells, whistles, and flashing lights of a modern simulator but, as impressive as it might be, the simulator is only a sophisticated teaching tool used by an experienced mariner with the aptitude and training to teach a well planned course covering the various aspects of vessel operations and shiphandling to cadets, pilots, and deck officers.

An uncodified but nationally and internationally accepted standard is evolving that requires very skilled mariners as instructors rather than a third mate cum instructor waiting for a job at sea, or a retired military officer with two years' sea time aboard military ships that are very different from today's large and often underpowered deep draft merchant ships. Instructors should be experienced pilots, master mariners, or maritime professionals who have in-depth experience in the particular maneuvers being taught and are also teachers trained in operating the simulator. At the better facilities, the instructors also have specialized training in adult education and the techniques for using simulation effectively as a training tool. When very specialized training is offered, the facility may use a *team concept* with two instructors, one trained in teaching with simulators and a second who is usually a professional with current experience in the specialty being taught.

Poor instruction only perpetuates the very shiphandling mistakes and poor operating procedures that the pilot, mate, or master came to the course to overcome, and courses taught by anyone other than senior, experienced mariners with training as instructors do a disservice to this area of maritime education.

Companies, pilot organizations, and the mariners using a facility should consider the qualifications of the instructor as well as the capabilities of the simulator when evaluating a simulator program, and simulator facilities should budget for well qualified instructors, not excessively expensive equipment. A simulator with limited capabilities in the hands of a skilled instructor with strong course material is an excellent training tool. The best full-task simulator is a weak teaching tool in the hands of a poor, professionally inexperienced instructor and an instructor who does not take simulation seriously.

There are ongoing studies by the International Maritime Organization, the U.S. Coast Guard, and several papers by various participants in the international conferences on marine simulation concerning accreditation of simulator instructors that will consider professional experience and training but, as yet, no such standards are in place in the United States. This certification should also include certification standards for courses that train the trainer.

DEGREE OF INSTRUCTOR INVOLVEMENT

There are two schools of thought regarding the degree to which the instructor should be involved in the simulator exercise.

Some believe instructors should be on the bridge working with the student group. The instructor would explain maneuvers and actively guide the shiphandler or mate through the exercise so that each maneuver is performed correctly.

Others feel the instructor should be at a separate operating console removed from the students, who would go through each exercise independently after the briefing session. The shiphandlers and mates are allowed to make mistakes and perform the exercise at their own pace, after which the instructors and students go through a detailed debriefing critiquing each other's work based on performance and records of the exercise. With the plethora of excellent measuring and monitoring equipment available, most facilities are using the latter method, which most students and more experienced instructors generally agree is more effective. Specialized courses sometimes use both alternatives. The expert simulator instructor works at the console, while a second instructor with specific skills in the subject matter taught works on the bridge.

THE SIMULATOR CURRICULUM FOR DECK OFFICERS

The curriculum is the third component of an effective simulator program.

It is interesting to watch experienced seamen get deeply involved in well planned shiphandling lessons on a real time simulator presentation, responding emotionally as the fog sets in or another ship approaches in a narrow channel. This is perhaps the best testimony for the effectiveness of such training.

On the job, deck officers do not routinely get enough closely supervised shiphandling training or hands-on experience in pilot waters, even if they glean as much information as possible from a pilot aboard their ship. For them, simulation is especially important. Shipboard work is, to a large extent, a solitary task, and mariners often carry bad habits throughout their career because there are limited opportunities in the normal course of a voyage for someone to point out their errors. The simulator is valuable if it does no more than provide a briefing and debriefing forum with peers, under the supervision of experienced shiphandlers and shipmasters with no obligations other than to teach professional skills.

As already stated, simulators are very effective aids for teaching a multitude of subjects. This text focuses on shiphandling and considers skills only to the extent that they impact on shiphandling. In this regard, ship model and computer simulators are both very effective for teaching basic shiphandling theory and specialized piloting and shiphandling techniques, but more advanced shiphandling skills must be honed to the level expected by the maritime community, and the public, by spending hundreds of hours actually handling ships.

It is generally agreed that detailed, carefully developed scenarios that reflect situations a pilot or deck officer will encounter in the course of their work should be used as a basis for instruction rather than a rote lesson. Plan a very detailed scenario that includes all the navigation, radio communications, and intraship communications, watch reliefs, and other routine events in an arrival, docking, undocking, departure, or other evolution being practiced.

Based on discussions with experienced instructors and students, it is apparent that scenarios that closely track real world situations are more effective than impossible situations that degrade the simulator session to the level of a video game. Avoid the temptation to overdo problems to the point where exercises become unrealistic, no-win situations, but include all the work a shiphandler or pilot will have to do during the same evolution aboard ship so the work load and priorities reflect on-the-job experience. Ideally, the problems developed in those scenarios increase in difficulty at the student's pace until realistic limits, rather than the limits of the computer, are reached.

Subjects covered on the simulator vary depending on the intent of the program, since a third mate needs different material than a master preparing to command a VLCC, but as a minimum the program should include:

1. An introduction to general ship maneuvering characteristics.
2. Basic maneuvers as discussed in the master's trials.
3. The Williamson Turn maneuver to demonstrate steering characteristics.
4. Watchkeeping scenarios requiring maneuvering a ship at sea in close meeting and crossing situations (both when aboard the giving way vessel and the standing on vessel), stressing the importance of a round turn maneuver in such situations.
5. Maneuvers to arrive at a pilot station and make a lee to embark a pilot in all types of weather and sea conditions.

6. Maneuvering to make a lee to launch a lifeboat or recover a person from the water.
7. Maneuvering in narrow channels and with traffic, including stopping a ship in a narrow channel in the minimum time while maintaining good control of the ship.
8. Use of tugs in narrow channels and while docking and undocking.
9. Response to own ship machinery failures and failures aboard approaching ships.
10. Methods for handling a ship with sternway, with and without strong winds.
11. Comparison of high sided versus low freeboard ships and their behavior in strong winds.
12. If within the capability of the simulator, demonstrate techniques for working with bank suction, intership action, and strong river currents.
13. Proper communication techniques using sound signals, running lights, and radio, and stressing the importance of limiting such communication only to necessary information.

Insist on proper procedures for every task and teach the full range of work involved in a shiphandling exercise including navigation, rules of the road in traffic situations, bridge organization, bridge resource management, a command presence, decision making and leadership skills, and voyage planning techniques under routine and emergency situations, not just shiphandling itself. All these skills impact on shiphandling. The pilot or deck officer must master the entire package of professionals skills and techniques of bridge resource management to utilize the crew and equipment to advantage. Utilize the simulator's capability to its fullest extent so that the mariner is practicing the skills in as close to a real world environment as possible. That is the very essence of the simulator experience.

Bridge organization is discussed briefly in this text to the extent it impacts on shiphandling, and some excellent texts on voyage planning and bridge resource management are listed in the Bibliography. Develop these skills as part of the study of shiphandling since they are an integral part of that work. The simulator is the most effective tool for putting the concepts of voyage planning and bridge management into practice, both of which are integrated into every well planned simulator program.

Plan exercises under progressively worsening weather conditions with increasing winds and reduced visibility. Analyze maneuvers done under clear conditions compared with those done as conditions deteriorate. Incorporate several lessons into one exercise as the ship is brought from sea to a dock. Practice maneuvering in traffic, applying the Rules of the Road, making a lee and picking up a pilot, and learn to work with tugs, communicate, organize the bridge in pilot waters, and understand hydrodynamic effects all in one exercise by being creative with carefully planned scenarios. Be sure to do the same work under night conditions since the same jobs appear different in the dark.

The simulator also makes seafarers, and particularly the younger ship's mate, comfortable with the idea that a ship is designed to be maneuvered. This may sound basic, but too many deck officers are reluctant to take action when a problem develops due to a stigma of inviolability attached to the bridge and its equipment. Effective course material takes this into consideration during training in shiphandling, maneuvering in traffic, and bridge resource management. The "hands-on drill" discussed elsewhere in this text is also applicable to the first day on a simulator and, after several days of simulator training, the reluctance to maneuver should be gone.

THE SIMULATOR CURRICULUM FOR PILOTS

As previously stated, deck officers and masters are having an increasingly difficult time finding opportunities to practice shiphandling to the degree needed to develop strong shiphandling skills. Fortunately, this is not the case for pilots who have no problem accumulating shipboard experience. By the very nature of their work, pilots have daily access to ships for training and practice of shiphandling and bridge management skills. They are aboard ships in pilot waters, maneuvering, at all hours under all conditions. They learn and practice their skills on a routine basis, under tutelage of experienced, skilled pilots at no cost other than their time—they train aboard the ultimate ship simulator, the ship, and that training is free!

Simulators, in their present state of development, do not give pilots a sense of depth and distance or the subtle visual cues and hydrodynamic effects needed to master close quarters shiphandling. It is still the ship that best demonstrates all the nuances of ship behavior at the level required to develop total competence under all the conditions encountered by a working pilot. Simulators, in their present state, are effective tools to *enhance* pilot skills but they don't replace the ship for most pilot training.

Simulators do not presently replace the traditional apprenticeship-oriented training methods that have served pilots so well, and any claim to the contrary does a disservice to the development and acceptance of simulators, but they definitely are a useful tool for pilots for many purposes including:

1. Theory and basic techniques of shiphandling, including training in emergency situations.
2. Bridge resource management and bridge organization.
3. Familiarization with new or unusual ship types not customarily handled in a pilot's home waters.
4. As a forum for pilots to demonstrate and compare various job techniques with peers in a structured training environment.
5. Radar, ARPA, navigation, and communications training to update knowledge of new equipment and techniques.
6. Port development and improvement studies to reconfigure ports and establish parameters for handling new, larger, or unique ship types.
7. New methods for dealing with specialized pilot tasks, such as handling new or larger vessels and maneuvering in realigned channels and new port configurations.

Technical reports from CAORF published in March 1985 discuss simulator training for pilots in depth, and those reports provide an excellent basis for planning a generic pilot training program. More definitive training must be developed in conjunction with the pilots' association for the port or area simulated because piloting is inherently port specific and very specialized. That is the very reason pilots exist. No one other than the pilots themselves appreciate the techniques used and the local knowledge needed to work safely and efficiently in a particular port.

Like ship's officers, pilots need training in navigation, radar, bridge operations and bridge resource management, and emergency maneuvers. Apprentice pilots especially must make full use of the ship features and equipment, rather than concentrating on shiphandling alone, since they need the same training and experience in bridge operations as the third mate. Again, scenarios should be planned to include all aspects of a passage through pilot waters, not just shiphandling techniques, even though the pilot may be inherently more interested in the shiphandling aspects of the exercise, and the scenarios must be challenging but realistic, so the exercise remains a job to be done rather than a game to be won.

Spend time discussing hydrodynamics and theory of ship behavior with pilots who benefit from a better understanding of why ships behave as they do rather than just knowing how they behave. An appreciation of hydrodynamic principles and shiphandling gives pilots the basis for anticipating ship behavior on the job rather than reacting to it. *Have the pilot role-play as master,* working with another pilot to better appreciate the master's position in the pilot-master relationship. Take a ship into familiar ports. Broaden the pilots' experience by placing them in challenging situations with larger ships and different ship types from those being handled in the pilot's home waters. Use the recording and replay capabilities of the simulator to *facilitate self analysis and peer critiques* of not only the actual shiphandling performance but also bridge demeanor and bridge resource management. Even the most skilled and experienced pilots find, when reviewing graphs and videos of their exercises, that they may give many unnecessary orders or show signs of stress that create unnecessary tension on the bridge in challenging situations. Pilots are using the playback and review process routinely and pilot organizations are participating in bridge resource management courses on a routine basis.

Bridge operations and resource management have become increasingly difficult for pilots who work more and more with multicultural crews without advance preparation to move a ship safely through pilot waters. The pilot organizations recognize this and the American Pilot's Association is promoting bridge management training for all pilots.[1] In fact, pilots insist that a simple *requirement to communicate in a common tongue,* usually English, would do more to increase marine safety than a wheelhouse full of new instruments or a volume of regulations. Communications and bridge organization remain a major challenge to working pilots, and simulator exercises provide an excellent opportunity to sharpen the pilot's skills in bridge resource management and communications.

Training exercises should include both *vessel-specific exercises* for more senior pilots and *nonspecific exercises* for less experienced pilots learning the basics of shiphandling using generic ships operating over the pilot's route. Insist that all pilots involved in the course follow

[1] *APA Promotes BRM Training for Pilots.* Washington, DC: American Pilots' Association, October 5, 1993.

correct procedures and make every aspect of the training scenario as realistic as possible.

Pilots are also using simulators for port studies, familiarization with new vessel types, and as a forum with peers in the workplace, practicing shiphandling exercises and exchanging ideas on their work. Pilots are most familiar with ships that routinely call in the waters on which they serve and, when radically different types of sizes of ships begin serving that port, they sometimes have to reinvent the wheel. Increasingly, pilots are getting together with peers from another port who have experience with that ship type and are *using simulators as a tool for transferring knowledge and experience within the profession.* This forum aspect of the simulator exercise provides a unique opportunity, since pilots normally work alone with little opportunity to critique each other's work and discuss shiphandling. Piloting is by nature a solitary job with little routine contact between peers and the simulator can change this —serving as a catalyst for professional discussion among pilots that can be quite beneficial.

So, is simulation effective in improving piloting skills? The pilots must think so since they attend both model- and computer-based simulators at their own expense. They see the value of training that enhances their abilities both in broad shiphandling skills and specialized areas peculiar to their own port and work. Cost is an important consideration though, since simulators are expensive. Perhaps it is time for a *nationally uniform training surcharge on* all pilotage fees that is retained by each association to pay the cost of training and educating its members. This equalizes the cost of training between ports and creates a fund so that even the smallest associations can afford training paid for by the beneficiaries of that training: the shipowner whose ships are moved safely and expediently in that port.

THE THREE STEPS OF SIMULATOR TRAINING

As stated previously, there are *three steps to simulator training: a briefing session* where theory and an outline of the simulator exercise are discussed in a classroom environment, *the simulator exercise itself,* and a *debriefing session* to review performance. Simulator training time seems to be broken down about evenly between these three steps, so that only *approximately a third of the total training time is actually spent on the bridge simulator.* This is logical since instruction and appraisal is done by the instructor through a well planned course and, without intensive instruction and evaluation, the pilot, master, or mate would only be using simulator time to practice and reinforce weak or improper work habits.

BRIEFING AND DEBRIEFING SESSIONS

Time must be allotted for a classroom *briefing* before each simulator period to discuss the theory and hydrodynamics involved in each problem and plan the intended passage. Charts and tide tables must be studied and a passage plan developed. The more carefully the passage is discussed and planned, the more beneficial the subsequent simulator period will be.

After the simulator exercise, there should be a lengthy, carefully moderated *debriefing* where bridge work is reviewed and the performance of each of the individuals involved in the lesson is critiqued. Most of the learning from a simulator session is done during this debriefing when the users are led by the instructor to look critically at their performance and the results of their work and analyze what they might have done differently. The mates and pilots are usually allowed to critique their own performance with guidance from the instructor using reruns of selected sections of the passage, and a review of video, audio, and chart records gives mariners a clear picture of what occurred during the simulator exercise. Without this review, the period on the simulator becomes a high priced video game since the lessons are never really fixed in the user's mind.

It is surprising how often mistakes are not recognized during the session but immediately seized on and discussed during the debriefing. Even the most experienced mariners and pilots often comment on work habits they hadn't realized they had developed during years of work aboard ship. This peer to peer review is especially helpful to experienced pilots and shipmasters since they rarely have an opportunity to compare techniques and develop improved work habits through discussion with their peers.

The third segment of the simulator training, the time actually spent on the simulator, has already been discussed in preceding sections of this chapter.

THE FUTURE OF SIMULATION

Simulation is a developing field. Technology, need, and application are changing and improving rapidly as the simulator is more widely accepted as a useful training and testing tool in the marine community.

Each generation of simulator offers more accurate presentations and better visual detail as more and faster computers are put into smaller spaces at lower cost.

There may be a time when desktop simulators have a capacity to drive small simulators installed directly aboard ship so that officers can learn the rules of the road, ARPA and radar operation, navigation, and all the other skills taught on today's simulators, and even familiarize themselves prior to arrival with ports on the ship's itinerary.

Computers are developing because of universal demand. There is obviously a much smaller demand for research and data needed to increase the usefulness of simulation for teaching and testing. Research is needed to develop the human side of simulation and collect more complete data on the effectiveness of instruction and *the degree to which simulator training transfers to work aboard ship*. Research is also needed on *ship behavior* in shallow water. The accuracy of mathematical models is still limited because cost and tight schedules make it difficult to collect data aboard ships operating in shallow water and, without that information, much of the basis for current models is theoretical and extrapolated from deep water sea trials and tank tests. The effectiveness of simulator training and testing will increase as this information becomes available.

Computers will be used more for testing and license examinations after better testing criteria are developed. In the future, the simulator may be used both for original license examinations and for upgrading and license renewal where testing can be performance-based on several subjects simultaneously in a realistic shipboard scenario. The U.S. Coast Guard and the Maritime Administration are sponsoring studies on the use of simulation for these purposes by the National Research Council's Marine Board. Recent International Maritime Organization reports include recommendations for *performance-based testing* of underlying skills rather than dependence on written knowledge-based testing.[2] These studies reflect a significant change in testing methodol-

[2] *Review of the 1978 Standards of Training and Watchkeeping,* IMO Sub-committee on Standards of Training and Watchkeeping, Section 4.2.3, October 5, 1993.

ogy away from traditional written multiple-choice examinations that test memorization more than the ability to do a job.

This will require developing meaningful *criteria for measuring performance* (no easy task) and *an examination board of senior industry professionals* skilled in the work being tested. It isn't possible for a junior Coast Guard officer to examine merchant marine officers and pilots if tests are going to be subjective in nature and require discretionary grading based on experience rather than a pass-fail question and answer format. A new marine licensing authority of senior officers, independent from or contracted to the U.S. Coast Guard, is probably needed to do this. Again, the technological development of simulation has outpaced its application.

In addition to license examinations, time spent in simulator training may soon be considered as on-the-job experience when computing service requirements for original, upgraded, and renewed marine licenses. There is a definite shift to a policy of equating written tests and licensing, classroom time, and standardized training requirements with "hands-on" training, and there are international and national precedents for substituting simulator and classroom time at some multiple of days credit for each day of training.[3] There is serious doubt among professionals about this practice and many feel simulation should be seen as an additional tool for raising standards to meet the requirements of an increasingly demanding profession rather than as a substitute for other experience and training. Pilots especially seem to feel simulator training enhances shipboard experience but does not replace it.

Supporters of granting service credit at some ratio of equivalency contend the structured simulator experience provides better training than on-board experience. Opponents of equivalency contend time aboard ship is meant to provide experience, not training, and that it is irreplaceable precisely because it is not structured. They maintain that broad and random experience seasons and prepares the officer for promotion and command. The latter group also feel the work of mates, masters, and pilots encompasses much more than just bridge operations, and reducing time requirements also reduces important experience in areas not addressed in a simulator exercise.

[3] Standards of Training and Watchkeeping 1978 Regulation 11/4, Article IX, (1) Equivalents, and CFR Title 46—Shipping, Part 10.304—Substitution of training for required service.

The U.S. Coast Guard currently grants up to six days' sea time credit for each day spent on a simulator with a maximum credit equal to 25 percent of the total required time being granted. Whether this practice continues in this form will probably depend on the findings resulting from present studies and input from the industry. It is possible that, in the foreseeable future, mates will both prepare and be examined for upgraded licenses on a simulator.

Simulation has matured into a widely used and effective training tool for teaching basic shiphandling and other bridge skills. Simulation's place in maritime training is in a state of flux, but there is no doubt it will play an increasing part in the education and testing process for mariners and operating professionals in many other high skill fields.

CHAPTER ELEVEN

MASTER/PILOT RELATIONSHIP

> If a pilot undertakes the Conduct of a vessel . . . and fails
> of his Duty therein . . . and the Merchants Sustain
> Damage thereby, he shall be Obligated to make full
> Satisfaction for the same . . . and if not, lose his head.
>
> —Rule 23
> *Laws of Oleron*

It must first be stressed that this chapter is not a legal treatise on the complex relationship between shipmaster and pilot; it is a discussion of the day-to-day working arrangements between two professionals. An excellent discussion of the legal aspects of the master/pilot relationship can be found in *Law of Tug, Tow, and Pilotage.** This text was used as the principal reference for the discussion that follows.

At first glance the master/pilot relationship appears poorly defined. Areas of responsibility seem nebulous and conflicting, with the master appearing responsible for much of the work performed by a pilot whom the master does not select and is usually compelled by statute to employ. The case law in this area further befogs the relationship, leaving the mariner to figuratively "navigate under Rule Nineteen."

In practice though, the master and pilot are experienced professional seamen working together to complete a passage safely, understanding the relationship between their two positions that has evolved through custom and practice over centuries. The arrangement works well and thousands of ships are moved each year without incident. It is only when a casualty occurs that this informal but well understood and workable arrangement becomes unnecessarily complicated.

THE PILOT ABOARD SHIP

The pilot comes aboard to take charge of the navigation of the ship from the pilot station to her destination, or to some intermediate point if multiple pilots are used. The pilot moves the ship toward her destination

*Alex L. Parks and Edward V. Cattell, Jr., *Law of Tug, Tow, and Pilotage,* 3d ed., Centreville, Md.: Cornell Maritime Press, 1994.

using both local knowledge and a degree of shiphandling skill that the seagoing master generally is not expected to possess. Local knowledge is such a broad term that it might be said to encompass the whole of the pilot's expertise, but at least it would include:

1. Local tides and currents.
2. Bottom and channel depths and configurations.
3. Courses, distances, aids to navigation, and significant geographic features enroute.
4. Local customs and practices for ship movements.
5. Local weather patterns.
6. The shiphandling skills necessary to move vessels in the waters employed.

The pilot must, of course, possess many of the mariner's skills including a knowledge of the Rules of the Road, navigation, and the use of all forms of navigation equipment. Obviously then, the landsman's picture of the quaint old pilot standing at the master's side mumbling pithy bits of local wisdom and advice, as the ship proceeds under the master's direction toward her destination, is patently incorrect and unrealistic.

A clear distinction must be made between voluntary and compulsory pilots. A voluntary pilot is one engaged for the convenience of the vessel. A North Sea pilot employed to take a ship between the Rotterdam and Bremerhaven sea buoys would be one example of a voluntary pilot. No statute requires a ship to have a pilot aboard, but the master or owner may hire a pilot to aid in making the passage expeditiously.

The owner, through the master, has great control over the voluntary pilot. The pilot need not be hired in the first place, or the pilot's services can be rejected during the passage and the vessel continue to her destination. The voluntary pilot is in a significantly different position aboard ship than the compulsory pilot. *Homer Ramsdell Transportation Company v. Compagnie Generale Transatlantique,* 182 U.S. 406 (1901). Practically speaking then, the master can feel much more free to advise or relieve a voluntary pilot—the voluntary pilot is in much the same position as the ship's mates.

A compulsory pilot, on the other hand, is one that is required by law to be aboard while the ship is navigating certain specified areas. Penalties such as fines or imprisonment, or both, are the hallmarks of compulsory pilotage laws. If a ship is allowed by statute to refuse the services of a pilot provided she pays a portion of the pilotage fee, the pilotage is not compulsory. *The Merrimac,* 81 U.S. (14 Wall.) 199, (1872).

The relationship between master and compulsory pilot is in many ways unique in that it is usually defined by custom, practice, and statute rather than contract. While the pilot is generally neither an employee of the ship nor a member of her crew, he is ultimately subordinate to the master, although the degree of subordination is less than popularly perceived. The public and the industry benefit from this working arrangement and from the degree of overlapping responsibility that compels both pilot and master to be concerned about a vessel's safety.

The compulsory pilot is not aboard in a purely advisory capacity. That pilot is in charge of the navigation of the ship while aboard and the ship's crew is required to obey the compulsory pilot's orders relating to navigation unless the master determines it is necessary to intercede for reasons yet to be discussed. A compulsory pilot is responsible for his own actions and receives a significant fee because of this responsibility. In the presence of the compulsory pilot, a master's responsibility is not total and forever. Both master and pilot have a job to do and bear an unusual degree of responsibility not only to the vessel, cargo, and crew, but also to the public.

Except for American flag vessels operating in the coastwise trade under enrollment, ships are required to have a pilot aboard in most inland waters of the United States to provide local knowledge and ship-handling skill. Most pilots are compulsory and it is that type of pilot that is referred to throughout this chapter unless specifically noted otherwise.

An exception is found to the traditional master/pilot relationship at the Panama Canal. The Panama Canal Commission accepts a greater degree of liability in exchange for greater control of ships' navigation in that strategic waterway. Inside the locks of the Panama Canal the Commission is liable for payment for injuries to the vessel, cargo, crew, or passengers arising out of a passage through the locks under the control of employees of the commission, unless the commission shows that the injury was *caused by a negligent act of the vessel.* Outside the locks the Commission is liable for payment for injuries to a vessel, cargo, crew, or passengers *when such injuries are proximately caused by the negligence or fault of a Canal Commission employee* . . . provided that in the case of a ship required to have a Panama Canal pilot on duty, damages are

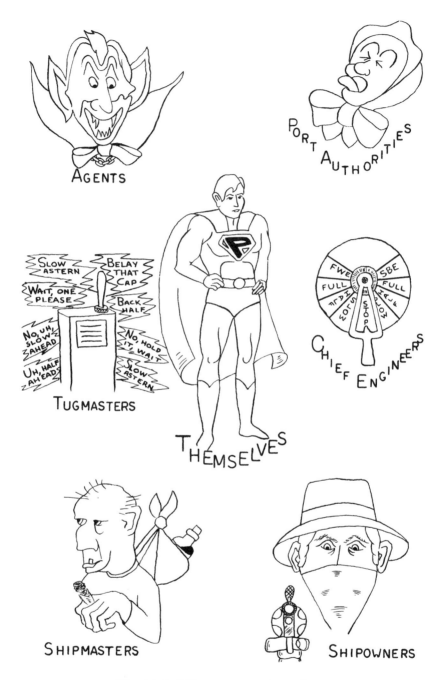

Fig. 11-1. "Pilots as seen by . . ."

only payable if at the time of injury the navigation was under the control of the Panama Canal Pilot.

Shipmasters should be aware of the manner in which the traditional master/pilot relationship is distorted in this special circumstance.

THE MASTER'S RESPONSIBILITIES IN PILOTAGE WATERS

The master retains overall responsibility for the vessel and her operation, for having a competent watch on duty and seeing that they perform their work efficiently, for being sure a proper lookout is maintained, and for compliance with all regulations and statutes including the Rules of the Road (COLREGS). The master's authority is never completely in abeyance even while a pilot (compulsory or not) has immediate charge of the ship's navigation. The master is also responsible for his own professional competence, including having sufficient knowledge and experience to be able to judge the pilot's performance and recognize significant pilot error, and to have studied the local waters and be able to recognize known and published dangers.

The master has a duty to advise or relieve a pilot in cases of :

1. Intoxication.
2. Gross incompetence to perform the task at hand.
3. When the vessel is standing into danger that is not obvious to the pilot.
4. When the pilot's actions are in error due to a lack of appreciation of particular circumstances, including the limitations of the particular ship being handled.

In carrying out these responsibilities the master may either advise or relieve the pilot, at the master's discretion. In practice, there is a real burden upon the master to justify relieving the pilot should some casualty result, so the action of relieving must not be arbitrary. There are several ways to do a job and, while admittedly some are more expeditious than others, the master must not relieve simply because he feels that he can do a better job—the pilot should only be relieved when the master feels, based upon professional experience and training, that the vessel, crew, or cargo is being placed in real and imminent danger because of that pilot's present course of action. On the other hand, the master is negligent if action is not taken when required. The master first objects to an action, then recommends an alternative, and only in the rare case when the pilot refuses to accept a recommendation does the master relieve a pilot in a timely manner—while it is still possible to avoid an accident.

The decision about when to become involved is more difficult than the absolute problem of whether it is necessary to do so. There is a natural reluctance to act because of the ramifications in case of a casualty, yet the question of timing is most critical. Relief usually occurs when it is too late—when the situation has deteriorated so far that even the most competent shiphandler could not correct matters and the master's efforts then only complicate an already bad situation. There is no requirement that a ship be *in extremis* before the pilot is relieved, only that the master foresees danger should a present course of action continue.

It is imperative that the master be sufficiently skilled in shiphandling to recognize a problem early, and have sufficient confidence in those skills to take prompt and decisive action if it is necessary to relieve a pilot. The correctness of action taken reflects the training and experience that a master has had, and *it is too late to compensate for years of neglect in this area at such a time.* The decision to relieve a pilot is not an easy one, but a master who instead stands by as the vessel heads for certain catastrophe remains a responsible party and must take action. It is a judgement that can only be made based on professional experience and is but one example of why the title "shipmaster" bears a connotation of unusual responsibility.

"RELEASE FROM LIABILITY" FORMS

Occasionally a master is presented with a form to be signed releasing the pilot from liability. These forms may be based on local practice or special circumstances, such as a tugboat strike. The validity of these forms in a particular case is questionable and depends on local laws and regulations of which the master cannot reasonably be expected to have knowledge.

Inasmuch as the master may be under pressure not to delay the vessel, and may not be able to consult with anyone about the advisability of signing a release, he may elect to sign and note over the signature that the release is "Signed under protest so that the vessel may proceed." An entry to that effect should be made in the ship's log. Forward a copy of the release to the owners so they can advise you about signing such documents in the future.

In any case, the form will have no immediate practical effect since the master has ultimate responsibility for the ship in any case, and the document in no way alters the master's conduct during the docking or other work at hand.

SOME PRACTICAL CONSIDERATIONS

The real world must be kept in mind when discussing a relationship between master and pilot. In practice, the pilot will not refuse to work more safely, or to slow down, or use an additional tug when requested to do so by the master, so it is extremely rare that a conflict over relative authority arises between pilot and master aboard ship. No reasonable pilot is going to reject a master's request to work more safely, nor would any master object to such a request by a pilot. *This duality of interest works to the obvious benefit of all concerned.* So long as one of the two parties has an interest in working safely, the ship is handled in a proper manner, and when both work professionally the concerns of one tend to amplify those of the other.

It is a fact that very few casualties occur in pilot waters that do not involve some degree of acquiescence on the part of the master. In many cases, if the master had done no more than suggest that the pilot reduce speed in fog or clarify a proposed meeting arrangement with an approaching vessel, no accident would have occurred since the pilot will not refuse to handle a situation more safely in such conditions. In most reports of marine casualties it is obvious that the master was reluctant to get involved and allowed the pilot to act alone until it was too late to avoid an accident.

It is again stressed that the master must not wait until the situation is hopeless before getting involved. It is time to get involved, to at least question a pilot's intentions, at the first moment that there is any doubt about the correctness of the pilot's actions.

What options do the compulsory pilot or master have when an irreconcilable disagreement arises about a course of action?

The pilot can accept the master's recommendations, or take the vessel to the nearest safe anchorage until the matter is resolved, or stand aside and allow the master to complete the job. The master can relieve the pilot, complete the maneuver if conditions require it, and then either return the conn to the pilot or put the ship to anchor. It is again stressed though, that the master intervenes only when the pilot's work is endangering the ship, cargo, crew, or assisting tugs—not because the master feels a job can be done in another, more expeditious manner.

Let me reiterate for emphasis. It would be wrong to give an impression that such differences occur with any regularity. They do not! Both the master and pilot are professionals with a common interest and the fact is that irreconcilable differences almost never occur because of the context in which objections to a course of action are made.

Recently, the relationship between the master and pilot has been complicated by the growth in popularity of the "team concept" of shipboard organization. The pilot is often said to be another member of a team that is to navigate a ship from one point to another, as if the pilot were employed as a crew member for the passage. This is clearly not the case with a compulsory pilot who is providing a one-time service to the ship, and it is unrealistic to attempt to put any pilot into that position.

The team concept in its intended form is not new. The well-organized crew has always operated as a team under the master, each member performing assigned tasks to move the ship expediently from point to point, and the concept is valid as long as it is kept in that context. The team is organized vertically with the mate and helmsman, engineer on watch, and others involved in the navigation of the ship performing tasks as assigned by the pilot, through the master. These tasks might involve machinery operation, log and record keeping, position fixing, or radar plotting—all jobs being performed *to support the master or pilot* who has the conn. It is important to differentiate between this vertically organized *team* and a horizontally organized *committee*. There is no place for the latter aboard ship—any concept that diffuses *responsibility* beyond the master or pilot only confuses the relationship that exists between those two and is counterproductive to safety and sound operation. The shipboard team should exist only to supply information and assistance as assigned by the responsible master or pilot.

THE COST OF RESPONSIBILITY

Authority, responsibility, and liability are inseparable, so fault will inevitably be assigned after any casualty according to perceived responsibility. Fortunately, the day when pilots and mariners paid with their lives for errors is long past, so present day penalties are primarily in the form of lost income or fines.

Perhaps these penalties satisfy a perceived need to enforce standards of performance and assign blame. Unfortunately, it is inevitable that they become a consideration when the master thinks about relieving a pilot. The penalties might in fact be counterproductive since their existence can cause the master to delay in taking corrective action. In any case, it is doubtful that they serve any real purpose since casualties usually are the result of errors in judgment rather than gross negligence or intentional misconduct. To make matters worse, the penalties are assigned after the fact by a third party who usually has only a limited appreciation of the marine profession and the context within which the mariner's judgments are made and actions are taken. Unfortunately, there is no reason to expect this situation to change.

It is essential that neither the master nor the pilot get too bound up in considerations of legality and liability in the course of their work. While these considerations are significant, there is an overriding professional and moral obligation for both of them to exercise all their professional talents to safely and expeditiously move ships. Both must appreciate the circumstances under which they labor, but their actions should be instinctive and in the best interests of the ship in which they are serving. When the master or pilot hesitates to act as they see proper because of concern for some later review or liability, it is time for them to seek some other career.

CHAPTER TWELVE

VESSEL OPERATIONS

> Many officers spend much time in perfecting them-
> selves in deep sea navigation, where the ship is not
> endangered, but make no effort to acquaint them-
> selves with conditions such as tides, currents, etc.,
> when coming into port, because the Captain or pilot
> will then be taking responsibility. This is where
> danger really exists. . . .
> —*Merchant Marine Officer's Handbook*

PLANNING THE PASSAGE

Columbus wasn't sure what he would find at his destination or what
would be encountered en route, but he planned his passage with meticu-
lous care and made the best use of information available at that time.
He planned a stop at Gomera in the Canary Islands, and a track down
the twenty-eighth parallel which he felt would take him to his destination. Through the centuries masters and ship's officers have continued
to plan each passage using all available information to safely and
expeditiously reach their destination. Passage planning is neither new
nor any less important today whether a passage is offshore or in pilot
waters.

Further, as discussed in Chapter 7, the need to plan a passage does not
diminish with experience on a particular route or body of water; too
often, a mate or master neglects planning because "I've made this run
a hundred times." This is illogical, since no one plans a passage more
thoroughly than a pilot who has probably made a thousand trips over a
route. Because of the pilot's competence and experience the planning
may at times seem effortless and sketchy although, in fact, the pilot has
planned the passage in great detail; an apparent contradiction since the
pilot already has such detailed knowledge of the area being navigated.
The fact is the mariner may not have sufficient local knowledge to
appreciate the planning that is required. The pilot checks currents and
tides at several points, not just at the pier as the mariner tends to do,
and compares dead reckoning to actual positions continuously during a

Fig. 12-1. "Look, Chris, just because the Satnav is kaput is no reason
to scrub the voyage."

passage. Notices to Mariners are checked even though the aids long ago
became so well known that positions are reconciled almost without
conscious thought. Distances off points and aids are checked, times for
standing by the anchors and taking tugs are discussed, times for rising
and setting of the sun and moon are computed because of their effect on
available light during a passage, and weather conditions along the route
are studied. If the pilot considers all this work essential, it is only logical
that the mariner who is less familiar with an area should plan at least
as carefully.

The hazard of overplanning and its effect on handling the ship must
also be considered—and more significantly, the dangers of following an
inflexible passage plan regardless of conditions that develop. Do not
plan the placement of every mooring line at the dock and then attempt
to blindly follow that plan regardless of the 30-knot wind that develops
off the dock after the planning is done, or despite the freshet found to
be running across the berth. Select an area to anchor, but use your
professional skill to adjust when you find a ship anchored in your
planned location. This may sound obvious, yet a few years ago a ship's
mate religiously followed an overly detailed passage plan until the ship's

Fig. 12-2. "No one plans a voyage more thoroughly than a pilot."

bow was 50 feet over the Cristobal breakwater! It is not uncommon for a pilot to board a ship and find bridge personnel overly concerned because another ship has stopped ahead on the preplanned track line that "we have to follow." The plan is meant only as a formalized dead reckoning and does not replace good seamanship, navigation, and shiphandling ability.

The at-sea passage plan begins in an abstract tabular format that includes:

1. Planned track with waypoints and junction points.
2. Courses to steer from point to point, or between waypoints.
3. Distances from point to point, and for the passage.
4. Estimated time of arrival at various points computed for selected speeds at half-knot intervals.
5. Lights and aids to navigation expected en route, with characteristics and range of visibility.
6. Notations of banks, shoals, and other points of particular interest.
7. Port and pilot requirements, VHF working frequencies and reporting requirements, times of high and low water at the port.

8. Set and draft expected from ocean and local currents.
9. Particular information required by any unusual conditions existing along the track.
10. Local vessel traffic control practices and requirements.

This information is also put on all the necessary charts as a reference that will remain throughout the passage—a graphic plan that is even more important and useful than the tabular plan, since good navigation practice calls for all navigation to be done directly on the charts of an area. As the passage plan is laid down on the chart, the charted data is compared to the tabular plan for errors or unforeseen dangers along the planned route. Put this information on the chart *in ink* so it will remain in its original form. This avoids the cumulative errors which occur when penciled courses are continually shifted as fixes are obtained during a passage. Daily navigation is done in pencil for comparison with the planned track. Lay down arcs of visibility for all lights that will be used, and put all distance, course, expected currents, and other information that is shown on the tabular plan into the chart.

Additional information is required in pilot or inland waters including:

1. Courses and distances in each reach or leg of a port passage.
2. Each turning point, with a reference buoy or bearing and distance off a prominent aid or point of land.
3. Set and drift at several significant points along the route.
4. Time of high and low water at similar points.
5. Location of anchorages, pilot boarding areas, and the location where tugs will be met and made fast.
6. Shoals and hazards, highlighted to bring them to the navigator's attention during the passage.

Again, everything except the times of tides and current changes should be in ink, both to avoid mistakes and to save future work, since the courses and distances will not be lost when the chart is erased and will be available for subsequent passages.

THE COURSE CARD

In addition to the chart, a pocket size course card (described in Chapter 7) is prepared by the master for reference during the passage to or from the dock (Fig. 12-3). The pocket card minimizes distraction from the ship's operation and allows the master to remain at the centerline

PILOT VHF 16 & 12

SEA TO NEWTOWN WHARF

FROM	TO	CHARACTERISTIC	COURSE	DIST.
LT. TOWER	BUOY #8	QK.FL R.	311	2.4
BUOY #8	BUOY #17	QK.FL.W.	319	1.9
BUOY 17	JONES PT.	GP. FL.W.(5SEC)	327	2.7
JONES PT.	BUOY "2PR"	QK. FL. W	322	2.2
BUOY "2PR"	BUOY "17PR"	FL.W. (4 SEC)	337	3.6
BUOY "17 PR"	BASIN		332	1.9
BASIN	DOCK #6		322	0.5
		TOTAL DIST.		15.7 MI.
		VARIATION 3.5 W.		

Fig. 12-3. Pocket course card.

window to conn the ship or observe the pilot's work rather than having to shift between the wheelhouse and chartroom. The pilot has a course card even though he is able to draw the chart of the port from memory; how can the master effectively conn the ship without one? The card shows the reaches in order with the course, length of the reach, turning point at the end of each reach, and the characteristics of turning point lights noted. Put the information on one or two 3-by-5-inch cards which are kept in the shirt pocket. The cards are meant to supplement the charted information and to minimize distracting trips to the chartroom, rather than to replace the use of the charts completely. The card must cover the entire area between the sea and dock, not just the portion of the passage that is made without a pilot.

This card will be especially appreciated when that heavy rain squall or fog sets in midway down river and the master needs only to glance at the course card to check the heading as the ship feels her way to sea.

BRIDGE DESIGN

Good bridge design is essential if the mariner and shiphandler are to work safely and effectively. It is difficult to use improperly located equipment, or to bring a ship onto a range that can't be seen because of obstructions placed in the shiphandler's line of sight. The mariner must insist that naval architects give the same consideration to good bridge design as is given to hull and engine room design, so the bridge is planned to fit the deck officer's and pilot's work habits. The cost of installation should be secondary to good design and ease of maintenance; the bridge layout affects the operation and navigation of the ship throughout her life.

An excellent study was done by a committee of master mariners and pilots chaired by Captains Wilbur H. Vantine and Robert D. Valentine in 1975,* to develop practical criteria for bridge design. The study has since been adopted by the International Maritime Pilots' Association, has been reviewed and approved by over two hundred ship designers, builders, and owners, and was included by IMO in the internationally accepted standards for bridge design. This study is available from those groups, and should be consulted by mariners, naval architects, and operations managers when designing or updating a ship's bridge. Design criteria are presented, rather than a standardized bridge design, so there is no risk of institutionalizing present-day technology.

Standardized designs are neither necessary nor practical; different types of vessels, their manning scales, and their intended service all affect design so that an "all ship" bridge is not feasible. Guidelines and minimum requirements do have value though, especially if developed by experienced seafarers and pilots so that design fits use, and good work habits do not have to be compromised to adapt to impractical design. A small, bridge-controlled coaster that docks with one man on the bridge requires a more centralized layout than a VLCC, and the height and open design required with a 900-foot-long containership is not necessary for the coaster. It is counterproductive, then, for any study to be overly specific: only those features desirable on all vessels should be presented.

Aboard new ships, miniaturized equipment should be grouped in clusters or stations that don't interfere with the shiphandler or mate on watch. It is now technically possible to place all bridge equipment in one console, but this is counterproductive since several people must then work in one area. Gear should be grouped by use so it isn't necessary to move from one side of a 100-foot-wide wheelhouse to the other to perform a single task, and place each console-mounted group in that area of the wheelhouse where it is most useful (Fig. 12-4).

No two mariners or pilots will agree on the exact placement of bridge equipment, but there are general principles upon which all experienced pilots and mariners concur:

*Wilbur H. Vantine, "Good Bridge Design from a Master Mariner's Point of View," 99-104.

Fig. 12-4. Group bridge equipment in clusters or stations. Courtesy Sperry Marine Systems.

1. A clear view must be provided on the centerline, or as near the centerline as possible, from the wheelhouse to the stern.
2. The wheelhouse windows must be large and give a clear all-around view of the horizon, with as few bulkheads and pillars as possible.
3. There must be unobstructed access to the centerline wheelhouse windows so the shiphandler can see both forward and abeam without having to move around the wheelhouse.
4. A conning station is required around the centerline windows.
5. At sea, navigation equipment should be located so there is as near to a 360-degree clear view as possible from the chart table.
6. The helmsman's station should be located on the centerline well back from the windows.
7. A ship control console is required near the center of the wheelhouse, located well back from the windows, where the officer on watch can clearly hear all helm and engine orders.
8. The wheelhouse should be soundproofed; too many casualties occur because the mate or helmsman cannot hear orders clearly.
9. A conning station is required on each bridge wing.
10. A clear walkway is needed from one bridge wing to the other, through the wheelhouse, with all equipment other than the conning station located aft of the walkway.

Naval architects seem to have a misconception about the helmsman's duties, so a significant number of modern ships have the wheel located forward at the wheelhouse windows. Ships with the wheel in this improper location seem inevitably to sign on a helmsman who is 7-feet tall, making it physically impossible for the master or pilot to see! On future ships the helm station should be placed well back from the window and equipped with a gyro repeater, gyro pilot controls, rate of turn indicator, and wheel and rudder angle indicators (Fig. 12-5).

If your ship's helm station is improperly located adjacent to the wheelhouse windows, give the helmsman a stool to sit on in pilot waters. The pilot or conning officer can then at least see over the helmsman's head.

Arrange a conning station around the centerline windows, the equipment being bulkhead mounted over the windows and on a console aft of the window facing forward *to keep access to the windows clear*. It is important that the shiphandler and mate on watch have an unobstructed view ahead and abeam while working. This becomes especially significant when a light rain covers the windows with beads of water and it is impossible to see out without getting right up to the glass. This simple detail—providing unobstructed access to the centerline windows—materially increases the margin of safety when handling the ship. If you can't get up to the bridge windows aboard your present ship, it might be possible to move a bulkhead table or other equipment to create the needed access.

This conning station is designed to group in one location all the equipment needed for shiphandling. Any changes you can make in your present ship, such as shifting a tachometer, VHF transmitter, fathometer, or rudder angle indicator so they can be used while you remain at the center windows will be worth the effort. Even if only a few pieces of gear are shifted, you can create at least a minimal conning station. The optimum station would include a digital fathometer, VHF transceiver, wind direction and force indicators, whistle control, Doppler speed indicators, bow thruster controls, gyro repeater, tachometer, rate-of-turn indicator, and rudder angle indicator. The radar/CAS should be placed to starboard of this location, good seamanship dictating that the horizon off the starboard bow of a ship should be visible from the radar, so it can be used by the officer working at the conning station. If this equipment is placed at one station, the mate or pilot can obtain needed information without having to move about the wheelhouse. This is important, since it is difficult to remain oriented to ship motion, particularly lateral motion, if the shiphandler must continually move from one location to

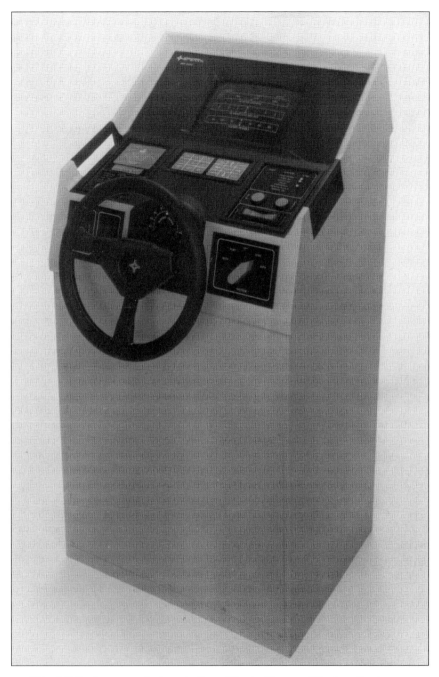

Fig. 12-5. A proper helm station. Photo Sperry Marine Systems.

Fig. 12-6. Provide unobstructed access to the centerline wheelhouse windows.

another to work (Fig. 12-6). Japanese ships generally have such well arranged conning stations that they could be a model for ships of other nationalities.

A similar station should be placed on each wing. Less equipment is needed at this station, since the pilot or master normally works from the bridge wing only when embarking or disembarking a pilot, or conning alongside a dock, a small boat, or other vessel. A tachometer, gyro repeater, the VHF and internal communications handsets, rudder angle indicator, and bow thruster controls should be placed here. If the telegraph is not visible from this station, a small repeating indicator is needed on the wing. If your ship lacks these wing indicators, have them installed. Aboard larger ships, or ships with a high level of bridge noise, a communications system is needed between the bridge area, helmsman, and mate on watch to eliminate the shouting that leads to misunderstood commands and accidents. Use an answerback system so the mate and helmsman can acknowledge orders, either via a talkback hailer arrangement or a walkie-talkie. Japanese ships routinely have a microphone mounted at the steering console so the helmsman can repeat commands back to the conning officer on the bridge wing, and you could easily fit such equipment aboard your present ship.

Mariners and pilots should be consulted when designing the bridge layout prior to construction of a new ship; once the ship is built, seamen can make changes only where practical and then work around remaining restrictions placed upon them by poor design. Mariners must insist, through the Council of American Master Mariners and other professional groups, on having some impact on future design and regulation of the ship's bridge and its equipment. Even if no change is made in bridge design other than countering the trend toward blocking access to the wheelhouse windows with a helm station and operating console, a major improvement in design will have been made.

BRIDGE HEIGHT

Bridge height is a critical design consideration. Several years ago, a major European containership operator put a class of vessel into service with a wheelhouse so low that the tops of the containers were above the lower part of the wheelhouse windows, making it physically impossible to conn the ship from that location. The ship was a masterpiece of engineering, yet the pilot worked hanging over the bridge wing like an old-time locomotive engineer. The wheelhouse must be raised, even if it requires an extra unused deck, so the berth alongside and areas ahead are visible at a reasonable distance. This is especially important aboard bridge aft ships, since that design restricts visibility over the bow under the best of conditions.

Keep in mind when working from the greater bridge heights common aboard modern ships that distance and speed of advance are greatly distorted as height of eye increases. The ship appears to be moving much more slowly and to be much closer to points of reference than it actually is. The height of eye aboard a modern LNG ship, for example, is 110 to 130 feet—working from that height is similar to working from the roof of a ten- to twelve-story building (Fig. 12-7).

Automobile carriers, LASH ships, RO/RO, smaller passenger vessels, and similar ships commonly have the wheelhouse placed extremely close to the bow. Working 75 feet from the stem makes it difficult to estimate turning rates, so work looking aft, "Great Lakes fashion," when maneuvering in restricted areas and narrow channels. It is especially

Fig. 12-7. "Working from greater bridge heights creates new problems."

important that these types of ships have a clear view from the wheel-house to the stern, both from the bridge wings and from amidships, and that the bridge wings extend outboard to the maximum beam of the ship so the parallel midbody is visible. Some arrangement must be provided that overcomes the short bridge to bow distance that greatly reduces perspective. Most commonly, markers are placed on the centerline—a pole or high vertical jackstaff at the bow and a marker on the centerline window in the wheelhouse—to provide a "gunsight effect" to make small changes of heading more obvious. Since competent shiphandlers normally watch the stern as much as the bow when working, a wheelhouse located in the extreme forepart of the ship presents no significant obstacles, as long as the bridge is properly designed (Fig. 12-8).

Prepare a visibility diagram for every ship you serve aboard, showing areas not visible from the wheelhouse in light and loaded conditions, with and without containers if carried, and post the diagram in the wheelhouse. The diagram is simple to construct using basic trigonometry and the basic ship dimensions such as bridge height, bridge to bow distance, ship's beam, etc. The diagram is especially helpful when maneuvering around piers and in restricted channels (Fig. 12-9).

Fig. 12-8. Ships with a bridge well forward need a centerline marker.

NIGHT VERSUS DAYLIGHT MANEUVERING

Darkness creates new problems for the shiphandler and there are two pilotages in any water—a daylight and a night pilotage.

1. Speed and distance become more difficult to estimate, since depth perception is lost at night, and *relative size and changes of relative motion must be used to judge distance.*
2. It is even more important to look abeam or aft at night than during the day, since it is *impossible* to estimate speed during hours of darkness by looking ahead of the ship.
3. On a clear night objects appear *closer,* yet when visibility deteriorates they appear further away.
4. Unlighted buoys and shoreline are no longer visible, so more reliance must be placed on radar presentation and local knowledge to stay clear of shoals and banks.
5. A poorly lighted stringpiece must be avoided by instinct because it is not visible during docking.

Even the smallest increase in light helps, since some degree of depth perception is regained. Do not make a passage without computing the time of moonrise and moonset for the night in question, and, given a chance, delay a particularly difficult passage until daybreak if there is not at least a gibbous moon at the needed time. The ship's ETA is often

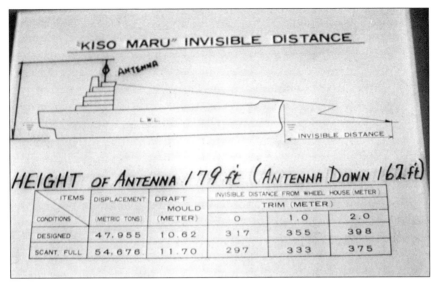

"KISO MARU" INVISIBLE DISTANCE

HEIGHT OF ANTENNA 179 ft (ANTENNA DOWN 162 ft)

ITEMS	DISPLACEMENT	DRAFT MOULD	INVISIBLE DISTANCE FROM WHEEL HOUSE (METER) TRIM (METER)		
CONDITIONS	(METRIC TONS)	(METER)	0	1.0	2.0
DESIGNED	47,955	10.62	317	355	398
SCANT. FULL	54,676	11.70	297	333	375

Fig. 12-9. Post a visibility diagram on the bridge.

an indication of the master's experience, since a more seasoned ship-master appreciates the problems caused by darkness and delays arrival until daybreak when there is no real need to arrive at an earlier hour.

Some degree of experience is needed on a dark night at sea to estimate distance from other ships, especially when masthead and range lights are poorly placed, although radar overcomes this problem to a great extent, and darkness is now much less a problem in open water navigation. Make it a practice to estimate distance off *before* going to the radar so you can develop the ability to judge distance visually with reasonable accuracy. This skill is greatly appreciated when the radar goes down or when conning by eye in an anchorage or congested area. Younger mariners especially need to make a conscious effort to develop this ability, since they do not acquire it by necessity, as did the senior officers who stood watches before radar was so widely accepted.

Depth perception is a result of binocular vision and unconscious evaluation of relative position. When this ability is lost at night, the mariner substitutes other techniques:

1. Relative size is an indication of distance. For example, the height of a buoy, and thus its distance off can be estimated at night since the light marks the top, while the reflection of that light on the water shows the base of the buoy.

2. Relative motion is quite helpful since at more than 2 miles' distance a buoy will appear nearly stationary, at 1 mile its change in bearing becomes more noticeable, and when the buoy is close at hand its movement nearly equals the speed of the ship.
3. Brilliance is helpful, but can be deceiving since it is affected by so many factors, such as atmospheric conditions, the aspect of the light, and motion of the light in the case of a buoy.
4. Techniques such as computing the arc of visibility and bobbing a light are applicable at greater distances than the shiphandler is generally concerned with, but can be used on occasion.

To expand on the importance of rate of changes in relative bearing, consider a ship turning inside a buoy. The apparent motion of the buoy is significantly greater as its distance from the ship decreases, and thus the change in motion can be used with reasonable accuracy to estimate the change in distance from the buoy as the ship turns. Again—*practice estimating distance in these conditions before looking at the radar* and the skill of handling a ship at night comes quickly.

RECORD KEEPING

The keeping of logs and records of maneuvers is inherent in proper shiphandling, although the two tasks often conflict when the record keeping becomes redundant or unnecessarily complicated. Proper organization and the use of autologging relieve the mate of some of the administrative chores, so more attention can be given to the navigation of the ship. Give priority to navigation rather than getting so involved in record keeping that problems are not recognized and acted upon. It is more important to avoid a casualty than to record the exact time of impact.

Good work habits develop with experience. Remember your first undocking as a cadet or green third mate? There seemed to be myriad tasks to accomplish and details to be noted and logged. With time, these responsibilities become second nature until, while accomplishing everything required, you had time for coffee and perhaps swapping sea stories with the pilot. When record keeping is properly organized, it can be done concurrently with other tasks and consumes little time. This sort of organization is essential while maneuvering in pilot waters.

Every ship should be fitted with an automatic bell logger. The mate's time is better spent checking the tachometer and rudder angle indicator to see that helm and engine orders are properly executed than in continuously recording the bells.

Eliminate all the separate books and limit all record keeping to *one scratch log/workbook and the chart* when in pilot waters. Important data is transferred to the deck log at a later convenient time and the mate does not have to shuffle bell books, navigation books, logbooks, sounding books, and whatever other record books might be required by company policy. Keep the book neatly, but don't waste time with elaborate entries that divert attention from the shiphandling and navigational duties at hand—after all, the book is called a "scratch log."

Refer to any of the classic navigation or seamanship texts for more detailed information about what should be included in the deck log when in pilot waters, but be certain to include:

1. Times and locations of course and speed changes, and times of changes to diesel fuel or maneuvering speeds.
2. Time of passing abeam of important lights, landmarks, buoys marking the end of a reach or other significant location, and the bearing and distance of those aids.
3. Times of encountering significant changes in depth of water under the keel.
4. Important meteorological information such as visibility, passing showers, fog, wind force and direction.
5. Engine maneuvers (recorded by the automatic bell logger).
6. Time of passing conning responsibility between master, pilot, and the deck officers.
7. Significant radio transmissions, such as those for making passing arrangements with ships being met or overtaken.

Note all the navigational information first on the chart, and then put essential information into the scratch log. Compare each position with the DR and the inked passage courses and notify the master and pilot of any set indicated. Don't end your duties with recording information while the vessel is set toward a shoal that only you are aware of, and *don't assume that the pilot is aware of the situation—tell the master or pilot about it*—information is gathered so you can supply it to the officer conning, not just so it can be recorded for historic interest.

Keep the passage plan nearby for reference and have it *preplotted* in ink on the charts used. This greatly reduces record keeping while maneuvering, and serves as a check on the ship's actual progress as compared to the passage plan. Graphic records are often more meaningful, and minimize the need for many distracting tabular records. Avoid redundant work by keeping the scratch paper off the chart table. *Enter bearings and other information directly into the scratch log* rather than putting them first on scratch paper, and reduce logging chores by nearly 50 percent. This helps you to record all necessary data without taking excessive time away from priority tasks. The scratch log is just that, a rough notebook for later reference, so anything of interest can be recorded in it while avoiding distracting and time-consuming double work.

REVIEW QUESTIONS AND PRACTICE MANEUVERS

Page numbers in parentheses indicate where in the text the answers may be found.

CHAPTER 1. ARRIVAL

Review Questions

1. In day-to-day work, the most useful unit of measurement for estimating turning circles and other distances is the ship's own length. (Page 9)
   a. true
   b. false

2. In shallow water, a ship's turning circle is: (Pages 9-10)
   a. larger
   b. smaller
   c. the same

3. An average-size ship's turning circle is usually slightly _____ when the ship turns to the right than when she turns left. (Page 10)
   a. larger
   b. smaller
   c. the same

4. A VLCC's turning circle to the right is usually _____ her turning circle to the left. (Page 10)
   a. larger than
   b. smaller than
   c. nearly the same as

5. When revolutions are increased during a turn, the tactical diameter becomes (or stays): (Pages 10-11)
   a. larger
   b. smaller
   c. the same

6. For a given rudder angle and engine speed, the rate of turn _____ as the depth of water decreases. (Pages 9-10)
    a. increases
    b. decreases
    c. does not change

7. A ship can be backed and filled in the smallest area when turned to the left. (Pages 11-12)
    a. true
    b. false

8. You are aboard an average-size, loaded, house-aft tanker proceeding through an open roadstead. The wind is blowing hard enough to overcome the normal twisting effect when your ship's engine goes astern. When you back your ship you would expect her to: (Pages 13-14)
   I. head into the wind while she has headway and back into the wind when she has sternway.
   II. head away from the wind while she has headway and back away from the wind when she has sternway.
    a. I only
    b. II only
    c. both I and II
    d. neither I nor II

9. Assuming there are no extraordinary wind, current, or bank effects, a ship should be swinging moderately to _____ before her engine is put astern. (Page 14)
    a. starboard
    b. port

10. A bow thruster is sometimes preferable to tugs because: (Page 15)
    I. it is located at the extreme end of the vessel.
    II. it is always available
    III. it is equally effective at slow and fast speeds.
    a. I and II
    b. II and III
    c. all of the above
    d. none of the above

11. Using a bow thruster has its disadvantages: (Pages 15-16)
    I. it usually provides less power than a tug.
    II. it has no effect on headway to slow or hold a ship.
    III. it can only be used at very light drafts.
    a. I and II
    b. II and III
    c. all of the above
    d. none of the above

12. A bow thruster is usually quite effective at speeds of up to 5 knots. (Pages 15-16)
    a. true
    b. false

13. The concept of using the "most effective maneuver" is important because: (Pages 16-17)
    I. the ship is maneuvered using the minimum number of engine and rudder orders.
    II. several tasks are accomplished simultaneously.
    III. it simplifies maneuvering because only one task is completed at a time.
        a. I and II
        b. I and III
        c. III only
        d. none of the above

14. How would you expect the following shiphandling characteristics to change as your ship moves from deep to shallow water? (Pages 17-18)
    A. Tactical diameter. _____   a. increase
    B. Twisting effect when backed. _____   b. decrease
    C. Rate of turn. _____   c. no significant change
    D. Speed loss during large course changes. _____
    E. Speed loss when engine stopped. _____
    F. Directional stability. _____

15. How would you expect the following to affect directional stability? (Pages 18-20)
    A. Increased length. _____   a. more positive (or less negative)
    B. Increased beam. _____   b. less positive (or more negative)
    C. Increased drag. _____   c. no significant change.
    D. Decreased under-keel clearance. _____
    E. Increased block coefficient. _____
    F. More full sections forward. _____
    G. Increased rudder angle. _____
    H. Ship trimmed by the head. _____
    I. Increased squat by the head. _____

16. Ships with large block coefficients are more likely to trim by the head in shallow water. (Page 20)
    a. true
    b. false

17. Which of the following statements is/are *true* for ships with *negative* directional stability? (Pages 18-20)
    I. A larger rudder angle is needed for a longer period of time to start a turn.
    II. A larger rudder angle is needed for a longer period of time to steady up after a turn.
    III. The ship's rate of turn increases when the rudder is put amidships during a turn.
    a. I only
    b. I and III
    c. all of the above
    d. none of the above

18. The only effective way to slow a ship is to stop the engine and, if necessary, go astern. (Pages 23-24)
    a. true
    b. false

19. A VLCC makes a hard-over turn. You would expect her to lose nearly ____ percent of her headway when her heading changes by 90 degrees. (Page 25)
    a. 10
    b. 20
    c. 25
    d. 50

20. A ship is on your port bow in a crossing situation and her bearing is steady. You reach the point where you doubt that collision can be avoided by her actions alone. Usually, it would be better to: (Page 25)
    I. back down
    II. make a round turn
    a. I only
    b. II only
    c. both I and II
    d. neither I nor II

21. A combination pilot ladder/accommodation ladder is required when the distance from the water to the top of the ladder exceeds____feet. (Pages 29-30)
    a. 10
    b. 20
    c. 30
    d. 50

22. A modern containership has more sail area than a full rigged sailing ship. (Page 33)
    a. true
    b. false

Practice Maneuvers

1. Make a hard-over turn in *deep water* and use the wake to measure the ship's tactical diameter. A brightly painted oil drum can be used as a reference or the diameter can be measured by radar using the display of the sea return generated by the ship's wake. How does the diameter of the turning circle compare with the ship's length?

   Make the same turn in *shallow water* (a depth less than 1.25 times draft) and measure the turning circle. How does the diameter of the turning circle in shallow water compare with that observed in deep water?

2. Your ship is dead in the water. Put the rudder hard over and put the engine progressively from slow, to half, and then to full ahead so the ship executes a complete circle with the revolutions increasing through the entire 360 degrees. Use the wake as in maneuver 1 above, to measure the diameter of this turn. Now, leave the engine on full ahead and again measure the turning circle diameter while making another complete 360-degree turn with the engine speed unchanged (a steady state turn). How does the diameter of the accelerating turn compare with that of the steady state turn?

3. Perform the *master's maneuvers* described in Chapter 1 while one of the ship's mates collects data on your ship's characteristics using a data sheet similar to Fig. 1-2 on page 9. Analyze these data and compare the rate of turn, time to stop, change of heading when stopping and backing, and other important characteristics with the data collected aboard other ships you have maneuvered. Study all the pertinent information so you have some feel for your ship and can predict her behavior with reasonable accuracy.

4. This exercise will give you a feel for, and appreciation of, using hard-over rudder to reduce speed. First, measure your ship's speed approaching an open anchorage or pilot station. This can be done with a Doppler log, or the ship's ARPA (plotting a fixed point while the ship's speed is manually input to zero knots so the "computed speed" of the fixed object is then your ship's speed), or by any other method you might choose. A series of simple fixes at frequent intervals can be used to at least get a rough measure of speed and changes in speed. Obviously, you can't accurately determine absolute speed with the latter method, but changes in speed will be quite apparent to the experienced mariner and this exercise can still be very useful even if your ship isn't fitted with equipment to measure speed accurately.

   Put the rudder hard over and change the ship's heading by at least 45 degrees. Measure the ship's speed again and calculate the reduction in speed. Repeatedly shift the rudder from hard over to hard over while continuing to measure or estimate speed through the water and changes in speed until the ship's headway is significantly reduced.

5. When sea room permits, make a practice of putting the rudder hard over toward the lee side (toward the side on which a pilot is boarding) a short time before the pilot begins boarding. Observe how this sweeps a smooth lee for the pilot and makes boarding quicker and safer.

CHAPTER 2. SHIPHANDLING IN A CHANNEL

Review Questions

1. To break a sheer in narrow channels a pilot should: (Page 44)
   - a. reduce engine revolutions
   - b. increase engine revolutions
   - c. turn away from the bank and increase distance
   - d. increase rudder toward the bank
   - e. both a and c
   - f. both b and d

2. Your vessel is steaming parallel to a shoal or bank. How does she behave?
   A. Her bow moves away from the bank or shoal. (Pages 44-45)
   - a. true
   - b. false

   B. Her stern moves toward the bank or shoal. (Pages 44-45)
   - a. true
   - b. false

   C. Her midbody moves laterally away from the bank. (Pages 44-45)
   - a. true
   - b. false

   D. Competent shiphandlers don't just react to the ship's behavior and decide on a course of action after a situation develops; they think ahead, anticipate situations,and plan alternative maneuvers. (Pages 46-47)
   - a. true
   - b. false

   E. Ships with variable pitch propellers steer best if speed is reduced quickly. (Page 49)
   - a. true
   - b. false

3. The tactical diameter and turning rate can be precisely adjusted during a turn by visually aligning an external fixed object, such as a buoy or point of land, with a reference point aboard ship.

A. The tactical diameter is ____ when the object moves ahead relative to the shipboard reference point. (Page 56)
   a. increasing
   b. decreasing

B. The rate of turn is ____ if the object moves ahead more rapidly. (Page 56)
   a. increasing
   b. decreasing

4. It is best to overtake and pass close by another ship in a narrow channel at a very slow speed, while the overtaken ship should increase her speed before being passed. (Pages 59-60)
   a. true
   b. false

5. The clicking sound made by the gyrocompass should be eliminated as it distracts the pilot. (Page 60)
   a. true
   b. false

6. A rate of turn indicator usually indicates turning rate in ____ per second or ____ per minute. (Page 62)
   a. meters/feet
   b. tenths of a degree/degrees
   c. degrees/degrees
   d. feet/feet

7. A ship changes draft when moving into shallow water. The change in mean draft indicates the ____ while the increase in deep draft, forward or aft, is called ____. (Page 64)
   a. squat/sinkage
   b. sinkage/squat
   c. squat/trim

8. Ships always trim by the stern in shallow water. (Page 64)
   a. true
   b. false

9. The pilot or ship's officer can reduce sinkage and squat by reducing the ship's: (Pages 64-65)
   I. block coefficient
   II. speed
   III. blockage factor
   a. I only
   b. II only
   c. II and III
   d. none of the above

10. Sinkage for a given speed and hull condition in confined water is ____ that in open water. (Pages 65-66)
   a. half
   b. twice

11. A useful formula for calculating approximate sinkage in open water is:

$$\text{Sinkage (feet)} = \text{block coefficent} \times \frac{(\text{speed in knots})^2}{30}$$

A. Calculate sinkage for a ship having a block coefficient of 0.8 proceeding at 6 knots in open water. (Pages 65-66)

B. Calculate sinkage for the same ship proceeding at the same speed in a restricted channel. (Pages 65-66)

C. Calculate sinkage for the same ship proceeding at 12 knots in a restricted channel. (Pages 65-66)

Practice Maneuvers

1. Closely observe the rudder angle indicator as a ship passes near banks and points of land. Compare the amount of rudder needed to hold a ship steady on her course as the bow passes each point of land with that needed when the stern reaches the same point.

2. Compare the amount of rudder and duration of time it is applied when starting a turn with the amount and time needed to check a ship's swing at the completion of the turn. Do this when your ship is trimmed by the head, and when she is trimmed by the stern. Is she directionally stable or unstable in each case?

3. Observe the change in rate of turn after the rudder has been put amidships for each case described in maneuver 2. Does the rate increase or decrease? Is your ship directionally stable or unstable?

4. Select a buoy or point that lies on the inside of a turn while making routine maneuvers at the pilot station or in an anchorage. Stand in a location that puts this buoy or point in line with the edge of a wheelhouse window, and turn your ship around this reference point without changing the rudder angle. Closely watch the object's relative motion as the ship turns. Did it move forward or aft relative to the reference point as the ship turned? How did the ship's distance from the reference object change in each case? How did the change in your ship's rate of turn affect the rate of relative motion of the reference object?

5. Make the same type of turn around the same or similar reference point and adjust the amount of rudder being used to keep the buoy fixed in position relative to your shipboard reference point. Did the ship then maintain the

same approximate distance off the reference object? You are now making controlled turns.

6. Carefully note the location of buoys and points, relative to your ship's pivot point, as a pilot begins each turn in a narrow channel. Develop a feel for the time at which turns should be started. (Note: Most inexperienced shiphandlers begin a turn too soon.)

7. Closely watch the rudder angle indicator as your ship meets and passes other ships in a narrow channel. Was more or less rudder used as the bows passed, or when the ships were abeam, or when their sterns were passing? Was the rudder toward or away from the other ship?

8. Watch the rudder angle indicator each time your ship overtakes and passes other vessels in a narrow channel. Note also any changes in engine speed made by the pilot while the other ships are being passed. Were the rudder and engine used in the manner described in shiphandling texts?

9. Make a habit of listening to the clicking sound of your gyrocompass while turning. It will soon become second nature and you will immediately know when your rate of turn is increasing or decreasing and to what degree.

10. Have the forward and after tugs read your draft as closely as possible while your ship is moving at 6 to 10 knots and again when they have made up and your ship is proceeding at bare steerageway. Note both sinkage (change in mean draft) and squat. Does your ship squat by the head or by the stern? How did this compare with your computed sinkage using the formula on page 65?

CHAPTER 3. USE OF TUGS

Review Questions

1. Prepare a sketch showing how a tug is typically made fast alongside in a U.S. port, using two lines. Label the backing line (head line) and the come ahead line (spring line). (Pages 71-72)

2. Make a similar sketch showing the tug made up with three lines, labeling the come ahead and backing lines as well as the additional stern line. (Page 72)

3. A tug being used for ship work can only be used to move a ship's bow or stern laterally. (Page 74)
   a. true
   b. false

4. You are docking a ship using two tugs. You have the quarter tug stand off until just before the ship enters the slip. Give two reasons for this. (Pages 76-77)

5. Match the following signals with one or more tug responses. (Page 73)
   A. Increase to full power. ____   a. one blast
   B. Tug is dismissed. Let go. ____   b. two blasts
   C. If working, stop. ____   c. three blasts
   D. If pushing, increase power. ____   d. series of short blasts
   E. Come ahead dead slow. ____   e. one long, two short blasts
   F. Back the tug, normal power. ____   f. one long blast
   G. If stopped, come ahead. ____
   H. Not a tug signal. ____
   I. If stopped, come ahead. ____
   J. If backing, increase power. ____

6. A bow thruster used correctly will have the same effects on the ship as a tug made fast on the ship's bow. (Page 74)
   a. true
   b. false

7. A tug's lines don't have to be heaved up tightly, when she is lashed up alongside to work, if she has good leads for both spring and head lines. (Page 80)
   a. true
   b. false

CHAPTER 4. APPROACHING THE BERTH

Review Questions

1. It is important that the pilot keep moving about the wheelhouse so as to always have a good view of every part of the ship while docking or doing other work. (Pages 83-84)
   a. true
   b. false

2. There are several techniques a shiphandler can use to hold a ship in position in a channel or other confined area, including: (Page 86)
   I. steam on the anchor at slow engine speeds.
   II. anchor to a short scope of chain with the current from ahead.
   III. simply back and fill in the channel.
   a. I only
   b. II only
   c. III only
   d. all of the above

3. Generally, the less experience shiphandlers have, the _____ they work. (Page 86)
   a. faster
   b. slower

4. Quickwater (propeller wash when backing) moves ahead at about the same speed as the ship when the ship is making about ____knots. (Pages 87-88)
   a. 1
   b. 2
   c. 3

5. Quickwater begins to move forward, up the ship's side, when the ship is making a speed of approximately _____ knots, and the quickwater reaches the ship's midships section when the ship is moving at a speed of ____knots. (Pages 87-88)
   a. 1/0
   b. 2/1
   c. 3/2

6. An experienced shiphandler always looks at objects ahead of the ship when estimating speed during a maneuver because it's difficult to detect movement by looking abeam or abaft the beam. (Pages 88-89)
   a. true
   b. false

7. Why is it better to approach the berth with less angle when docking a ship with a right hand propeller starboard side to the dock? (Page 90)

8. Sketch two alternative methods for making tugs fast when backing into a slip starboard side to the pier. (Pages 92-93)

9. Ships docking at a wharf in strong current can expect to be set off the berth just as they come alongside because of the ____and the ____, especially when there is a bank or solid face below the wharf. (Page 94)
   a. hydraulic cushion/Bernoulli effect
   b. Bernoulli effect/eddy current
   c. hydraulic cushion/eddy current

10. It is best to think of a ship as being docked stern first when she is docking with the current from astern. The docking is done as if the ship were moving ____ relative to the ____. (Page 94)
   a. ahead/water
   b. ahead/bottom
   c. astern/water
   d. astern/bottom

11. When docking at a wharf with the current from astern, the _____ is used to move her laterally the last few feet to the berth. (Page 94)
    a. current
    b. engine

12. Your ship is docking port side to a wharf parallel to the channel. There is a strong ebb current running as you come alongside, and tugs are made fast at the bow and stern. (Page 95)
    I. the tugs should come full ahead at a 90-degree angle to the ship to pin the ship tight alongside and prevent movement while lines are run.
    II. the tugs should work at an angle toward the ship, into the current, to hold the ship both alongside and in position.
    III. the tugs should come ahead parallel to the ship's side, against the current, to hold the ship in position while lines are run to keep the ship alongside.
    a. I only
    b. II only
    c. III only
    d. either I or III

Practice Maneuvers

1. Try to handle your ship without moving around the wheelhouse more than is absolutely necessary. Notice how your feel for the ship's movements (and especially lateral movement when turning, backing, working in currents, or using tugs) is significantly improved when you aren't constantly moving around the wheelhouse.

2. Make use of every opportunity to practice handling your ship at minimum speed. Stop the engine and keep her on course while approaching an anchorage or pilot station, using hard-over rudder as headway is lost. Be patient, watch the stem or jackstaff closely to detect movement as soon as possible, and learn how *slowly* your ship can be handled. When she no longer answers to rudder alone, use short kicks on the engine to start and check swing, and practice until you can handle your ship at less than 1 knot in all but the worst conditions with a minimum of engine maneuvers. Anyone can handle a ship at sea speed!

3. Look over the side and check the position of the quickwater every time you back the engine to slow or stop your vessel. Use the location of the quickwater to estimate headway when approaching an anchorage, berth, or pilot station. (Read page 88 for approximate speeds vs. quickwater position.)

4. If your ship is fitted with a Doppler log, check your speed through the water when the quickwater is moving forward at the same speed as your ship, when the quickwater starts moving forward along the ship's hull, and when the quickwater reaches amidships.

CHAPTER 5. DOCKING

Review Questions

1. A competent shiphandler plans a job so that wind and current can be used as aids to maneuvering rather than forces to be overcome. (Page 97)
    a. true
    b. false

2. A 1-knot current exerts the same force on a given surface area as _____ knot(s) of wind. (Page 98)
    a. 1
    b. 10
    c. 20
    d. 30

3. A ship moving at 2 knots moves approximately _____ in one minute (Page 100)
    a. 50 feet
    b. 100 feet
    c. 200 feet
    d. 200 yards

4. Lateral motion can be caused by: (Pages 100-101)
    I. wind and current.
    II. turning the ship.
    III. extended use of tugs.
    a. I and II
    b. I and III
    c. all of the above
    d. Ships do not move laterally.

5. You are docking a ship with a right hand propeller and she is about to come alongside and be stopped, in position, at the berth. The ship should be set up for backing to allow for, and use to advantage, the normal twisting effect as the ship goes astern. This is most commonly done: (Pages 101-2)
    I. when docking starboard side to, by "kicking" the engine ahead with hard port rudder before going astern.
    II. when docking port side to, by "kicking" the engine ahead with hard starboard rudder before going astern.
    III. when docking port side to, by going astern to take off headway and bring the ship alongside.
    a. both I and II
    b. both I and III
    c. III only
    d. none of the above

6. It's important to always put the rudder amidships before the engine starts turning astern. (Page 102)
    a. true
    b. false

7. Quickwater can have a significant effect, forcing the ship away from the berth when docking starboard side to. (Pages 102-3)
    a. true
    b. false

8. Ships must usually be forced into a berth and maneuvered using full revolutions ahead and astern, because shiphandling is not a subtle art. (Page 104)
    a. true
    b. false

9. Which of the following statements about landing a ship alongside a berth is/are true? (Pages 104-5)
    I. a ship should be parallel to the pier when she lands alongside so all frames along the parallel midbody can absorb equally the force of landing.
    II. a ship should be at an angle to the pier when she lands alongside the wharf or pier to minimize the effects of quickwater as she stops.
    a. I only
    b. II only
    c. both I and II
    d. neither I nor II

Practice Maneuvers

1. Measure the time required for your bridge to move between bollards on the pier. Estimate the distance between bollards by comparing that distance with your ship's beam. What was your ship's speed of approach?

2. Work to become more aware of lateral movement. Make a practice of standing on the centerline when approaching a berth and watching natural ranges (corners of buildings, stacks, flagpoles, rooflines, etc.) for changes that indicate lateral movement.

CHAPTER 6. UNDOCKING

Review Questions

1. Undocking is, by its very nature, a simple maneuver that requires less planning than a docking. (Pages 107-8)
    a. true
    b. false

2. In a ballasted condition, it's usually better to have too much drag than not enough, if such trim is necessary to get the propeller and rudder well submerged. (Pages 108-9)
    a. true
    b. false

3. It is best to approach a potential hazard such as pier or a shoal stern first because you can always put the engine ahead to reduce sternway. (Pages 118-19)
    a. true
    b. false

4. You are about to undock a ship berthed port side to at a wharf. Ships are berthed close ahead and astern, so the ship must be moved laterally to starboard, away from the berth, to clear those ships. Only one tug is available. Describe one way to accomplish this.

    A. The tug could be made fast _____ with at least one backing line from the tug's bow. (Page 111)
    a. forward
    b. aft

    B. The tug _____ at a 45-degree angle toward the stern, while the ship's engine turns ahead and her rudder is put hard to _____. (Pages 111-12)
    a. comes ahead/starboard
    b. backs/starboard
    c. comes ahead/port
    d. backs/port

5. Your ship is docked starboard side to her berth. A tug is made fast on the port bow and the last line has been let go. The ship has a right hand turning propeller. There is no ship berthed astern. The ship's engine is put astern.

    A. The stern will move_____the berth unless there is a strong current or wind countering the propeller's effect. (Pages 112-13)
    a. toward
    b. away from

    B. The bow moves _____ the berth as the ship's speed increases. (Pages 112-13)
    a. toward
    b. away from

    C. The tug will _____ to steady the ship as she moves astern out of the berth. (Pages 112-13)
    a. back
    b. come ahead

6. Your ship is berthed port side to her berth. One tug is available and is made up on the starboard bow. There is no ship berthed astern, but you will need to back approximately 300 feet to get clear of the ship. Describe one way to do this job.

A. The tug comes _____. (Page 113)
  a. ahead
  b. astern

B. This moves the ship's _____ toward the berth. (Page 113)
  a. bow
  b. stern

C. The tug continues _____ until the ship is at a significant angle to the pier. (Pages 113-14)
  a. pushing
  b. pulling

D. This is necessary because the stern will move _____ the pier when the engine goes astern and the ship backs from the berth. (Pages 113-14)
  a. toward
  b. away from

7. A ship's bow can be moved or canted toward a pier before undocking by: (Page 113)
I. pushing with a bow tug.
II. letting go the forward spring and then heaving on the headline.
III. coming ahead dead slow against the spring line with the rudder hard over toward the dock.
  a. I only
  b. I and II
  c. I and III
  d. all of the above

8. Face_____ when moving a ship stern first. (Page 120)
  a. ahead
  b. astern

9. When turning in a tidal basin, it's usually best to: (Pages 121-22)
I. turn the ship with some headway to complete the maneuver in the least time and to minimize effects of currents.
II. turn the ship in the up current side of the basin to avoid being set out of the basin before completing the maneuver.
III. have as much way off the ship as possible before starting to turn in a basin.
  a. I only
  b. I and II
  c. II and III
  d. none of the above

10. Ships fitted with variable pitch propellers respond in a _____ manner than ships fitted with conventional propellers when the engine goes astern. (Page 119)
    a. more predictable
    b. less predictable

11. Variable pitch ships should be fitted with ____ propellers. (Page 119)
    a. right hand
    b. left hand

12. Always dismiss the forward tug as soon as possible to reduce tug charges. (Page 123)
    a. true
    b. false

CHAPTER 7. DEPARTURE

Review Questions

1. The pilot's duties include clarifying the intentions of other ships and making safe meeting arrangements with those ships, and the master should not release the pilot at departure until this is done. (Page 125)
    a. true
    b. false

2. Safe speed at departure is to a large extent determined by: (Pages 125-27)
   I. the shiphandler's experience and confidence in his shiphandling ability.
   II. the depth of water, the speed of departing traffic, and the weather conditions.
    a. I only
    b. II only
    c. all of the above
    d. none of the above

3. By increasing ship speed and moving faster than other departing traffic, the shiphandler significantly reduces the potential for collision. (Page 125)
    a. true
    b. false

4. Modern bridge equipment has made it possible for the ship's master to conn a ship to sea with little or no assistance from the other ship's officers. (Pages 128-29)
    a. true
    b. false

5. Passage planning that stresses a pocket course card, formal pilot/master exchange of information, and charts with preplanned courses, turning bearings, distances, operating notes, and other navigation information noted in ink is preferable to pages of written instructions. (Pages 129-30)
   a. true
   b. false

CHAPTER 8. ANCHORING AND SHIPHANDLING WITH ANCHORS

Review Questions

1. A competent shiphandler can anchor safely in any anchorage and never has to lay off for conditions to improve. (Page 133)
   a. true
   b. false

2. Anchoring is one continuous evolution and considering it in parts makes it unnecessarily complicated. (Pages 134-35)
   a. true
   b. false

3. Allowance should be made one degree at a time for set and leeway when maneuvering at slow speeds in an anchorage. (Page 136)
   a. true
   b. false

4. A ship moving at 3 knots moves about _____ feet ahead in one minute. (Page 137)
   a. 50
   b. 100
   c. 200
   d. 300

5. A ship 600-feet-long, moving at 3 knots, would require about _____ minutes for her entire hull, bow to stern, to pass a fixed point. (Page 137)
   a. one
   b. two
   c. three
   d. four

6. A 1-knot current on the beam sets a 600-foot ship about _____ feet in that amount of time. (Page 137)
    a. 100
    b. 200
    c. 300
    d. 600

7. A ship can turn and maneuver to depart from a crowded anchorage by heaving short and maneuvering on her anchor. (Pages 139-40)
    a. true
    b. false

8. Ships lie at anchor on their final heading: (Page 141)
I. lying to the strong force, wind or current, affecting the ship.
II. lying to the resultant of all forces acting on the ship.
III. lying into the current.
    a. I only
    b. II only
    c. both II and III
    d. all of the above
    e. none of the above

9. List three reasons why it is preferable to have the ship on her final heading before letting go. (Page 142)

10. The difference between the apparent motion of closer ships or objects and farther objects or the shoreline can be used to accurately detect lateral motion and motion ahead and astern. (Pages 145-46)
    a. true
    b. false

11. Go astern to estimate ship's speed through the water _____ the final anchoring location, when anchoring _____. (Pages 147-48)
    a. when at/at night
    b. before reaching/at night
    c. when at/at all times
    d. before reaching/at all times

12. Always place the anchor halfway between ships anchored ahead and astern so your ship will lie at an equal distance from all ships when your anchor fetches up. (Page 148)
    a. true
    b. false

13. Ships at anchor always appear _____ your ship than they are actually lying. (Pages 151-52)
    a. closer to
    b. farther from

14. There is significant risk of damaging a ship's rudder and propeller with a stern anchor. Make sure the ship is _____ before letting go a stern anchor and that sternway is _____ when heaving the stern anchor. (Page 158)
    a. moving astern/increased
    b. stopped/minimized
    c. moving astern/minimized
    d. stopped/increased

15. It's important to use the proper amount of chain when handling a ship with her anchor. Used correctly, the anchor will drag along with considerable resistance, but it won't dig in and hold. (Pages 163-64)
    a. true
    b. false

16. It is unusual for anchors to be used in day-to-day shiphandling because anchors are ineffective with today's larger ships. (Page 166)
    a. true
    b. false

17. An anchor is only used for shiphandling in emergencies when maneuvering today's larger ships. (Pages 159 and 166)
    a. true
    b. false

18. A ship sheers immediately and violently to the side on which an anchor is dropped. (Pages 160-61)
    a. true
    b. false

19. The offshore anchor is recommended when docking a ship because: (Pages 161-62)
    I. there is more chance of the anchor digging in and holding.
    II. there is less chance of damaging the hull and chain.
    III. the offshore anchor may be used later to heave off the berth and undock with minimum damage to hull and chain.
    a. I only
    b. II only
    c. both II and III
    d. all of the above
    e. none of the above

20. Static friction (when the wildcat is not turning) between the asbestos brake band and the windlass's brake drum is approximately _____ times as great as dynamic friction (when the wildcat is turning). (Page 163)
    a. two
    b. three
    c. five
    d. ten

21. When docking with the anchor, using the correct amount of anchor chain: (Page 165)
    I. the bow is steadied.
    II. the ship loses headway when the engine is stopped.
    III. the ship responds to her rudder without gaining headway at low RPMs.
    IV. the ship can be moved ahead by further increasing revolutions.
    a. I only
    b. II and III only
    c. all of the above
    d. none of the above

22. A ship can be turned in a considerably smaller area using an anchor. (Page 167)
    a. true
    b. false

23. In an emergency, let go at least one anchor with enough chain to be certain the anchor will dig in and hold, and not drag, as the ship moves ahead. (Page 164)
    a. true
    b. false

Practice Maneuvers

1. Select a pilot station or anchorage with a fairly uniform sand or mud bottom and a depth 10 to 20 feet greater than your ship's draft. Arrive an hour or more before the ship's pilot time and practice using the anchor.

    a. Head across the wind and stop the engine. Try to steer using the rudder alone as the ship loses headway. Note the wind's effects on the ship.
    b. Come ahead, if necessary, and increase the ship's speed to approximately 2 knots. Stop the engine and let go the windward anchor and one shot of chain well in the water. Slack more chain, as necessary, until the drag of the anchor begins reducing the ship's headway (a length of chain equal to approximately twice the depth of water). Note how the ship is steadied by the anchor as compared to maneuver 1a above and that there is no immediate or violent change in the ship's heading when the anchor is used.
    c. Come dead slow or slow ahead and use the ship's rudder to maintain the ship's heading across the wind. Slack out more chain if necessary so the ship remains dead in the water at low RPM and note how the ship's heading and position can be maintained, even when lying across the wind.

    d. Increase revolutions until the ship begins moving ahead again and use the rudder to maintain the selected heading across the wind. Increase and reduce revolutions to increase and decrease the ship's headway. Observe the ship's behavior under control of the anchor, including the change of headway when engine RPM is changed; the time required for the ship to lose all headway when the engine is stopped; and speed through the water at a given RPM with the anchor on the bottom, as compared to the speed at the same RPM without the anchor.

    e. Reduce to dead slow ahead, and when the ship is dead in the water, use the rudder to change heading to port and starboard. Note the effect of rudder on rate of turn and how quickly the ship steadies up with the rudder amidships. Also pay attention to the forward shift of the pivot point toward the bow; the reduced diameter of the ship's turning circle; and leeway, or, more accurately, the lack of leeway as the ship is held on a particular heading.

    f. Increase and decrease RPM and again alter the ship's heading, this time with headway. Note that it's possible to make very controlled maneuvers by coming ahead on a fixed heading to move the bow toward a desired point, and by reducing RPMs until headway is lost and then using the rudder to move the stern to one side or the other, as might be done to come alongside a berth.

All this should help you develop an understanding of, and a feel for, shiphandling under the control of an anchor. Think how useful maneuver 1c would be while holding a ship awaiting tugs or improved weather conditions. Ship behavior demonstrated in 1d would be useful in very narrow channels or in reducing speed without backing (or when you've lost the engine) while the practice in 1e becomes important when you have to maneuver in a narrow channel or into a narrow berth without a tug (by choice or circumstances), or need the anchor to break a sudden sheer while proceeding up the channel from sea. Maneuver 1f puts it all together and shows how a ship can make controlled maneuvers or come alongside a berth or another vessel under perfect control, using an anchor even when conditions are less than ideal.

  2. Hold your ship in position using the anchor and a short scope of chain while waiting for the pilot to board. This maneuver is most advantageous with a light ship in bad weather and you should try it at every opportunity to gain experience in all conditions of wind, tide, and ship's draft.

    a. Reduce speed to bare steerageway and put down one or two shots of chain (depending on the depth of water). Steam on the anchor, adjusting the rudder angle and engine revolutions to head the ship into the prevailing wind and sea.

    b. Adjust RPM and slack a bit more chain, if necessary, and continue coming ahead against the anchor. Hold the ship *stationary* relative to the bottom *on the same heading* into the prevailing wind and sea.

   c. Put the rudder hard over as the pilot boat approaches and increase engine RPM to change heading across the wind and sea/swell and make a lee for the pilot. Depending on circumstances, you could begin heaving the anchor after the pilot boards or steam on the anchor to bring the ship around to the initial course toward the channel while awaiting the pilot's arrival on the bridge.

This is certainly a lot safer and easier than backing and filling for half an hour in a crowded anchorage while awaiting the pilot launch!

CHAPTER 9. SPECIAL MANEUVERS

Review Questions

1. Currents at the entrance to locks can be caused by: (Pages 174-75)
I. spilling of water from the chamber.
II. difference between the density of the water in the chamber and the water outside the chamber.
   a. I only
   b. II only
   c. both I and II
   d. neither I nor II

2. The best heading for approaching a single-point mooring is indicated by the heading of anchored ships and the reciprocal of the direction in which the floating hoses trail from the buoy. (Page 181)
   a. true
   b. false

3. The wind has little effect on VLCCs, so these ships approach single-point moorings directly into the current. (Page 182)
   a. true
   b. false

4. The safest, most expedient approach to a single-point mooring is made by: (Page 183)
I. heading directly at the mooring, keeping the buoy dead ahead as ship's engine goes astern and stopping near the pickup buoy.
II. making a significant course change, preferably to port, to come to the final approach heading, and then keeping the buoy fine on the port bow as the ship approaches the SPM.
   a. I only
   b. II only
   c. either I or II
   d. neither I nor II

5. During ship to ship lightering operations, there is less chance of damage if the Yokohama fenders are rigged on the VLCC rather than the offtaker. (Page 188)
    a. true
    b. false

6. It is important that mooring wires used by ships engaged in ship to ship lightering have synthetic tails or pendants: (Pages 188-90)
I. even though they make the wires more difficult to handle.
II. because they make it possible for ships to break apart more quickly in an emergency.
III. because they absorb some of the surge that might otherwise part the wires.
    a. I only
    b. II and III
    c. III only
    d. Synthetic tails should not be used for this purpose.

7. When approaching the offtaker, the VLCC proceeds at ____ possible speed. (Page 190)
    a. maximum
    b. least

8. During this part of the operation, the VLCC should head ___the prevailing wind and swell. (Page 190)
    a. into
    b. across

9. At the same time, the offtaker ____ the VLCC's quarter and comes alongside. (Page 190)
    a. stays close to
    b. keeps clear of

10. Anchors can be used to steer a ship backing to a berth or mooring, because the ship's stern will move to port if the starboard anchor is held, and to starboard if the port anchor is held. (Page 196)
    a. true
    b. false

11. When making a Mediterranean moor, the ship should back with her engines until in position, close up to the berth, before running any lines. (Page 199)
    a. true
    b. false

12. Departing a multiple-buoy mooring or Mediterranean moor, it's usually best to: (Pages 198 and 200)

I. heave the weather anchor short.

II. steam on the weather anchor as required while heaving home the lee anchor.

III. steam away from the mooring as soon as the lee anchor breaks free, heaving on and dragging both anchors until well clear of the buoys or berth.

    a. I only

    b. II and III only

    c. all of the above

    d. none of the above

13. Williamson Turns are less effective with a VLCC because she maintains her speed longer and the vessel's path of travel is less predictable. (Page 200)

    a. true

    b. false

14. When making a Williamson Turn, a ship should always be steadied up 60 degrees from her initial heading before starting a hard-over turn in the opposite direction. (Pages 200-203)

    a. true

    b. false

15. Twin-screw ships fitted with single rudders are generally more responsive at slow speeds through the water when the engines are stopped. (Page 205)

    a. true

    b. false

16. Twin-screw ships can be moved laterally toward a berth by pushing the bow with a tug or bow thruster and *backing* the _____ engine while coming ahead on the other engine. (Pages 205-6)

    a. inshore

    b. offshore

17. VLCCs generally steer well at very slow speeds. (Page 209)

    a. true

    b. false

18. VLCCs usually go astern to avoid close quarters situations. (Page 209)

    a. true

    b. false

19. "Safe speed" is the same for all sizes of ships. (Page 210)

    a. true

    b. false

20. Shallow water effects are felt at greater depth-to-draft ratios by loaded VLCCs than by smaller ships. (Page 211)
    a. true
    b. false

21. The term "constrained by draft" should take into consideration both shallow water effects and danger of grounding. (Page 211)
    a. true
    b. false

22. Hydrodynamic effects are different for VLCCs. (Page 212)
    a. true
    b. false

23. VLCCs are less easily damaged when coming alongside a berth. (Page 212)
    a. true
    b. false

24. VLCCs should be closer to a berth than smaller ships before mooring lines are sent ashore. (Page 212)
    a. true
    b. false

25. Longer ships are more difficult to bring flat alongside because perspective makes the farther end appear much closer to the berth than the closer end (the "railroad track" effect). (Pages 212-13)
    a. true
    b. false

Practice Maneuvers

The Williamson Turn is used for man-overboard emergencies and for routine vessel maneuvers, both to bring a ship back to a desired point with a minimum of maneuvering and to help mates and masters appreciate a ship's handling characteristics at full speed at sea. Turning circles, the time and amount of rudder needed to make and check turns, and the amount of speed a ship loses making large course changes can all be demonstrated during a Williamson Turn.

1. Paint an oil drum or other object bright orange so it can be easily seen and used as a reference during the Williamson Turn. Puncture both ends of a 5-gallon paint pail and attach it to the drum with small diameter line. The pail serves as a drogue to minimize wind drift during the exercise. Also, prepare a data sheet, like the one described in Chapter 1 for the master's maneuvers, to collect data during the maneuvers. The information will be useful when studying the ship's performance and comparing handling characteristics under different conditions of loading.

2. Muster the crew prior to starting the Williamson Turn, and explain the maneuver and its purpose as both a man-overboard drill and a shiphandling exercise. The details of the man-overboard procedure are outside the scope of this book, so only the shiphandling aspects of the maneuver will be discussed here.

3. Throw the drum or reference object over the side, note the ship's base course, put the rudder hard over, and start the turn as described on page 202. Measure the time required for the ship to begin turning after the rudder is put hard over and compare the advance and tactical diameter with the ship's length, as the ship turns, using the drum as a reference. This information will be helpful both for maneuvering in close quarters situations at sea and in any future emergency situation that might arise. The time to turn, the tactical diameter, and the advance will probably be significantly less than you expected.

4. Continue the maneuver, shifting the helm from hard over to hard over when the heading has changed 55 degrees from the base course (point "A" in Fig. 9-15). Note the heading when the ship steadies up and begins swinging in the opposite direction. Calculate the number of degrees that the ship swings before she checks up and you'll know the arc of swing required to steady up from a hard-over turn.

5. Keep the rudder hard over as the ship turns through a circle toward the reciprocal of her initial heading. Apply the arc required to check her swing, as calculated in maneuver 2 above, and when the ship's heading is that number of degrees from the desired final heading (the reciprocal of the initial heading), reverse the rudder hard over again. The ship should check up on, or near, the final heading as the ship returns to her starting point alongside the reference oil drum.
Example: Object overboard on the starboard side, rudder hard right to turn the ship to starboard.

Original course	030	degrees
Initial change of heading	+ 55	
Heading to shift helm ("A")	085	
Ship steadies up	095	
Arc to check swing (difference)	10	
Final (reciprocal) heading	210	
Arc to check swing	10	
Heading to shift helm ("B")	220	degrees

The ship will have completed the Williamson Turn in a predictable manner with the least possible helm movements (three) and thus the minimum of variables. Note the total time to complete the maneuver, the speed through the water at the end of the maneuver, and the distance and bearing from the starting point. If desired, back down and stop the ship as close to the starting point as possible.

6. Perform the maneuver again using an initial change of heading at point "A" of 35 degrees. Did your ship return closer to or farther from her starting point using this smaller initial course change? The required initial change of heading is, to a large extent, determined by the ship's directional stability, and the more positive the directional stability, the farther the ship should be allowed to swing before shifting the helm at "A."

Practice this maneuver at light and loaded drafts, in various conditions of trim, and let all the ship's officers perform Williamson Turns so everyone learns the procedure. A great deal can be learned about shiphandling parameters and the effects of various loading and trim conditions by comparing the turning rate, most effective change of heading at point "A," tactical diameter, advance, etc.

CHAPTER 10. TRAINING

Review Questions

1. On-board training and experience is important because: (Pages 218-19)
I. it is impossible to teach some marine skills in a classroom.
II. priorities needed to apply theory to real world situations can only be learned on board the ship.
III. masters and senior officers can transfer the lessons gained from experience through shipboard training.
IV. it's possible to learn most skills, such as shiphandling, simply by watching senior officers and pilots at work.
    a. I only
    b. both I and III
    c. both II and III
    d. IV only

2. Deck officers can't become effective watch officers and shiphandlers until: (Pages 220-21)
I. they have twenty years' experience at sea.
II. they have "hands-on" drills and feel comfortable using equipment.
III. they learn not to touch equipment unless absolutely necessary.
    a. I only
    b. II only
    c. III only
    d. I and III

3. Simulators are innovative training aids because they make it possible to: (Pages 226-27):

I. learn to prioritize tasks and perform several tasks concurrently.

II. watch experts work.

III. transfer classroom theory to real time situations.

IV. learn most shipboard work without spending a great deal of time aboard ship.

    a. I only

    b. II only

    c. II and IV

    d. I and III

4. Simulator type is more important than instructor experience when judging potential benefits of a training facility. (Page 239)

    a. true

    b. false

5. Professional instructors are preferable to professional mariners at simulator training facilities. (Page 239)

    a. true

    b. false

6. The following mariner's skills could be improved with simulator training: (Page 242)

A. Shiphandling.

    a. true

    b. false

B. Rules of the Road applications and maneuvering with other ships.

    a. true

    b. false

C. Bridge organization.

    a. true

    b. false

D. Watchkeeping practices.

    a. true

    b. false

E. Restricted visibility navigation.

    a. true

    b. false

F. Emergency procedures.

    a. true

    b. false

G. Ship to ship communication procedures.
  a. true
  b. false

7. The computer-based simulator is an advancement that is replacing the ship-model type simulator at most training facilities. (Pages 236-37)
  a. true
  b. false

8. The most important component of the simulator course is the: (Page 238)
  a. simulator
  b. instructor
  c. the curriculum
  d. all of the above

9. Performance-based testing on simulators should overload the student with scenarios that are more difficult than real world situations. (Page 241)
  a. true
  b. false

10. Time should be divided between the briefing, simulator session, and debriefing approximately: (Page 246)
  a. $\frac{1}{4}$, $\frac{1}{2}$, $\frac{1}{4}$
  b. $\frac{1}{3}$, $\frac{1}{3}$, $\frac{1}{3}$
  c. $\frac{1}{4}$, $\frac{1}{4}$, $\frac{1}{2}$
  d. the debriefing is only necessary if students make many errors.

CHAPTER 11. MASTER/PILOT RELATIONSHIP

Review Questions

1. It isn't particularly important that pilots possess traditional seagoing skills, because their main task is advising shipmasters of courses and speeds from point to point. (Page 252)
  a. true
  b. false

2. A pilot whose services are required by law is a ____ pilot. (Pages 252-53)
  a. compulsory
  b. voluntary

3. A pilot taken at the master's option is a ____ pilot. (Page 252)
  a. compulsory
  b. voluntary

4. A compulsory pilot is aboard in a purely advisory capacity and as such has no responsibility or liability for his actions. (Page 253)
   a. true
   b. false

5. There are no significant differences between the responsibilities of the compulsory and the voluntary pilot. (Page 252)
   a. true
   b. false

6. Should the shipmaster *immediately* relieve the pilot in the following situations? (Pages 255-56)

   A. The pilot is intoxicated.
      a. yes
      b. no

   B. The pilot demonstrates gross incompetence.
      a. yes
      b. no

   C. The master knows a more expedient way to complete the maneuver at hand.
      a. yes
      b. no

   D. The vessel is standing into danger that is not obvious to the pilot.
      a. yes
      b. no

   E. The pilot's actions are in error due to circumstances or the limitations of the ship being handled.
      a. yes
      b. no

   F. The master recommends a change that the pilot rejects.
      a. yes
      b. no

   G. A master must wait until the ship is "in extremis" before relieving a compulsory pilot. (Page 256)
      a. true
      b. false

7. It is essential that the master be a competent shiphandler because, under certain circumstances, he has a responsibility to relieve a pilot in a timely and effective manner. (Page 256)
   a. true
   b. false

8. The traditional overlapping of responsibility between the master and pilot prevents many accidents. (Page 257)
   - a. true
   - b. false

9. Irreconcilable differences between master and pilot occur often in the course of moving ships in pilot waters. (Pages 257-58)
   - a. true
   - b. false

10. Penalties and liabilities for accidents which could occur should be foremost on the mariner's mind when deciding on a course of action. (Page 259)
    - a. true
    - b. false

CHAPTER 12. VESSEL OPERATIONS

Review Questions

1. Formal plans are only needed if the master and mates have not recently made a passage in a particular area. (Pages 260-61)
   - a. true
   - b. false

2. Passages can be overplanned. An inflexible passage plan, without alternatives based on professional planning and judgment, is as dangerous as no plan at all. (Pages 261-62)
   - a. true
   - b. false

3. Review the types of information that should be included in proper inland waters passage plans. (Page 263)

4. Passage plans and routes should never be put on charts in ink because that would make the chart less useful for future voyages. (Page 263)
   - a. true
   - b. false

5. Competent masters don't prepare and carry pocket course cards because they memorize charts and passage plans from sea to the dock. (Pages 263-64)
   - a. true
   - b. false

6. All bridges should be standardized with identical layouts and equipment. (Page 265)
   a. true
   b. false

7. There should be a clear view forward from large, unobstructed centerline windows. (Page 266)
   a. true
   b. false

8. The quartermaster's station should be as close to the forward wheelhouse windows as possible. (Pages 266-67)
   a. true
   b. false

9. Instruments should be clustered by use and placed where the user (mate, master, pilot, quartermaster) can use them without being diverted from other work. (Pages 265-66)
   a. true
   b. false

10. A conning station should be organized with equipment mounted on a bulkhead, console, or to keep windows clear. (Page 267)
    a. true
    b. false

11. Instruments and equipment should be kept off bridge wings. (Pages 269-70)
    a. true
    b. false

12. Which of the following statements are true regarding the effect of bridge location on shiphandling? (Pages 270-71)
    I. points of reference appear closer as bridge height is increased.
    II. your ship appears to be moving more slowly as height of eye increases.
    III. turning rate is more difficult to detect when looking ahead from a bridge located close to the bow.
    IV. visibility is improved when the bridge is higher and closer to the bow.
    a. I and II only
    b. I and IV only
    c. all of the above
    d. none of the above

13. There are significant differences between shiphandling in daylight and at night. Which of the following are true? (Page 272)
I. Loss of depth perception at night makes it more difficult to estimate distance.
II. speed cannot be determined at night by looking ahead.
III. speed cannot be determined at night by looking abeam or abaft the beam.
IV. lights and aids appear farther away on clear nights.
    a. I and II only
    b. III and IV only
    c. all of the above
    d. none of the above

14. Which of the following is/are true regarding record keeping? (Page 274)
I. logs and records are important aspects of proper vessel operation.
II. logs and record keeping often conflict with shiphandling, and redundant paperwork must be eliminated.
    a. I only
    b. II only
    c. both I and II
    d. neither I nor II

BIBLIOGRAPHY

Armstrong, Malcolm C. *Pilot Ladder Safety.* Woollahra, N.S.W., Australia: International Maritime Press, 1979.

Barrass, C.B. "Ship Squat and its Calculation." *Safety at Sea Magazine,* February, 1978.

Brady, Edward M. *Tugs, Towboats, and Towing.* Centreville, Md.: Cornell Maritime Press, 1967.

Cahill, R.A. "The Avoidance of Close Quarters in Clear Weather." *Journal of the Royal Institute of Navigation,* 1982.

Cameron, Ian. *The Impossible Dream, the Building of the Panama Canal.* New York: William Morrow & Company, Inc., 1972.

Crenshaw, R.S., Jr. *Naval Shiphandling.* Annapolis, Md.: Naval Institute Press, 1975.

Gray, W.O. *Esso Osaka Maneuvering Trials—Shallow Water Maneuvering of VLCC's.* Tarpon Springs, Fla.: American Petroleum Institute, 1978.

Hayler, William B., ed. *Merchant Marine Officer's Handbook,* 5th ed. Centreville, Md.: Cornell Maritime Press, 1989.

Hope, Brian H. *El Paso Consolidated Maneuvering Trials.* Cove Point, Md.: El Paso Marine Company, 1978.

International Maritime Organization (IMO). *Standards for Training and Watchkeeping.* London, 1978.

La Dage, John H. *Modern Ships.* Cambridge, Md.: Cornell Maritime Press, 1965.

MacElrevey, Daniel H. *El Paso Arzew Maneuvering Trials.* Cove Point, Md.: El Paso Marine Company, 1978.

———. *Master's Guide to Shiphandling.* Cove Point, Md.: El Paso Marine Company, 1978.

MarineSafety International. *Ship Performance Data for VLCC's.* New York, 1978.

Marton, G.S. *Tanker Operations,* 3d ed. Centreville, Md.: Cornell Maritime Press, 1992.

McCullough, David. *The Path Between the Seas.* New York: Simon & Schuster, 1977.

Meurn, Robert J. *Watchstanding Guide for the Merchant Officer.* Centreville, Md.: Cornell Maritime Press, 1990.

311

National Research Council Marine Board. *Minding the Helm: Marine Navigation and Piloting.* Washington, D.C.: National Academy of Sciences, 1994.

———. *Ship Bridge Simulator Training.* Washington, D.C.: National Academy of Sciences, 1995.

Oil Companies International Marine Forum. "Proceedings of the Safe Navigation Symposium." Washington, D.C., 1978.

Oil Companies International Marine Forum. *Ship to Ship Transfer Guide (Petroleum).* London: Witherby & Co.

———. *Standards for Equipment Employed in Mooring of Ships at Single Point Moorings.* London: Witherby & Co., 1978.

Panama Canal Commission. *Panama Canal Pilot's Handbook.* Balboa, Panama: 1980.

Parks, Alex L. and Edward V. Cattell, Jr. *Law of Tug, Tow, and Pilotage,* 3d ed. Centreville, Md.: Cornell Maritime Press, 1994.

Quick, George A. "Pilotage." *Proceedings—Maritime Transportation Research Board.* Washington, D.C.: National Academy of Sciences, 1980.

Reid, George H. *Shiphandling with Tugs.* Centreville, Md.: Cornell Maritime Press, 1986.

Ship Performance Data for VLCCs [Training Manual]. La Guardia, N.Y.: MarineSafety International, 1981.

Swift, Captain A.H., MNI. *Bridge Team Management—A Practical Guide.* London: The Nautical Institute, 1993

United Kingdom Board of Trade. "Navigation Safety/Guide to Planning & Conduct of Passages," MN854.

Vantine, Wilbur H. "Good Bridge Design from a Master Mariner's Point of View." *Ship Operation Automation,* ed. by Pitkin, Roche, and Williams. New York: North-Holland Publishing Company, 1976.

Werner, Norman A. "A View from the Bridge." *The Panama Canal Review,* Spring, 1976.

INDEX

Length affecting directional stability, 20. *See also* Directional stability
Length/beam ratio, 20
Letting go anchor for docking, 161-62, 164-66
Liability: in Panama Canal locks, 253; outside Panama Canal locks, 253-54; pilot, 258-59
Lifting quarter of twin-screw ship, 208
Lightering: discussed, 186-94; mooring lines, 188, 191-92
Light ship departing moorings, 198
Limits: for speed, 66-67; for mooring at SPM, 182-83; lightering, 190
Lines: fouling twin-screws, 208
Little Creek, Va.: model-based simulator, 227
Local knowledge: importance, 85, 128, 260-61; defined, 252
Lockage: density current, 175; approach, 175-76; discussed, 177-78; techniques, 177-78; piston effect, 178; wall effects, 178-80; filling, 179; departing, 180; flush out, 180;
Lock wall suction, 180
Lookout in pilot waters, 255
LOOP terminal, 181
Loss of engine: stopping ship, 25

M
Making fast, 105-6
Making lee: simulator training, for pilot boarding, 241, 243; for lifeboats, 242
Maneuvering: most effective, 17; pilot station, 26-28; information, 38, 40-42; in channel, 53-55, 67-68; fuel, 130; simulated traffic, 242
Maneuvering characteristics: importance of, 40-42, 133-34, 138, 220; learning, 133; changes in, 18-20, 133, 138; wind effects, 33-35, 97-98, 133; departing anchorage, 140
Maneuvering plot for helicopter operation; 217

Maneuvering ship: replenishment at sea, 214-16
Manning: bridge, 128; anchor, 140, 160
Man overboard, 200, 202-4; drill, 202
Manropes, 31
Master: trial maneuvers, 7-9; relationship to pilot defined, 251, 253; relationship to pilot in practice, 251, 255, 257; exercising responsibility, 255; disputing pilot's actions, 255-56
Master's trials: simulator, 241
Mate's duties: on watch, 128, 274-75; anchoring, 140, 149
Maximum submerged area, 52-53
McMillin, Captain Earl R., 198
Measuring: performance by simulation, 227, 237, 247; equipment, 237, 247
Mediterranean moor: discussed, 198-200; anchors, 198-99; mate's duties, 199; departing, 200
Meeting: simulated in a channel, 228, 232, 234, 235, 236, 237, 241
Meeting ships in channel, 57-58, 59
Messengers: at SPM, 183; for tug lines, 123
Midships section affecting shiphandling, 64, 65; and squat, 64-65
Model-based simulators: discussed, 227-30, 235-36; advantages, 228-30; hydrodynamic effects, 229-30; anchor work, 230; model accuracy, 232, 235; limitations, 235-36; disadvantages, 235, 236-37; compared to computer simulation, 236-37; preferences, pilot vs. deck officer, 237
Mooring: discussed, 154-56; running moor, 154; flying moor, 154; methods, 154-56; spread anchors, 154; standing moor, 154; clear hawse, 154-55; clearing chain, 155-56
Mooring bitts at SPM, 184-85
Mooring lines: discussed, 85, 105-6, 109, 113; lightering, 188, 191-92;

Mooring lines – *continued*
5-point moorings, 194, 196; twin-screw ship, 207, 208
Mooring master's duties, 181, 183-85, 190-92, 195-96, 197-98
Motion: detecting general, 28, 61, 82-83, 101. *See also* Lateral motion
Moving: astern, 14, 15; laterally, 100-101, 117; with tug, 111-12, 117-18; ship sideways, twin-screw, 204
Mules in Panama Canal, 176, 178

N

Narrow channel: backing in, 13; discussed, 44, 57; meeting ships, 57-58; holding position, 86; using anchor, 166-67, 168, 171; simulated maneuvers, 242; holding simulated, 242; twin-screw, 207
Navigation: anchoring, 141, 145-46; by eye, 141; leading marks, 141, 145-46; simulation, 226, 237
Navigation training for pilots, 222-23, 244
Navigational aids: simulating, 234
Negative directional stability. *See* Directional stability
Neutral directional stability. *See* Directional stability
Night: estimating speed, 28, 86-87, 88; vision, 42; passage, 272-74
Notices to Mariners, 261

O

Offshore anchor. *See* Anchors
Offshore lightering: discussed, 185-91; offtaker, 185; departing from, 191
Open stern, 19
Outboard propeller: walking ship, 206, 207
Overtaking, 59-60

P

Panama Canal: discussed, 173-74; locomotives, 176, 178; locks

entrance, 175-76, 177-79; locks departure, 180; master/pilot relationship, 253-55
Part task simulators, discussed, 232
Passage planning: discussed, 17, 129-30; for anchoring, 133, 134, 135; for maneuvering, 137, 138, 139; briefing officers, 140, 149; need for, 260-63; excessive, 261-62; on charts, 129-30, 263; affecting record keeping, 274
Peer review, 240, 244, 245, 246, 247
Penalties: master's errors, 258-59; counterproductive, 259
Performance-based testing, 248-49; vs. written examinations, 248-49; criteria, 249
Permanent crews, 96-97
Perspective, 212, 213
Pilot-Master relationship, simulator training, 245
Pilot(s): embarking, 23; maneuvering at pilot station, 26-28; ladder, 29-32; hoist, 33; qualifications, 222-23, 252; training, 222-24, 243-46; federal licensing, 224; tailoring simulators, 232; simulated boarding, 241, 243; curriculum, 243-46; on-board vs. simulated training, 243; simulator-enhanced training, 243; simulator as forum, 244-45; duties, 251-52; responsibility, 251-55; relief by master, 255-56
Piston effect, 64-65, 66
Pivoting moment of anchor, 160-62
Pivot point: discussed, 51, 92, 110, 116, 121, 167-68; turning, 53; undocking, 111-12; anchor affecting, 160-61
Planning ahead: for wind, 35; discussed, 46-47, 48, 97-98, 107, 108, 170; passage, 46, 129-30; docking, 74; undocking, 107-8; anchoring, 134, 135-36, 149; stern anchor, 157; Mediterranean moor, 198-99; with VLCC, 209-10

324

INDEX

Twin-screw: tugs, 72-73; disadvantages, 204-5; slow speed, 204-5;
starting, 208; turning, 201-2,
204-5; ships discussed, 204-9;
compared to single-screw, 204;
diesel vs. turbine, 204, 204-9;
single-rudder, 204; twisting, 204;
rudder flow, 204-5; inboard turning
vs. outboard turning, 206
Twisting effect: backing, 13; shallow
vs. deep water, 13, 18; discussed,
48-49, 101-2, 138; diesel, 204;
turbine, 204; twin-screw, 204,
205; technique, 205; VLCC, 211;
simulated, 233

U
ULCC: single-point moorings, 181;
handling, 209-14. See also SPM
Undocking: tug lashed up, 80-82,
117; planning, 107-8; current
astern, 111; vessel ahead, 111;
from wharf, 110-12; wind on
berth, 115-16; slack water 112;
from slip, 112-16; stern in, 116-
17; twin-screw, 206-7; mooring
lines, 208; simulated, 233
Unit crews, 96-97
Unmooring: stern anchor, 158-59
Unstable, simulated directional, 233
Unstable ship. See Directional
stability

V
Valentine, Robert D., 265
Validation: simulator model, 235,
238, 248
Vantine, Wilbur H., 265
Variable pitch: discussed, 48-49,
112; steering, 48, 49; astern, 49;
docking, 49; flow to rudder, 49;
vs. fixed pitch, 49; vs. turbine,
49; left hand turning, 119
VHF: use of, 25, 35-38, 127; at arrival,
26; in traffic, 35, 36, 37; call iden-
tification, 36; meeting situations,

37; terminology, 36-37; effectiveness, 37; at dock, 106; simulator
training, 242, 243; installation, 267,
269
Vibration in shallow water, 17, 66,
126
Video, simulator tool, 238, 247
Visibility: simulating, 234; arc of,
235; bridge height, 270-71;
diagram, 271, 273
VLCCs: diameter of turn, 10, 52;
shallow water, 21-23; low speeds,
61; steering, 61, 182; SPM, 181-86;
sail area, 33, 182; Williamson
turn, 200-204; handling, 209-14;
stresses, 210-11; helicopter operations, 216-17; storing, 216; bridge
design, 265. See also ULCC
Voith-Schneider, 72-73, 79
Voluntary pilot, 252
Voyage planning, simulator training, 242

W
Walking ship, 204; technique, 205-
6; high power ships, 206-7; at
berth, 206; forces, 207; special
cases, 206-7
"Walking the stern": twin-screw, 205-8
Watchkeeping: training, 220, 221,
240-43; pilot waters, 263, 274,
275-76
Watchkeeping experience, simulation, 225, 241; theory vs. practice,
225; instruction, 226, 243
Weather conditions: SPM, 186;
lightering, 191-92; 5-point
moorings, 197-98; using anchor,
166-67
Wharf: importance of solid face, 94
Wheelhouse windows, 266, 267, 271
Whistle signals: supplementing
VHF, 36, 37; discussed, 127;
simulator training, 242
Williamson turn: defined, 200; variables, 200-202; simulator, 241

ABOUT THE AUTHOR

Captain Daniel H. MacElrevey was reared near the Delaware River, where he developed an interest in the sea watching the ships come and go from the port of Philadelphia. He graduated from the United States Merchant Marine Academy in 1963 and went to sea as a deck officer with Moore-McCormack Lines aboard cargo and passenger ships trading to south and east Africa, South America, and northern Europe. He also worked with the same company in marine operations and stevedoring in New York.

He and his family moved to Panama in 1970 where he worked as a Panama Canal pilot. Living in Panama provided the opportunity for him to pursue another strong interest—ocean sailing—and later he and his family lived aboard and cruised for a year before he returned to sea for four years as master, and to work as mooring master for VLCCs at the Louisiana Offshore Oil Port.

The moving of ships continues to be Captain MacElrevey's primary work. He spends part of each year at the Panama Canal, where he now has over twenty years' experience as a pilot, and the rest of the year he provides consulting, training, technical writing, and shiphandling services to the marine industry through the Offshore Services Company, which he formed in 1980. He has become increasingly involved in marine education and the use of simulation for training and licensing of ship's officers and pilots. Captain MacElrevey served as a member of the Committee on Ship Bridge Simulation Training sponsored by the National Academy of Science's Marine Board in 1993 and 1994.

ISBN 0-87033-464-6

53500